BRIEF REVIEW in

Earth Science

BRIEF REVIEW in
Earth Science

JEFFREY C. CALLISTER
Newburgh Free Academy
Newburgh, New York

Prentice Hall
Needham, Massachusetts   Englewood Cliffs, New Jersey

Credits

Editorial   Julia A. Fellows, Ann L. Collins, Natania Mlawer
Marketing   Arthur C. Germano, Joel Gendler
Design   Alison Anholt-White, Jack Pollard
Production   David Graham, Jo-Ann Connolly, Leanne Cordischi, Virginia Shine
Manufacturing   Holly Schuster

Cover Design: Richard Hannus

PRENTICE HALL
A Division of Simon & Schuster
Needham Heights, Massachusetts 02194
Englewood Cliffs, New Jersey 07632

ISBN 138316864

Printed in the United States of America
1 2 3 4 5 6 7 8   99 98 97 96 95 94

CONTENTS

ABOUT THIS BOOK

Brief Review in Earth Science is a concise text and review aid for the current New York State Syllabus in Earth Science and a means of preparing for the Regents Examination in this subject. The following features will be of special interest to teachers and students.

1. Brief, simple explanations of all concepts and major understandings included in the syllabus.

2. Organization by *Topics* closely following the syllabus.

3. Particular emphasis on essential vocabulary. Each important term is printed in **bold type** where it is defined and discussed in the text. These terms are also presented for review at the end of each Topic and are defined in the *Glossary*.

4. An abundance of illustrations. There are more than 100 drawings in the text alone, each designed to help students visualize and understand the concepts and vocabulary of the subject. They also familiarize students with the types of diagrams they will be required to interpret in Regents Examination questions.

5. Hundreds of practice questions covering all the major understandings of the syllabus. Some questions are reproduced from past Regents Examinations, while other questions are of Regents type. The questions have been selected to review specific concepts and are grouped in the order in which concepts are discussed within each Topic. Many questions review the newest changes in the *Earth Science Reference Tables*.

6. Four complete Regents Examinations. The four most recent examinations are included in their entirety. For convenience in using these exams as an additional source of questions for each Topic, a question number key is provided at the beginning of the Questions section of each Topic.

7. An exceptionally complete index. The index has been carefully planned and compiled to make it easy for the student to locate the portion of the text where any specific term is defined and any specific subject matter is treated.

I believe this book will be highly effective in helping every student achieve mastery of the course content and objectives of the New York State Syllabus in Earth Science. The author would appreciate suggestions on how to make future editions of this book even more useful.

I would like to acknowledge the invaluable contributions of Vernon G. Abel, Bertram Coren, Lois B. Arnold, and my wife Angie to earlier editions of this book. I would also like to thank Tim Denman, Elizabeth A. Jordan, Ronald Macey, and hundreds of students for their suggestions regarding this newest edition.

Jeffrey C. Callister

TOPIC I   Observation and Measurement

OBSERVATION.   An **observation** occurs through the interaction of one or more of the **senses**—sight, hearing, touch, taste, or smell—with a part of the environment. The ability of the senses to make observations is limited in range and precision. **Instruments** are devices invented by people to extend the senses beyond their normal limits and thus enable them to make observations that would otherwise be impossible or highly inaccurate. For example, a microscope makes it possible to see objects and details that are too small for the unaided eye to detect; a magnet allows one to observe something that the senses do not respond to at all.

INFERENCE.   An **inference** is an interpretation of observations. It is a mental process that proposes causes or explanations for what has actually been observed. For example, the observation of an impression in mud, shaped like a dog's foot, leads to the inference that a dog has been present. This inference may or may not be correct. Additional observations may make the inference more likely to be true. A prediction of an event, such as an earthquake or snowstorm, is also a type of inference.

CLASSIFICATION.   Scientists group similar things together in order to make the study of objects and events in the environment more meaningful. This grouping is called **classification,** and it is based on the observed properties of the objects or events.

MEASUREMENT.   A **measurement** is a means of expressing an observation with greater accuracy or precision. It provides a numerical value for some aspect of the object or event being observed. Every measurement includes at least one of the three basic *dimensional quantities*—length, mass, and time.

   Length may be defined as the distance between two points.

   Mass is the quantity of matter in an object. It is often determined by weighing the object, but mass should not be confused with *weight,* which is the pull (force) of the earth's gravitation on an object. The weight of an object may vary with its location, but its mass remains the same.

   Time may be described as our sense of things happening one after another or as the duration of an event.

   Some types of measurements require mathematical combination of basic dimensional quantities. For example, a unit of volume is actually a unit of length cubed, as in 25 cm³ (25 cubic centimeters). Other examples are density (mass per unit volume, as in 4 g/cm³); pressure (force per unit area—15 lb/ft²); speed (distance per unit time—9.8 km/sec).

   All measurements of the basic quantities (length, mass, and time) are made by a direct comparison with certain accepted *standard units* of measurement. For example, length is measured by comparing it with a

1

standard unit such as the centimeter, mass with a unit such as the gram, and time with a unit such as the second. A measurement must always state the units used; for example, 27.9 *grams.*

ERROR.   No measurement is perfect, because it is limited by the imperfection of the senses and of instruments. Human error may also result from carelessness or from improper use of an instrument. Any measurement is therefore an approximation of a true, or absolute, value and must be considered to contain some error.

PERCENT DEVIATION.   Often in science there is an accepted value for a given quality (for example, the density of water). It is then possible to determine the accuracy, or amount of **error,** of a given measurement by comparing it with the accepted value. When the amount of error is expressed as a percentage, it is called **percent deviation** (or **percent error.**) The percent deviation is obtained by dividing the difference between the measured and accepted values by the accepted value and multiplying the result by 100%.

$$\text{percent deviation} = \frac{\text{difference between measured value and accepted value}}{\text{accepted value}} \times 100\%$$

For example, suppose a student measures the mass of an object as 127.5 grams and the accepted value is 125.0 grams. Then,

$$\begin{aligned}
\text{amount of deviation} &= \text{difference between measured value and accepted value} \\
&= 127.5 \text{ grams} - 125.0 \text{ grams} \\
&= 2.5 \text{ grams} \\
\text{percent deviation} &= \frac{\text{amount of deviation}}{\text{accepted value}} \times 100\% \\
&= \frac{2.5 \text{ grams}}{125.0 \text{ grams}} \times 100\% \\
&= 2.0\%
\end{aligned}$$

DENSITY.   The concentration of matter in an object is known as its **density.** The density of an object is the ratio of its mass (quantity of matter) to its volume; that is, density is the mass in each unit of volume. (**Volume** is the amount of space an object occupies.) To determine the density of an object, its mass is divided by its volume:

$$\text{density} = \frac{\text{mass}}{\text{volume}}$$

The density of a material does not depend on the size or shape of the sample, as long as the temperature and pressure remain the same. For example, a cube of aluminum with a volume of 20 cm^3 has a mass of 54 grams. Its density is 54 g/20 cm^3 = 2.7 g/cm^3. An aluminum ball with a volume of 40 cm^3 (twice the volume of the cube) will have a mass of 108 g (twice the mass of the cube), but its density will be the same: 108 g/40 cm³ = 2.7 g/cm³.

FLOTATION.   An object immersed in a liquid is buoyed up by a force equal to the weight of liquid it displaces (Archimedes' Principle). If the density of the object is less than the density of the liquid, the weight of displaced liquid will be greater than the weight of the object. Therefore, the upward force will be enough to support the object, and it will float in the liquid. Flotation of objects in liquids (and in gases) is one method of determining their relative densities. The lower the density of a floating object, the higher it floats in the liquid, that is, the greater the percentage of its volume that is above the surface. As the density of a floating object increases, it sinks relatively deeper into the liquid. If its density is greater than that of the liquid, it will sink to the bottom. If an object and a liquid have exactly the same density (for example, a fish in water), the object can remain stationary anywhere in the liquid.

FACTORS THAT AFFECT DENSITY.   Changes in temperature and pressure affect the density of substances, especially of gases. If the temperature of a gas increases, and its pressure remains the same, its molecules move farther apart (that is, the gas expands). The temperature rise thus results in less mass per unit volume, so that the density of the gas decreases. This explains why hot air rises when surrounded by cooler air.

If the pressure on a gas increases, the molecules come closer together (the gas contracts). The pressure rise thus results in more mass per unit volume, and the density increases.

The expansion and contraction caused by temperature and pressure variations occur also in solids and liquids, but to a much smaller extent. Therefore the density of solids and liquids is less affected by such environmental changes.

PHASES OF MATTER.   Matter on earth exists in three main forms: solid, liquid, and gaseous. Each form is known as a **phase,** or **state,** of matter. The density of a substance changes with changes in its phase. Most substances increase in density as they change from a gas to a liquid, and from a liquid to a solid. They have their highest density as a solid because the atoms are closest together in that phase. Water is an exception, having its highest density in the liquid state at a temperature of 4° C. Therefore, solid water (ice) floats on liquid water, while in most substances the solid sinks in the liquid. Water at 4° C will also lie below layers of water at any other temperature.

VOCABULARY

observation	measurement	density
senses	mass	volume
instrument	error	phase (state)
inference	percent deviation or	
classification	percent error	

QUESTIONS ON TOPIC I—
OBSERVATION AND MEASUREMENT

Questions in Recent Regents Exams (end of book)

June 1991:   1, 4, 56–60
June 1992:   none
June 1993:   102
June 1994:   1, 2, 6, 102, 105

Questions from Earlier Regents Exams

1. Using a ruler to measure the length of a stick is an example of (1) extending the sense of sight by using an instrument   (2) calculating the percent of error by using a proportion   (3) measuring the rate of change of the stick by making inferences   (4) predicting the length of the stick by guessing

2. Which statement made by a student after examining a rock specimen is an inference?   (1) The rock is of igneous origin.   (2) The rock has rounded edges.   (3) The rock is light-colored.   (4) The rock contains large crystals.

3. Which descriptive term illustrates an inference?   (1) transparent (2) bitter   (3) younger   (4) smooth

4. A prediction of next winter's weather is an example of   (1) a measurement   (2) a classification   (3) an observation   (4) an inference

5. A classification system is based on the use of   (1) the human senses to observe properties of objects   (2) instruments to observe properties of objects   (3) observed properties to group objects with similar characteristics   (4) inferences to make observations

6. A measurement is best defined as   (1) an inference made by using the human senses   (2) a direct comparison with a known standard (3) an interpretation based on theory   (4) a group of inferred properties

7. Using the centimeter ruler provided in the *Earth Science Reference Tables*, what is the length of line segment *X-Y*?

(1) 5.8 cm   (2) 6.1 cm   (3) 6.4 cm   (4) 7.1 cm

8. The diagram below represents the scale of a triple beam balance. What mass is indicated by this scale?

(1) 130 g   (2) 151 g   (3) 517 g   (4) 571 g

9. A student determines the density of an ice cube to be 0.80 gram per cubic centimeter, when it is actually 0.90 gram per cubic centimeter. What is the percent deviation (percent error) in this calculation? [Refer to the *Earth Science Reference Tables.*]   (1) 6%   (2) 11%   (3) 13% (4) 88%

10. Which term is best defined as a measure of the amount of space a substance occupies?   (1) mass   (2) volume   (3) density   (4) weight

11. Which is the best definition for the mass of an object?   (1) the amount of space the object occupies   (2) its ratio of weight to volume (3) the quantity of matter the object contains   (4) the force of gravity acting on the object

12. Which characteristic of an object will always change as the object travels from the earth to the moon?   (1) mass   (2) volume (3) density   (4) weight

Base your answers to questions 13 through 17 on your knowledge of earth science, the *Earth Science Reference Tables,* and the diagrams below. Objects *A* and *B* are solid and made of the same uniform material.

(A)

(B)

13. If object *B* has a mass of 173 grams, what is its density? (1) 0.37 g/cm^3 (2) 2.7 g/cm^3 (3) 3.7 g/cm^3 (4) 5.7 g/cm^3

14. Object *A* expands when it is heated. Which graph best represents the relationship between the temperature and the density of object *A*?

15. A student measures the mass of object *B* to be 156 grams, but the actual mass is 173 grams. The student's percent deviation (percentage of error) is approximately   (1) 1%   (2) 5%   (3) 10%   (4) 20%

16. A third object is made of the same uniform material as object B, but has twice the volume as object B. How does the density of this third object compare to the density of object B?   (1) It is one-half as dense as B.   (2) It is the same density as B.   (3) It is twice as dense as B. (4) It is four times as dense as B.

Note that question 17 has only three choices.

17. How does the mass of object B compare to the mass of object A?   (1) The mass of B is less than the mass of A.   (2) The mass of B is greater than the mass of A.   (3) The mass of B is the same as the mass of A

Base your answers to questions 18 through 21 on your knowledge of earth science and on the graph at the right, which shows the masses and volumes of four different earth materials.

18. Which material has the greatest density?
(1) A
(2) B
(3) C
(4) D

MASSES AND VOLUMES OF EARTH MATERIALS

19. If the density of water is 1 g/cm^3, which material will float on water?   (1) A (2) B (3) C (4) D

20. What is the mass of sample C if its volume is 3.0 cubic centimeters?   (1) 7.5 g   (2) 2.1 g   (3) 3.0 g   (4) 21 g

21. Which material has a density of 4.0 g/cm^3?   (1) A (2) B (3) C (4) D

22. The two solid blocks below are made of the same material and are under the same temperature and pressure conditions. If the mass of block X is 54 grams, what is the mass of block Y?

(1) 18 g   (2) 27 g   (3) 54 g   (4) 108 g

23. Substances A, B, C, and D are at rest in a container of liquid as shown by the diagram below. Which choice lists the substances in the order of lowest density to highest density?

(1) A, B, C, D (2) A, D, C, B (3) D, C, B, A (4) C, B, A, D

24. Substances A, B, C, and D are at rest in a container of liquid as shown in the accompanying diagram. Which substance probably has the same density as the liquid?

(1) A (2) B (3) C (4) D

25. In which phase (state) do most earth materials have their greatest density?   (1) solid   (2) liquid   (3) gaseous

26. Which graph represents the behavior of water as it is warmed from 0° C to 16° C?

TOPIC II The Changing Environment

CHARACTERISTICS OF CHANGE.   Observations reveal that most of the properties of the environment are undergoing **change** at all times. As a result, the description of a portion of the environment is never exactly the same in all details at two different times. The occurrence of a change in the properties of an object or a system is called an **event.** Events may be almost instantaneous, as in the case of a meteor, or they may occur over long periods of time, as in changes in sea level.

FRAMES OF REFERENCES.   Change can be described with respect to time and space (location). Time and space are called the **frames of reference** for studying change. As an example, we say that the moon changes because we observe it in different locations and different phases at different times.

RATE OF CHANGE.   **Rate of change** describes how much a measurable aspect of the environment (a field) changes in a period of time (years, hours, or seconds). Rate of change is determined by use of the following equation, which is found in the *Earth Science Reference Tables.*

$$\text{rate of change} = \frac{\text{change in field value}}{\text{change in time}}$$

CYCLIC CHANGE.   Many changes in the environment occur in some orderly fashion in which the events constantly repeat themselves with reference to space and time. Such orderly changes are called **cyclic change,** and they include the movement of celestial objects (sun, moon, stars, planets), seasonal events, and the water and rock cycles.

PREDICTION OF CHANGE.   A prediction is a type of inference about the conditions of the environment in the future. Predictions can be made if the amount, type, and direction of change can be determined. Because eclipses are cyclic, for example, astronomers can predict the occurrence of solar and lunar eclipses many hundreds of years in the future.

ENERGY AND CHANGE.   All change involves a flow of energy from one part of the environment (which loses energy) to another part (which gains it). For example, in the movement of the water in a stream, friction causes the stream to lose energy, while the environment around the stream gains energy (in the form of heat). Energy is usually exchanged across an **interface,** which is the boundary between regions with different properties. In the case of the stream, there is an interface between the water and the air and another between the water and the stream bed.

ENVIRONMENTAL EQUILIBRIUM.   Although change occurs continuously throughout the environment, certain general characteristics tend
to remain constant. For example, the wooded shore of a lake tends to
look the same from one day to the next. Although it may go through a
cycle of seasonal changes, it tends to look the same each year at the
same season. This is the result of a natural balance among all the changes
taking place, called **environmental equilibrium.** This equilibrium is easily
upset on a small scale, for example by the burrowing of a worm in the
soil, but is normally not upset on a large scale. Human activities, however, often abruptly upset the natural environmental equilibrium. For example, construction equipment can rapidly change a rain forest into a city, thus
introducing change on a large scale.

POLLUTION OF THE ENVIRONMENT.   **Pollution** of the environment
occurs when the concentration of any substance or form of energy reaches
a proportion that adversely affects people, their property, or plant or
animal life.

CAUSES OF POLLUTION.   Many forms of pollution are the result of
human technology, which often produces substances and forms of energy
in harmful quantities. Some forms of pollution are the results of natural
events or processes and would occur without the presence of people.
High concentrations of pollen in the air, and ash and gases from volcanic
eruptions, are examples of natural pollution.

   Pollutants (things that pollute) include solids, liquids, gases, biologic
organisms, and forms of energy such as heat, sound, and nuclear radiation. People, through their technology, add pollutants by individual
action, community action, and by industrial processes. Many forms of
pollution vary with the time of day or season of the year because the
causes are cyclic. Air pollution in cities, for example, may increase at
the times people are going to and from work because the automobile is
one of the greatest contributors to air pollution.

VOCABULARY	
change	interface
event	environmental equilibrium
rate of change	pollution
frames of reference	pollutants
cyclic change	

QUESTIONS ON TOPIC II—THE CHANGING ENVIRONMENT

Questions in Recent Regents Exams (end of book)

June 1991:   2, 69
June 1992:   2, 7
June 1993:   96
June 1994:   15

Questions from Earlier Regents Exams

1. What always happens when a change occurs?   (1) Pollution is produced.   (2) The temperature of a system increases.   (3) The properties of a system are altered.   (4) Dynamic equilibrium is reached.

2. Which statement best explains why some cyclic earth changes may *not* appear to be cyclic?   (1) Most earth changes are caused by human activities.   (2) Most earth changes are caused by the occurrence of a major catastrophe.   (3) Many earth changes occur over such a long period of time that they are difficult to measure.   (4) No earth changes can be observed because the earth is always in equilibrium.

3. Which graph represents the greatest rate of temperature change?

4. Refer to the data table below. At approximately what rate did the temperature rise inside the greenhouse between 8:00 A.M. and 10:00 A.M.?

Time	Average Inside Temperature
6:00 A.M.	13°C
8:00 A.M.	14°C
10:00 A.M.	16°C
12:00 noon	20°C

(1) 1.0°C/hour   (2) 2.0°C/hour   (3) 0.5°C/hour   (4) 12.0°C/hour

5. The rising and setting of the sun are examples of   (1) noncyclic events   (2) unrelated events   (3) predictable changes   (4) random motion

6. Future changes in the environment can best be predicted from data that are   (1) highly variable and collected over short periods of time   (2) highly variable and collected over long periods of time   (3) cyclic and collected over short periods of time   (4) cyclic and collected over long periods of time

7. An interface can best be described as   (1) a zone of contact between different substances across which energy is exchanged   (2) a region in the environment with unchanging properties   (3) a process that results in changes in the environment   (4) a region beneath the surface of the earth where change is not occurring

8. Which condition exists when the rates of water flowing into and out of a lake are balanced so that the lake's depth appears to be constant? (1) equilibrium   (2) transpiration   (3) hydration   (4) saturation

9. Why were laws passed that made some insecticides, such as DDT, unavailable to the general public?   (1) Some insecticides were not effective against insects.   (2) Some insecticides' colors were causing a change in the environment's physical appearance.   (3) Some insecticides' concentration in the environment became harmful to other animal life as well as to insects.   (4) Some insecticides' effects were weakened when diluted by the atmosphere and hydrosphere.

10. When the amounts of biologic organisms, sound, and radiation added to the environment reach a level that harms people, these factors are referred to as environmental   (1) interfaces   (2) pollutants   (3) phase changes   (4) equilibrium exchanges

11. People who live close to major airports are most likely to complain about which form of pollution?   (1) sound   (2) heat   (3) radioactivity   (4) particulates

12. Which energy source is *least* likely to pollute the environment? (1) uranium   (2) petroleum   (3) coal   (4) wind

Additional Questions

1. Which statement is *not* true about earth changes?   (1) Most changes are cyclic.   (2) The scope and direction of most changes are not predictable.   (3) Change is the natural state of the environment. (4) A change in the environment also involves a change in time and space quantities.

2. Most changes in the environment are   (1) cyclic   (2) destructive (3) sudden   (4) unnatural

3. Which statement is true about the environment of most of the earth?   (1) It is usually greatly unbalanced.   (2) It is usually in equilibrium and hard to change.   (3) It is usually in equilibrium but easy to change on a small scale.   (4) It is normally heavily polluted by natural occurrences.

4. Why have humans been such a big factor in the pollution of the environment?   (1) They have had many wars.   (2) They are larger in size than most animal forms.   (3) Their technology creates pollutants. (4) They are the only form of life that can adapt to almost all the environments on the earth's surface.

5. Which statement is true about the pollen, carbon monoxide, and sound found in an urban community?   (1) Their concentrations change with time.   (2) They are not forms of pollution because they can be caused by natural events.   (3) They are always considered pollutants because they adversely affect the environment in any concentration. (4) They are produced by the technology of people and are thus considered forms of pollution.

TOPIC III   Measuring the Earth

SIZE AND SHAPE OF THE EARTH

THE EARTH'S SHAPE.   The earth's shape is an **oblate spheroid;** that is, it is a sphere with a slight flattening at the polar regions and a slight bulging at the equatorial region. As a result, the equatorial diameter and circumference are larger than the polar diameter and circumference respectively, as Figure 3-1 shows.

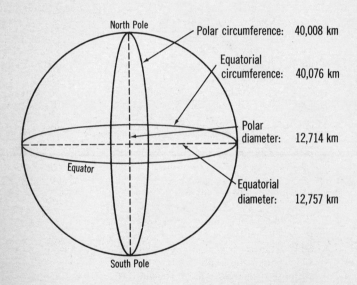

Figure 3-1. Polar and equatorial dimensions of the earth.

However, the differences are very small compared to the actual dimensions; for example, the difference between the two circumferences is only 68 kilometers. This variation from a spherical shape could not be detected in a model of the earth, such as an ordinary globe. Such models are therefore made in the shape of a sphere. (A **model** is any way of representing the properties of an object or system. A model may be an object, such as a globe to represent the earth, or it may be a drawing, diagram, graph, chart, table, or even a mathematical formula or equation. Scientists construct models of these various kinds as aids in studying and understanding the environment.) Besides being very close to a perfect sphere, the earth's surface is very smooth (has very little relief) compared to its diameter.

EVIDENCE FOR THE EARTH'S SHAPE

1. Altitude of Polaris. The **altitude** of an object in the sky is its angle above the horizon. The **latitude** of a point on the earth's surface is its angle north or south of the equator. The star **Polaris** (also called the *North Star*) is almost directly over the North Pole of the earth. From the geometry of a sphere, it can be shown that the altitude of Polaris at any point in the Northern Hemisphere should be the same as the latitude of that point. That is, the altitude of Polaris should change from 0° at the equator to 90° at the North Pole. In the Northern Hemisphere, the altitude of Polaris is equal to the latitude of the observer. (See Figure 3-2).

Figure 3-2. Showing that the altitude of Polaris should be the same as the latitude of the observer on a spherical earth. Note that the **geographic poles** are at the ends of the earth's **axis** of rotation.

The altitude of Polaris, however, does not vary exactly in step with latitude. The observed variation is evidence that the earth is not a perfect sphere but is slightly oblate.

2. Photographs from space. Extremely precise photographic observations of the earth taken from satellites and manned spacecraft confirm the oblateness of the earth's shape.

3. Gravity measurements. *Gravity* is the force that attracts all objects toward the center of the earth. The amount of this force on an object is called the object's *weight*. The law of gravitation states that this force is inversely proportional to the square of the distance between the centers of the earth and the object. That is, as the distance from the center of the earth increases, the weight of an object decreases. On a perfectly spherical earth, the weight of a body should be the same at any latitude, since all points of the surface of a sphere are the same distance from the center. However, measurements show that an object weighs more near the poles than near the equator. Part of the reason for this is an apparent outward force caused by the earth's rotation. But when this is accounted for, there is still a greater gravity force at the poles than at the equator, indicating an oblate shape for the earth. (See Figure 3-3).

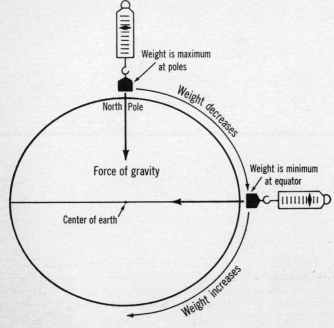

Figure 3-3. Gravity varies with latitude. Because of the flattening of the earth at the poles the distance from the center of the earth is less at the poles than at the equator. As a result, the force of gravity is greater at the poles than at the equator. (Flattening greatly exaggerated in this drawing.)

4. "Sinking" ships. As a ship sails away from shore, it appears to sink at the horizon. Although this effect does not prove that the earth is spherical, it is evidence that the earth's surface is curved.

MEASURING THE EARTH. In our space age, measurements of the earth's dimensions can be made from space. However, it has long been possible to estimate the earth's circumference quite accurately from earth by using fairly simple methods.

About 200 B.C. a Greek scientist named Eratosthenes measured the circumference of the earth using angles of the sun at noon. (Refer to Figure 3-4.) Eratosthenes knew that on a particular day each year the sun shone directly down to the bottom of a well in one city in Egypt. In another city due north, the sun cast a shadow at noon on that day. Eratosthenes measured the distance between the two cities and calculated the earth's circumference using the following equation, which is also found in the *Earth Science Reference Tables.*

$$\frac{\text{shadow angle}}{360°} = \frac{\text{distance of surface}}{\text{circumference}}$$

Figure 3-4. Determining the circumference of the earth.

Using this formula, Eratosthenes calculated a circumference equal to about 40,000 km, which is close to present-day measurements. Once the circumference of the earth is estimated, its radius, diameter, surface area, and volume can also be calculated (see Figure 3-5).

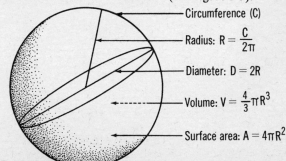

Figure 3-5. Relationships among the dimensions of a sphere.

THE OUTER PARTS OF THE EARTH

THE LITHOSPHERE. The **lithosphere** is a layer of rock that forms the solid outer shell of the earth (see Figure 3-6). The lithosphere is approximately 100 km thick. The upper portion is called the crust.

THE HYDROSPHERE. The **hydrosphere** is the layer of water that rests on the lithosphere. The hydrosphere consists of the ocean, which covers about 70% of the earth's surface, plus the water in bodies such as lakes, streams, and rivers. The ocean layer is relatively thin, averaging only 3.8 kilometers in thickness; in fact, even the thin line labeled "hydrosphere" in Figure 3-6 is too thick to show the hydrosphere in correct relation to the lithosphere and atmosphere.

Figure 3-6. A cross section of the earth showing the three outer spheres. The drawing has not been made to scale, but the relative thicknesses of the parts of the earth are close to proportion.

THE ATMOSPHERE The **atmosphere** is the shell of gases that surrounds the earth. It extends out several hundred kilometers into space, but nearly all of its mass is confined to the first few kilometers from the earth's surface. The atmosphere is *layered,* or *stratified,* into zones with their own distinct characteristics, such as temperature and composition. (See *Selected Properties of Earth's Atmosphere* in the *Earth Science Reference Tables.*)

LOCATING POSITIONS ON THE EARTH

COORDINATE SYSTEMS.   To fix the location of a point on any two-dimensional surface, such as the surface of the earth, two numbers, called *coordinates,* are needed. The system for determining the coordinates of a point is called a **coordinate system.** The *latitude-longitude system* is the one commonly used to locate points on the earth. Latitude and longitude are measured in angular units: degrees (°), minutes ('), and seconds (").

LATITUDE.   **Latitude** is an angular distance north or south of the equator. If a line is drawn from any point on the earth's surface to the center of the earth, the latitude of that point is the number of degrees in the angle between the line and the plane of the equator. All points that have the same latitude lie on a circle that is parallel to the equator. These circles are called **parallels** of latitude. The **equator** may be considered to be the parallel of latitude 0°. Latitude increases north and south of the equator to a maximum of 90° at each pole.

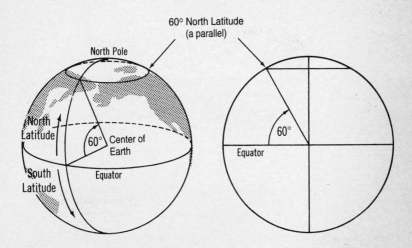

Figure 3-7. The meaning of latitude. Latitude is the angular distance north or south of the equator. On the left, the earth is shown as a sphere with the 60° parallel of North Latitude shown as a circle parallel to the equator. On the right, the earth is shown with the North-South axis vertical; the equator and the parallels of latitude then becomes horizontal lines.

MEASURING LATITUDE.   As shown in Figure 3-2 on page 13, the altitude of Polaris equals the degree of latitude. In the Southern Hemisphere, latitude can be determined by measuring the altitude of certain other stars. In both cases, astronomical tables are used to make adjustments for date and time if extreme precision is desired.

LONGITUDE. **Longitude** is an angular distance east or west of the Prime Meridian. A **meridian** is any semicircle on the earth's surface connecting the North and South Poles. The meridian that passes through Greenwich, England, has been designated the *Prime Meridian,* or the meridian of zero longitude. The longitude of any point on the Prime Meridian is 0°. The longitude of any other point on the earth's surface is the number of degrees between the meridian that passes through the point and the Prime Meridian. This angle can be measured along the equator or along any parallel of latitude. Since a full circle is 360°, longitude increases east or west of the Prime Meridian from 0° at the Prime Meridian to 180° at the meridian that is the continuation of the Prime Meridian on the other side of the earth.

Figure 3-8. The meaning of longitude. Longitude is the angular distance east or west of the Prime Meridian, which is the meridian passing through Greenwich, England. Latitude and longitude together provide a system of coordinates for locating any point on the earth. The coordinates of Point P₁ are 40° N. Lat. and 75° E. Long. Those for Point P₂ are 30° S. Lat. and 60° W. Long.

MEASURING LONGITUDE. *Local noon* (12:00 noon) at any point on the earth occurs when a line from the sun to the center of the earth cuts the meridian of that point. At that moment the sun reaches its highest altitude of the day, so that the instant of local noon can be determined by observing the sun. Since the earth rotates from west to east at the rate of one rotation per day, or 360° in 24 hours, it rotates 15° per hour. Therefore, the occurrence of local noon moves from east to west at the same rate of 15° per hour. Longitude can be calculated if, when local noon occurs, the observer knows what time it is at Greenwich, England. For example, if local noon occurs at 1:00 P.M. Greenwich time (G.M.T.), one hour has passed since the sun crossed the Prime Meridian; the local longitude is therefore 15° west. In general, longitude can be calculated by finding the time difference in hours between local sun time and Greenwich time, and multiplying by 15°. If local time is earlier than Greenwich time, the longitude is west; if later, it is east. Greenwich time can be determined if the observer has a clock that has been set to keep Greenwich time, or by means of radio signals that are broadcast regularly for that purpose.

FIELDS

DEFINITION.   A **field** is any region of space or the environment that has some measurable value of a given quantity at every point. Examples of field quantities are gravity, magnetism, elevation or depth, atmospheric pressure, wind, and relative humidity.

VECTOR AND SCALAR FIELDS.   Some fields need only an amount, or *magnitude,* to be completely described. These fields are called **scalar fields** and include such things as temperature, atmospheric pressure, and relative humidity. Other fields need a magnitude plus a *direction* to totally describe them. These fields are called **vector fields** and include such things as magnetism, gravity, and wind.

ISOLINES.   The varying values of a field are often represented on a map of the region by the use of lines, called **isolines,** which connect points of equal value. Some common examples of isolines are *isotherms* (which connect points of equal temperature), *isobars* (which connect points of equal air pressure), and *contour lines* (which connect points of equal elevation).

ISO-SURFACES.   Isolines show field values over a *two-dimensional* field or surface. For example, isotherms on a weather map show temperatures at one level only (usually ground level). To show field values throughout a *three-dimensional* region or volume of space, it is necessary to use *iso-surfaces.* An **iso-surface** is a surface all of whose points have the same field value. (See Figure 3-9 on page 20.)

CHANGES IN FIELDS.   Since the environment is constantly changing, field characteristics usually change with time. This means that any model of a field, such as a weather map, shows the field for only one particular time.

GRADIENT.   The rate at which a field changes from place to place within the field is called the **gradient** or *slope.* It can be calculated from the following formula:

$$\text{gradient} = \frac{\textbf{change in (amount of) field value}}{\textbf{change in distance}}$$

For example, if a weather map shows a change in temperature of 12°C between two locations 3 km apart, the gradient between the two locations is 4°C per km.

Figure 3-9. Isothermal surfaces in the 3-dimensional temperature field inside a room. All points in any of the iso-surfaces have the same temperature. Where the iso-surfaces meet the ceiling, a 2-dimensional field of isothermal lines is formed. A similar 2-dimensional field can be seen in the right-hand wall.

USING CONTOUR MAPS

CONTOUR MAPS. A **contour map** (topographic map) is a commonly used model of the elevation field of the surface of the earth. The **contour lines** are isolines that connect points of equal elevation above sea level. Other symbols are used to show other features.

The difference in elevation between consecutive contour lines is the *contour interval.* In reading contour lines, pay attention to these points: (1) When contour lines cross a stream, they bend uphill toward higher elevations. Contour lines "point" upstream.   (2) *Depression contours* are marked with small lines pointing toward the center of a depression. (Refer to the upper left-hand corner of Figure 3-10.)

DISTANCE ON MAPS. To find the horizontal distance between two places on a map, you compare the distance on the map with the map scale. For example, the length of the road with the number 84 on the map in Figure 3-10 is approximately 4 miles.

MAP DIRECTION. Most maps, including contour maps, usually show directions by indicating north with some type of arrow. The map in Figure 3-10 indicates north by ★, which stands for "geographic north." On most maps, the top faces north. There is usually a north arrow or a compass rose like the one at the right. Compass directions are often shown on maps.

Figure 3-10. A topographic map.

MAP GRADIENT. For practice, compute the gradient of the Newburgh River in Figure 3-10 from the 180-foot contour line to the 100-foot contour line. Your result should be 20 feet per mile. On any map of a field, the relative amount of gradient can be estimated by the distance between the isolines. The more closely spaced the lines, the greater the gradient. In the map example, the gradient is great, or steep, just to the east of Vails Gate Mountain because the contour lines are close together. In the area around the Denman Orchard, the gradient is small, or gentle, because the contour lines are far apart.

PROFILES. The three-dimensional nature and the gradient of a field can be shown by drawing a profile. Profiles of contour maps are often drawn to show the shape of the earth's surface. The method of making a profile of a contour map is illustrated in Figure 3-11. The profile is drawn for the region between X and X' in the southeast corner of the map in Figure 3-10.

TOPOGRAPHIC MAP EXERCISE

Answer the following questions based on the map in Figure 3-10.

1. What is the maximum altitude of Denman Orchard?   (1) 140 feet   (2) 150 feet   (3) 159 feet   (4) 161 feet

2. What is the longitude of the middle of Coren Swamp?   (1) 37°53' North   (2) 37°53' West   (3) 74°32' North   (4) 74°32' West

3. What is the total distance of Hennessey Street on the map from the margin of the map to where it meets Route 84?   (1) 2½ miles   (2) 3 miles   (3) 3½ miles   (4) 4 miles

4. What is the gradient of the Kennedy River from the 200-foot contour line to the contour line before the Kennedy River meets the Newburgh River?   (1) 5 to 10 feet/mile   (2) 15 to 20 feet/mile   (3) 25 to 30 feet/mile   (4) 35 to 40 feet/mile

5. What is the latitude of the school?   (1) 74°34' North   (2) 74°34' West   (3) 37°41' West   (4) 37°41' North

6. Which side of Temple Hill has the steepest gradient?   (1) north   (2) south   (3) east   (4) west

7. The most gentle slope is found in the vicinity of   (1) Abel Pond   (2) Denman Orchard   (3) Temple Hill   (4) Zemp Creek

8. What direction is Vails Gate Mountain from Callister City?   (1) north   (2) northwest   (3) northeast   (4) west

9. In what direction is the Kennedy River flowing?   (1) south   (2) southwest   (3) north   (4) northeast

10. Which of the profiles above represents the shape of the landscape from A to B on the map?   (1) 1   (2) 2   (3) 3   (4) 4

Figure 3-11. Constructing a profile along the line X-X′ on the contour map of Figure 3-10. The edge of a strip of paper is placed along the line, and a mark is made wherever the paper crosses a contour line. The marks are labeled with the corresponding altitude. The marks are then projected upward to locate dots on a piece of lined paper as in Drawing B. Finally the dots are connected with a smooth curved line, and the profile is complete.

VOCABULARY		
oblate spheroid	atmosphere	scalar field
model	coordinate system	vector field
altitude	latitude	isoline
Polaris (North Star)	parallels	iso-surface
geographic poles	equator	gradient
axis (of rotation)	longitude	contour map
lithosphere	meridians	contour line
hydrosphere	field	

QUESTIONS ON TOPIC III—MEASURING THE EARTH

Questions in Recent Regents Exams (end of book)

June 1991: 6–8, 52, 64, 72, 105
June 1992: 1, 4, 9, 13, 17, 56–60, 63, 64, 74
June 1993: 1–4, 56–60, 104
June 1994: 3, 4, 7, 16, 56–60, 97

Questions from Earlier Regents Exams

1. The true shape of the earth is best described as a   (1) perfect sphere   (2) perfect ellipse   (3) slightly oblate sphere   (4) highly eccentric ellipse

2. In the diagram, what is the latitude of the observer?

(1) 30°N   (2) 60°N   (3) 90°N   (4) 120°N

3. Which set of photographs taken over a period of one year would supply the best evidence of the earth's shape?   (1) photographs of the sun from the earth   (2) photographs of the earth from the moon (3) photographs of the earth's shadow on the moon   (4) photographs of the star paths from the North Pole

4. Measurements taken with gravity meters would be most useful in providing information concerning the   (1) magnetic field intensity (2) shape of the earth   (3) tidal range   (4) distance from the sun

5. Which statement provides the best evidence that the earth has a nearly spherical shape?   (1) The sun has a spherical shape.   (2) The altitude of Polaris changes in a definite pattern as an observer's latitude changes.   (3) Star trails photographed over a period of time show a circular path.   (4) The lengths of noontime shadows change throughout the year.

6. The actual polar diameter of the earth is 12,714 kilometers. The equatorial diameter of the earth is approximately   (1) 12,671 km   (2) 12,700 km   (3) 12,714 km   (4) 12,757 km

7. Based on the diagram below, what is the circumference of planet Y?

(1) 9,000 km   (2) 12,000 km   (3) 16,000 km   (4) 24,000 km

8. According to the *Earth Science Reference Tables,* the radius of the earth is approximately   (1) 637 km   (2) 6,370 km   (3) 63,700 km   (4) 637,000 km

9. The water sphere of the earth is known as the   (1) atmosphere   (2) troposphere   (3) lithosphere   (4) hydrosphere

10. In the diagrams below, the dark zone at the surface of each wedge-shaped segment of the earth represents average ocean depth. Which segment is drawn most nearly to scale?

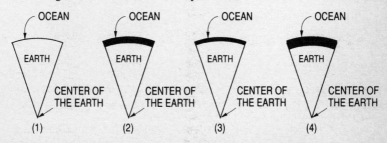

11. What is the approximate altitude of the mesopause in the atmosphere?   (1) 50 km   (2) 66 km   (3) 82 km   (44) 90 km

12. Which statement most accurately describes the earth's atmosphere?   (1) The atmosphere is layered, with each layer possessing distinct characteristics.   (2) The atmosphere is a shell of gases surrounding most of the earth.   (3) The atmosphere's altitude is less than the depth of the ocean.   (4) The atmosphere is more dense than the hydrospherc but less dense than the lithosphere.

13. In which group are the spheres of the earth listed in order of increasing density?   (1) atmosphere, hydrosphere, lithosphere   (2) hydrosphere, lithosphere, atmosphere   (3) lithosphere, hydrosphere, atmosphere   (4) lithosphere, atmosphere, hydrosphere

14. As a person travels due west, the altitude of Polaris will (1) decrease   (2) increase   (3) remain the same

15. Polaris is used as a celestial reference point for the earth's latitude system, because Polaris   (1) always rises at sunset and sets at sunrise   (2) is located over the earth's axis of rotation   (3) can be seen from any place on earth   (4) is a very bright star

16. An airplane takes off from a location at 17°S latitude and flies to a new location 55° due north of its starting point. What latitude has the airplane reached?   (1) 28°N   (2) 38°N   (3) 55°N   (4) 72°N

17. The diagram below represents a portion of the earth's latitude and longitude system. What are the approximate latitude and longitude of point *A*?

(1) 15°S 20°W   (2) 15°S 20°E   (3) 15°N 20°W   (4) 15°N 20°E

18. What is the location of Binghamton, New York?   (1) 42°06′ N lat., 75°55′ W long.   (2) 42°06′ N lat., 76°05′ W long.   (3) 42°54′ N lat., 76°05′ W long.   (4) 42°54′ N lat., 75°55′ W long.

19. A person knows the solar time on the Prime Meridian and the local solar time. What determination can be made?   (1) the date   (2) the altitude of Polaris   (3) the longitude at which the person is located
(4) the latitude at which the person is located

20. Which weather variable has both magnitude and direction (vector quantity)?   (1) temperature   (2) air pressure   (3) wind   (4) relative humidity

21. If no elevation values were given, which general rule could be used to establish that a river shown on a contour map flows into a lake? (1) Rivers shown on maps generally flow southward.   (2) Rivers always flow toward large bodies of water.   (3) Contour lines bend upstream when crossing a river.   (4) A large body of water is generally the source of water for a river.

22. The map below represents an elevation field.

Which graph best represents the elevation profile along a straight line from point *A* to point *B*?

Base your answer to question 23 on the topographic map shown below.

23. What is the most likely elevation of point *A*? (1) 1,250 (2) 1,650 (3) 1,750 (4) 1,850

Base your answers to question 24 and 25 on the diagram below, which represents a contour map of a hill.

24. On which side of the hill does the land have the steepest slope? (1) north (2) south (3) east (4) west

25. What is the approximate gradient of the hill between points *X* and *Y*? [Refer to the *Earth Science Reference Tables*.] (1) 1 m/km (2) 10 m/km (3) 3 m/km (4) m/km

Additional Questions

1. Which is a model? (1) a globe (2) a ruler (3) a hand lens (4) a mineral specimen

To answer questions 2 and 3 refer to the diagram below, which shows a satellite in a polar orbit around the earth. Assume that the satellite contains photographic equipment.

2. Which of the following could not be easily determined from data from the satellite? (1) the thickness of the lithosphere (2) the circumference of the earth (3) the shape of the earth (4) the surface area of the earth

3. If the satellite were in a perfectly circular orbit, which of the following statements would be true of its distance from the surface of the earth? (1) it would be constant (2) it would be greatest at the poles (3) it would be greatest at the equator (4) it would sometimes be greatest at the poles and at other times greatest at the equator

4. Which of the following cannot be determined about the earth when the only dimension known is the circumference? (1) mass (2) volume (3) diameter (4) surface area

5. Which makes up most of the earth's surface? (1) the atmosphere (2) the lithosphere (3) the hydrosphere

The diagrams below illustrate systems that can be used to determine position on a sphere. Refer to them to answer questions 6 and 7.

6. Systems of lines like those illustrated above are called (1) latitude systems (2) coordinate systems (3) great circle systems (4) axis systems

7. Which of the systems illustrated is most like the latitude-longitude system used on the earth? (1) A (2) B (3) C (4) D

TOPIC IV The Earth's Motions

APPARENT MOTIONS OF CELESTIAL OBJECTS

CELESTIAL OBJECTS. A **celestial object** is any object outside the earth's atmosphere. The stars, the sun, the planets, and the moon are examples of celestial objects. The solar system is the sun and the portion of space containing celestial objects that revolve around the sun. See *Solar System Data* in the *Earth Science Reference Tables*.

DAILY MOTION. Most celestial objects appear to move across the sky from east to west. The paths of these apparent motions are circular, and the motion occurs at a constant rate of approximately 15° per hour. This is called **daily motion.** See Figure 4-1.

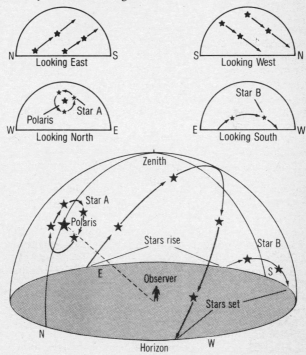

Figure 4-1. The apparent daily motion of the stars. To an observer in the mid-latitudes of the Northern Hemisphere, most stars appear to move from east to west in circular paths, or along parts of circles called **arcs,** at an angular rate of 360° in 24 hours (15° per hour). The center of these circular paths and arcs is very near the star Polaris. The complete circular path can be seen for stars in the northern part of the sky around Polaris. Other stars rise over the eastern horizon and set at the western horizon.

MODELS TO ACCOUNT FOR CELESTIAL OBSERVATIONS. The most obvious way to explain the daily motion of celestial objects is to assume that the earth is stationary and that the celestial objects are revolving around it at a rate of 15° per hour. This is called the *geocentric* ("earth-centered") model. It is the model that was employed by the ancient Greek scientists and that was accepted up to the 16th century. However, the geocentric model fails to explain certain observed **terrestrial motions** (motions related to the earth). In modern times it has been replaced by the *heliocentric* ("sun-centered") model. In this model the earth is rotating on its axis at the rate of 15° per hour and is revolving around the sun once per year. (**Rotation** of a body is the turning of the body on its own axis, in the manner of a spinning toy top. **Revolution,** or revolving, of a body is its movement around another body in a path called an **orbit.**) The heliocentric model accounts for all observed motions of celestial objects and terrestrial objects in a simpler way than the geocentric model. (Additional discussion of these two models will be found on pages 42–44.)

MOTIONS OF THE PLANETS. As seen from the earth, the planets also exhibit daily motion similar to that of the stars, but over extended periods of time they appear to change position with respect to the *star field* around them. This apparent movement relative to the stars is not uniform. According to the heliocentric model, the apparent motion of the planets is the result of the revolution of the earth and the planets around the sun at different rates (see Figure 4-2 on page 31).

The **apparent diameter** of an object is the diameter or size the object appears to have to an observer, not the actual diameter. The apparent diameter of each planet changes in a regular, or cyclic, manner. This occurs because the distance of the planets from the earth varies as the planets and earth revolve around the sun. The closer a planet is to the earth, the larger its apparent diameter, just as a distant object on earth seems to become larger as we approach it.

When observed over a period of time, identifiable features of the planets, such as volcanoes, appear in different locations on the face of the planet. These changes in location occur in a uniform direction in a cyclic manner and therefore indicate that these planets rotate. Additional evidence indicates that all the planets rotate.

MOTIONS OF THE MOON. As viewed from the earth, the moon shares the daily motion of all celestial objects. In addition, it appears to move relative to the stars in an orbit around the earth at the rate of one revolution per 27⅓ days. The apparent diameter of the moon varies in a cyclic manner at the same rate. These observations can be explained by the revolution of the earth and the moon in elliptical orbits around the center of mass of the earth-moon system, while the system as a whole revolves around the sun.* The moon's changes in apparent diameter can be explained by the revolution of the moon around the earth in an elliptical orbit.

---

*Elliptical orbits are discussed on page 37.

Figure 4-2. Apparent motion of a planet. Diagram A shows successive positions of the earth and Mars along their orbits at monthly intervals during part of a particular year. The dashed arrows show the sight lines from the earth to some fixed star. These sight lines are practically parallel because of the great distance of the star. The solid arrows are the sight lines toward Mars. As the diagram shows, the sight line in January was to the right of the star. From January to March, Mars appeared to move to the left. From March to June it appeared to move to the right. From June to September, it appeared to move to the left again. As a result, the apparent position of Mars changed with respect to the star as shown in Diagram B. Because the orbits of the earth and Mars are tilted with respect to each other, the altitude of Mars with respect to the fixed star also changed. In the following year, a similar motion would be observed, but in a different region of the heavens.

Figure 4-3. Motions of the earth-moon system as viewed from above the North Pole. Diagram A shows that the centers of the earth and the moon revolve around their common center of mass. This center of mass is so near the earth's center that it is actually inside the earth, about 1700 kilometers below the surface. Diagram B shows the motion of the earth-moon system as it revolves around the sun. The oscillations of the orbits are greatly exaggerated. If drawn to scale, the radius of the moon's orbit in Diagram B would be about 1/50 inch.

MOON PHASES. Half of the moon is always receiving light from the sun at any given time. Since the moon revolves around the earth, an observer on the earth sees varying amounts of the lighted half as the moon changes position in its orbit. Those varying amounts of the lighted moon are known as its **phases** (see Figure 4-4).

Because the revolution of the moon around the earth-moon focus is cyclic, the phases of the moon are also cyclic. However, because of the revolution of the earth-moon system around the sun, the cycle of phases is somewhat longer than the time of one revolution of the moon. The period from one full moon to the next is 29½ days, whereas the period of revolution is 27⅓ days. (See Figure 4-5.)

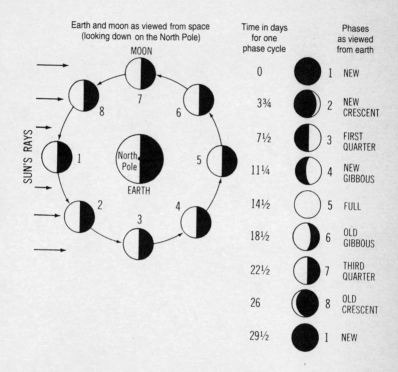

Figure 4-4. The phases of the moon. The half of the moon facing the sun at any given time is illuminated. The other half is dark. An observer on the earth sees varying portions of the illuminated half, depending on the position of the moon in its orbit. The appearance of the phases for eight positions in the cycle is illustrated.

MOTIONS OF THE SUN. Like all other visible celestial objects, the sun also goes through daily motion in the sky. The sun's apparent path, extending from sunrise to sunset, has the shape of an **arc** (part of a circle). As shown in Figure 4-6, that path changes position and length with the seasons. The greater the length of the path, the longer the daylight period. Figure 4-6 also shows how the position of the sun at sunrise and sunset varies predictably with the seasons.

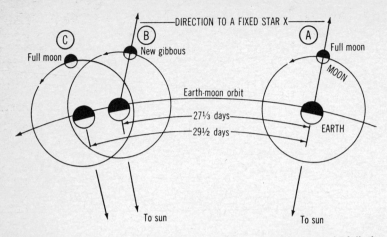

Figure 4-5. Period of one phase cycle. At Position A, the moon is full. At Position B, the moon has made one complete revolution about the earth. However, it is not full until it reaches Position C (about 2 days later).

Figure 4-6. The changing path of the sun during the year at 42° north latitude. Note that the path of the sun is longest on June 21, shortest on December 21, and average in length on March 24 and September 23.

ALTITUDE OF THE NOON SUN. The sun always reaches its highest position in the sky at local noon (see page 18). However, the altitude of the sun at noon depends on the time of year and the latitude of the observer. Only between latitudes 23½° N and 23½° S can the noon sun ever be directly overhead. Thus the noon sun is never directly overhead anywhere in the continental United States. Figure 4-7 shows how the latitude at which the noon sun is overhead changes during a year.

If you know the latitude at which the noon sun is directly overhead on a particular date, you can calculate the altitude of the noon sun for any other location on that date. First find the number of degrees between the latitude of the observer and the latitude at which the noon sun is overhead. Then subtract that number of degrees from 90°. For example, to find the altitude of the noon sun at 40° N on December 21, first note that on December 21 the noon sun is directly overhead at 23½° S. The number of degrees between 23½° S and 40° N is 63½° (23½° S to 0°, plus 0° to 40° N). Now subtract 63½° from 90°. The result is 26½°. This is the altitude of the noon sun at 40° N on December 21.

Figure 4-7. The changes in latitude where the sun is directly overhead (at the zenith point) at noon in the course of one year. Point 1—June 21   Point 3—Dec. 21   Point 2—Sept. 23   Point 4—March 21

ROTATION OF THE EARTH

The main motions of the earth are its rotation and its revolution. The earth's rotation is the spinning of the earth on its axis, the imaginary line from the North Pole to the South Pole through the planet. The earth rotates from *west to east* 360 degrees in 24 hours, an angular rate of 15 degrees an hour. The linear rotational speed (as in km/h) of a point on the earth's surface depends on its latitude. As shown in Figure 4-8, the circumference of the circle of rotation increases as you go from the poles toward the equator. Therefore, the linear speed of rotation also increases in the same way.

Figure 4-8. Circles of rotation showing linear rotation rates at different latitudes. Angular rotation rate is 15 degrees per hour at any latitude. Solar time changes 1 hour for each 15 degrees of longitude. When it is noon on the side of the earth facing the sun, it is midnight on the opposite side.

EVIDENCE OF ROTATION

1. The Foucault pendulum. When the Foucault pendulum is allowed to swing freely, its path will appear to change in a predictable way, as shown in Figure 4-9. This is evidence for the earth's rotation, because if the earth did not rotate, the pendulum would continue to swing in the original path (A-A'). What is really happening is that the earth is rotating under the pendulum, so that the pendulum's path appears to change.

Figure 4-9. Apparent motion of Foucault pendulum. An observer sees a pendulum swing in the direction A-A'. Several hours later, the pendulum has changed its direction of swing to the line B-B'. Actually, the pendulum swings in a fixed direction in space, while the earth, carrying the observer with it, rotates under the pendulum.

2. The Coriolis effect. The **Coriolis effect** (**Coriolis force**) is the tendency of all particles of matter moving at the earth's surface to be deflected from a straight-line path. The deflection is to the right in the Northern Hemisphere and to the left in the Southern Hemisphere. The deflection occurs because the earth is rotating, and therefore the earth's surface is moving with respect to the path of the particles. The following example can help to explain the effect: You are at the center of a merry-go-round that is rotating counterclockwise. Your friend is near the rim of the merry-go-round. You throw a ball directly at your friend. By the time the ball reaches the rim of the merry-go-round, your friend has been carried to the left. The ball reaches the rim at a point that is now to the right of your friend. With respect to the moving merry-go-round, the ball has been deflected to the right. In a similar manner, ocean currents and winds are deflected with respect to the earth's surface.

REVOLUTION OF THE EARTH

A planet's revolution is its motion around the sun in a path called an **orbit.** The shape of the earth's orbit (and those of the other planets) is a closed curve called an **ellipse.** Within the ellipse are two fixed points called **foci** (singular, **focus**). The sum of the distances between any point on the ellipse and the two foci is a constant; that is, the sum of those distances for one point is equal to the sum for any other point on the curve. The sun is at one of the foci of each planetary orbit in the solar system (see Figure 4-10).

The flattening of an ellipse is measured by its **eccentricity.**

$$\text{eccentricity of an ellipse} = \frac{\text{distance between foci}}{\text{length of major axis}} = \frac{d}{L}$$

If you measure d and L in the ellipse of Figure 4-10 and apply the formula, you should find the eccentricity to be 0.25. As the foci of an ellipse are brought closer together, the ellipse becomes more like a circle and the eccentricity decreases toward zero. The eccentricities of the planets are listed in *Solar System Data* in the *Earth Science Reference Tables.*

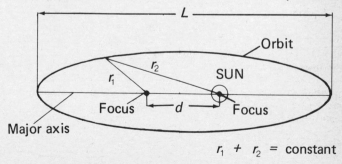

$$r_1 + r_2 = \text{constant}$$

Figure 4-10. An elliptical orbit of a planet with the sun at one focus. Flattening of ellipse and separation of foci are greatly exaggerated.

VARYING DISTANCE OF PLANETS FROM THE SUN. The elliptical shape of planetary orbits causes the planets to vary in distance from the sun during a revolution. For example, the earth is 147,000,000 kilometers from the sun when closest (**perihelion**, January 3) and 152,000,000 kilometers from the sun when farthest away (**aphelion**, July 4). The difference between these two distances is the same as the distance between the two foci (5,000,000 km). Since this distance is relatively small compared to the major axis (299,000,000 km), the eccentricity of the orbit is small (0.017) and the orbit is very nearly a circle.

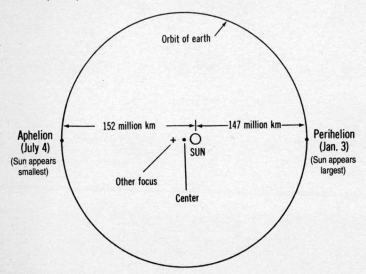

Figure 4-11. The earth's orbit. If drawn exactly to scale, the two foci would be about 1 mm apart.

The changing distance of the earth from the sun causes the sun's apparent diameter to change in a cyclic fashion during the year. The sun's apparent diameter is greatest on January 3 when the sun is closest to the earth and smallest on July 4 when it is farthest.

GRAVITATION. The earth and the other planets orbit the sun under the influence of **gravitation**, which is the attractive force that exists between any two objects in the universe. The gravitational force is proportional to the product of the masses of the objects and inversely proportional to the square of the distance between their centers. This can be expressed as

$$F \propto \frac{m_1 m_2}{d^2}$$

where m_1 and m_2 are the two masses, d is the distance between the *centers* of the two objects, and F is the gravitational force.

Figure 4-12. Cyclic energy transformation and changing orbital speed of a planet. Elliptical shape of orbit greatly exaggerated.

ORBITAL SPEED. The force of gravitation between the sun and a planet is always pulling the planet toward the sun. The planet does not fall into the sun because of the outward force related to its orbital motion. However, when the planet is in a part of its orbit that is bringing it closer to the sun, the force of gravitation is aiding the motion, causing the planet to speed up. The planet at such times is actually "falling" toward the sun, and some of its **potential energy** (stored energy or energy of position) is converted to **kinetic energy** (energy of motion). As the planet enters the part of its orbit that takes it away from the sun, the force of gravitation tends to oppose this motion. The planet's speed therefore decreases as it "climbs" to a higher distance from the sun. At such times its kinetic energy is being converted back to potential energy. Thus we see that there is a cyclic energy transformation between potential energy and kinetic energy as a planet revolves around the sun (see Figure 4-12). In the case of the earth, it is closest to the sun (perihelion) and has its greatest orbital speed around January 3. It is farthest from the sun (aphelion) and has its least orbital speed around July 4.

Changes in the orbital velocity of a planet always take place according to a definite principle: *An imaginary line connecting the sun and the planet always sweeps through equal areas during equal intervals of time.* This principle is illustrated in Figure 4-13. Since equal areas must be covered in equal intervals of time, the planet's orbital speed must be fastest at perihelion and slowest at aphelion.

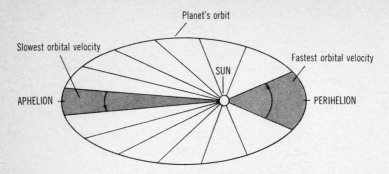

Figure 4-13. A line from the sun to a planet will sweep out each of these equal areas in the same time.

PLANET PERIOD. The **period** of a planet is the amount of time it takes the planet to make one orbit, or revolution, around the sun. This equals one **year** for that planet. The period of a planet is related to the planet's distance from the sun. The closer a planet is to the sun, the smaller its orbit, and the shorter its period. More precisely, for any planet the square of its period of revolution is proportional to the cube of its mean radius of orbit or mean distance from the sun. The relationship is expressed symbolically as $T^2 \propto R^3$, where T is the period of the planet and R is the mean radius of orbit. When T is expressed in earth years and R in Astronomical Units, then $T^2 = R^3$. One Astronomical Unit is the mean distance of the earth from the sun or about 150 million kilometers.

The relationship of period to distance can be easily verified. The period of Mars is 1.88 earth years and its distance from the sun is 1.52 times the average earth distance, or 1.52 Astronomical Units.

$$T = 1.88 \qquad\qquad R = 1.52$$
$$T^2 = 1.88 \times 1.88 \qquad R^3 = 1.52 \times 1.52 \times 1.52$$
$$= 3.53 \qquad\qquad\qquad = 3.51$$

Although the results are not equal, they are close enough to verify the relationship.

TIME AND EARTH MOTIONS

THE YEAR. The length of the **year** (or period of revolution) is equal to the time it takes the earth to make one revolution around the sun.

THE APPARENT SOLAR DAY. As explained on page 35, the sun reaches its highest point in the sky once each day at noon. The time it takes for the earth to rotate from noon to noon on two successive days at any fixed location on the earth is called the **apparent solar day.** Time based on the actual motions of the sun in the sky is called **apparent solar time,** or **sundial** time, because a sundial is used to measure it. As shown by Figure 4-14, the apparent solar day is always longer than one rotation of the earth. If the earth did not revolve in its orbit, it would take exactly one rotation to bring a point on the earth into the same position with respect to the sun. However, because the earth does move along its orbit, it has to rotate a small additional amount to bring the point into the same position relative to the sun.

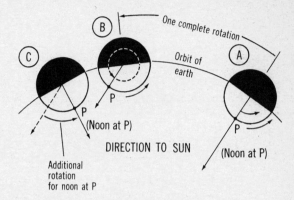

Figure 4-14. Length of apparent solar day. At Position A, it is noon at Point P on the earth. After one complete rotation, the earth is at Position B, but it is not yet noon at Point P. The earth must rotate an additional amount to bring Point P in line with the sun again, when it is again noon at P. The earth will have moved to Position C in this time. (The drawing is exaggerated to make the principle clear.)

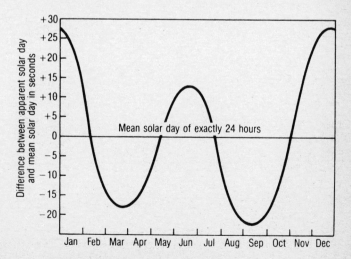

Figure 4-15. Variations in the length of the apparent solar day. This curve shows the difference between the apparent solar day and the mean solar day during the course of one year.

MEAN SOLAR DAY. If the earth moved around the sun in a circular orbit at constant speed, the apparent solar day would have a constant length. However, the earth's speed around the sun varies in a cyclic manner in the course of the year. As a result, the length of the apparent solar day also varies during the year. The inclination of the earth's axis, and the varying curvature of its orbit, also have an effect on the apparent solar day. The combination of these effects produces the cyclic variation in the apparent solar day shown in Figure 4-15. For convenience in timekeeping, a solar day of average length, called the **mean solar day,** has been established. This mean solar day has been divided into exactly 24 hours. On most days of the year, the apparent solar day is either slightly more or slightly less than 24 hours in length (as already noted in Figure 4-15).

MODELS FOR EXPLAINING CELESTIAL MOTIONS

GEOCENTRIC MODEL. An early concept of celestial objects and their motions is the **geocentric model** ("earth-centered"). In this model, the earth is stationary and all celestial objects revolve around it, as shown in Figure 4-16.

Figure 4-16. Geocentric model of celestial objects. The earth is stationary. The moon, sun, and fixed stars revolve about the earth in circular orbits at different speeds. The planets revolve in small circles, while the centers of these circles move about the earth in circular orbits. These additional circles for the planets are needed to explain their irregular motions.

Some of the major points about the geocentric model are:

1. It explains the apparent motions of celestial objects. The daily motion of the sun and stars is explained by their revolution around the earth. The irregular motion of the planets is explained by assuming that they move in small circular paths in addition to their revolution around the earth.

2. This model does not explain certain terrestrial motions, such as motions of the Foucault pendulum and the Coriolis effect.

3. The need for auxiliary circles for the planetary motions makes the model complex.

HELIOCENTRIC MODEL. The modern concept of the motions of celestial objects is the **heliocentric model** ("sun-centered"). In this model, the earth and the planets revolve around the sun; in addition, the earth rotates on its axis. (See Figure 4-17.)

Figure 4-17. Heliocentric model. The sun is stationary. The earth and the planets revolve about the sun at different speeds in elliptical orbits. The stars are stationary and are located at great distances from the solar system.

The major points about the heliocentric model are:

1. It explains the apparent motions of celestial objects. The daily motion is the result of the earth's rotation. The irregular motion of the planets is the result of the revolution of the earth and the planets around the sun at different rates.

2. This model accounts for observed terrestrial motions, such as motions of the Foucault pendulum and the Coriolis effect.

3. It is less complex than the geocentric model because each planet requires only one type of orbital motion.

VOCABULARY

celestial object	perihelion
daily motion	aphelion
arc	gravitation
terrestrial motions	orbital speed (or velocity)
rotation	potential energy
revolution (revolving)	kinetic energy
orbit	period (of revolution)
apparent diameter	year
phases (of the moon)	apparent solar day
Foucault pendulum	apparent solar time
Coriolis effect	sundial
ellipse (elliptical)	mean solar day
focus (of an ellipse)	geocentric model
eccentricity	heliocentric model

QUESTIONS ON TOPIC IV—THE EARTH'S MOTIONS

Questions in Recent Regents Exams (end of book)

June 1991: 3, 9–12, 61, 62, 64, 65, 104
June 1992: 3, 5, 6, 8, 10, 61, 62, 65
June 1993: 5, 6, 61–65
June 1994: 8, 9, 17, 24, 55, 61–65, 72, 75, 98

Questions from Earlier Regents Exams

1. According to the *Earth Science Reference Tables,* what is the approximate average density of the earth?   (1) 2.80 g/cm^3 (2) 5.52 g/cm^3 (3) 9.55 g/cm^3 (4) 12.0 g/cm^3

2. The apparent rising and setting of the sun as seen from the earth are caused by the   (1) rotation of the sun   (2) rotation of the earth   (3) revolution of the earth   (4) revolution of the sun

3. How many degrees does the sun appear to move across the sky in two hours?   (1) 15°   (2) 30°   (3) 45°   (4) 60°

4. If the earth rotated from north to south, the North Star would appear to   (1) set in the south   (2) set in the north   (3) move in a circle in the sky   (4) remain stationary

5. If viewed from the earth over a period of several years, the apparent diameter of Mars will   (1) decrease constantly   (2) increase constantly   (3) remain unchanged   (4) vary in a cyclic manner

6. How would a three-hour time exposure photograph of stars in the northern sky appear if the earth did *not* rotate?

(1)   (2)   (3)   (4)

7. An observer took a time-exposure photograph of Polaris and five nearby stars. How many hours were required to form these star paths?

(1) 6   (2) 2   (3) 8   (4) 4

8. A planet was viewed from earth for several hours. The diagrams below represent the appearance of the planet at four different times. The best inference that can be made based on the diagrams is that this planet is
(1) tilted on its axis   (2) changing seasons   (3) revolving   (4) rotating

Diagram A   Diagram B   Diagram C   Diagram D

Base your answers to questions 9 through 11 on the *Solar System Data Table* in the *Earch Science Reference Tables*.

9. Which planet has traveled around the sun more than once in your lifetime?   (1) Mars   (2) Uranus   (3) Neptune   (4) Pluto

10. On which of the following planets would the Coriolis effect be greatest?   (1) Mars   (2) Mercury   (3) Jupiter   (4) Neptune

11. Which planet has the most eccentric orbit?   (1) Venus   (2) Mars   (3) Saturn   (4) Pluto

Base your answers to questions 12 through 15 on the diagram below. The diagram represents the moon in various positions in its orbit around the earth. Letters *A* through *E* represent five of the moon's positions.

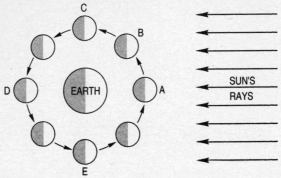

(NOT DRAWN TO SCALE)

12. Which diagram best represents the appearance of the moon to an observer on the earth when the moon is at position *B*?

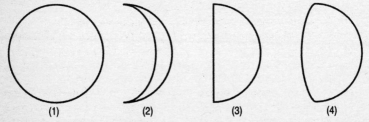

(1)   (2)   (3)   (4)

13. The moon would *not* be visible from the earth when the moon is at position   (1) *A*   (2) *E*   (3) *C*   (4) *D*

14. Why would an observer on earth see a complete cycle of phases of the moon in approximately one month?   (1) The moon rotates on its axis.   (2) The moon revolves around the earth.   (3) The earth rotates on its axis.   (4) The earth revolves around the sun.

15. If the distance of the moon from the earth were to increase, the length of time the moon would take to complete one revolution around the earth would   (1) decrease   (2) increase   (3) remain the same

16. To a person located at 43° north latitude, the sun appears to rise due east on   (1) December 22   (2) March 1   (3) March 21   (4) June 22

17. At noontime on June 21, the sun will make an angle of 23.5° with an observer's zenith if the observer is located at   (1) 0°   (2) 23.5°N   (3) 23.5°S   (4) 66.5°N

18. At 40° north latitude, for how many days a year is the sun in the zenith (directly overhead) position at noon?   (1) 1   (2) 2   (3) 3   (4) 0

19. In New York State, to see the sun at noon, one would look towards the   (1) north   (2) south   (3) east   (4) west

Base your answers to questions 20 through 23 on the diagram below. The diagram represents a plastic hemisphere upon which lines have been drawn to show the apparent paths of the sun on four days at a location in New York State. Two of the days are December 21 and June 21. The protractor is placed over the north-south line.

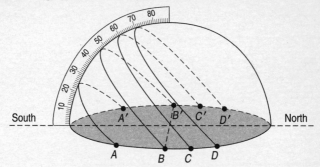

20. On which two dates could the sun have followed path C-C'? (1) October 22 and March 28   (2) September 9 and January 7   (3) January 27 and August 21   (4) May 7 and August 1

21. Which path was recorded on a day that had twelve hours of daylight and twelve hours of darkness?   (1) A-A'   (2) B-B'   (3) C-C'   (4) D-D'

22. Which would be the approximate length of the daylight period for the observer when the sun travels along the entire length of path A-A?'   (1) 9 hours   (2) 12 hours   (3) 15 hours   (4) 18 hours

23. Which observation about the sun's apparent path on June 21 is best supported by the diagram?   (1) The sun appears to move across the sky at a rate of 1° per hour.   (2) The sun's total daytime path is shortest on this date.   (3) Sunrise occurs north of east.   (4) Sunset occurs south of west.

24. According to the diagram below, the time at point C is closest to (1) 6 A.M.   (2) 12 noon   (3) 6 P.M.   (4) 12 midnight

25. A student in New York State obtained the data below by noting the altitude of the sun at noon for three consecutive months.

Month	Altitude of sun at noon
X	27.0°
Y	23.5°
Z	25.5°

The data for month Y were obtained during   (1) March   (2) June (3) September   (4) December

26. As one moves from the poles toward the equator, the linear velocity in km/hr of the earth's surface caused by the earth's rotation (1) decreases   (2) increases   (3) remains the same

27. The diagram below shows the rotating earth as it would appear from a satellite over the North Pole.

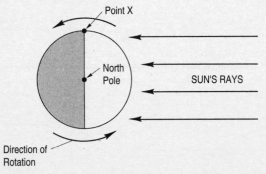

The time at point X is closest to   (1) 6 A.M.   (2) 12 noon   (3) 6 P.M. (4) 12 midnight

28. The Foucault pendulum provides evidence of the earth's (1) rotation   (2) revolution   (3) precession   (4) inclination

29. The diagram at the right represents a Foucault pendulum in a building in New York State. Points A and A' are fixed points on the floor. As the pendulum swings for six hours, it will   (1) appear to change position due to the earth's rotation (2) appear to change position due to the earth's revolution   (3) continue to swing between A and A' due to inertia   (4) continue to swing between A and A' due to air pressure

30. Planetary winds do not blow directly north or south because of (1) the Coriolis effect   (2) gravitational force   (3) magnetic force (4) centripetal force

31. The Coriolis effect provides evidence that the earth   (1) has a magnetic field   ((2) has an elliptical orbit   (3) revolves around the sun (4) rotates on its axis

32. Some stars that can be seen in New York State on a summer night cannot be seen on a winter night. This fact is a result of the   (1) rotation of the earth on its axis   (2) rotation of the stars around Polaris   (3) revolution of Polaris around the earth   (4) revolution of the earth around the sun

33. Based on the diagram below and the *Earth Science Reference Tables,* what is the eccentricity of the ellipse shown below?   (1) 1.0 (2) 0.5   (3) 0.25   (4) 0.13

34. If the pins in the diagram at the right were placed closer together, the eccentricity of the ellipse being constructed would   (1) decrease (2) increase   (3) remain the same

35. Which diagram best approximates the shape of the path of the earth as it travels around the sun?

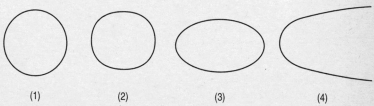

(1)   (2)   (3)   (4)

36. If the distance between the earth and the sun were increased, which change would occur?   (1) The apparent diameter of the sun would increase.   (2) The amount of insolation received by the earth would increase.   (3) The time for one earth rotation (rotation period) would double.   (4) The time for one earth revolution (orbital period) would decrease.

37. In the Northern Hemisphere, during which season does the earth reach its greatest distance from the sun?   (1) winter   (2) spring   (3) summer   (4) fall

38. If the distance from the earth to the sun were doubled, the gravitational attraction between the sun and earth would become   (1) one-fourth as great   (2) one-third as great   (3) twice as great   (4) four times as great

39. In the diagram below, letters *A* through *D* represent the locations of four observers on the earth's surface. Each observer has the same mass.

(NOT DRAWN TO SCALE)

The gravitational force is strongest between the center of the earth and the observer at location   (1) *A*   (2) *B*   (3) *C*   (4) *D*

40. Base your answer to the question on the diagram below, the metric scale in the *Earth Science Reference Tables,* and the equation for gravitational force.

Which would represent the change in gravitational force between sphere 1 and sphere 2 after sphere 2 is moved from position *A* to position *B*?   (1) ⅙ as great   (2) ½ as great   (3) ⅓ as great   (4) ⅑ as great

41. The diagram below represents a planet in orbit around a star. Which statement best describes how the planet's energy is changing as it moves from point *A* to point *B*?

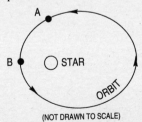

(NOT DRAWN TO SCALE)

(1) Kinetic energy is increasing and potential energy is decreasing.
(2) Kinetic energy is decreasing and potential energy is increasing.
(3) Both kinetic and potential energy are decreasing   (4) Both kinetic and potential energy are increasing.

42. When the orbital velocity of the earth is greatest, what is the season in the Northern Hemisphere?   (1) spring   (2) summer   (3) fall (4) winter

43. The elliptical shape of the earth's orbit causes   (1) Foucault pendulums to change direction   (2) the earth to have an oblate spheroid shape (3) the earth's axis to be inclined to its orbit   (4) changes in the orbital velocity of the earth

44. The diagram below shows a planet's orbit around the sun. At which location is the planet's orbital velocity greatest?   (1) A   (2) B   (3) C (4) D

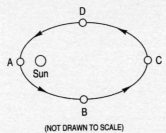

(NOT DRAWN TO SCALE)

45. Planet A has a greater mean distance from the sun than planet B. On the basis of this fact, which further comparison can be correctly made between the two planets?   (1) Planet A is larger.   (2) Planet A's revolution period is longer.   (3) Planet A's speed of rotation is greater. (4) Planet A's day is longer.

46. The diagram below shows the orbits of planets A and B in a star-planet system.

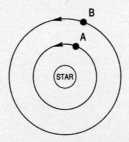

The period of revolution for planet B is 40 days. The period of revolution for planet A most likely is   (1) less than 40 days   (2) greater than 40 days (3) 40 days

47. Cities located on the same meridian (longitude) must have the same   (1) altitude   (2) latitude   (3) length of daylight   (4) solar time

48. When does local solar noon always occur for an observer in New York State?   (1) when the clock reads 12 noon   (2) when the sun reaches its maximum altitude   (3) when the sun is directly overhead   (4) when the sun is on the Prime Meridian

49. Upon which frame of reference is time based?   (1) the motions of the earth   (2) the longitude of an observer   (3) the motions of the moon   (4) the real motions of the sun

50. If the earth's rate of rotation decreased, there would be an increase in the   (1) length of the seasons   (2) sun's angle of insolation at noon   (3) number of observable stars at night   (4) length of time for one earth day

51. The graph below shows the time of apparent solar noon (maximum altitude of the sun) and the time of mean solar noon (clock time) during the year. How does the time of apparent solar noon compare with the time of mean solar noon?

(1) Apparent solar noon always occurs after mean solar noon.   (2) Apparent solar noon and mean solar noon never occur at the same time.   (3) The time of apparent solar noon changes with the seasons.   (4) The time of mean solar noon changes during the year.

52. For what reason did the heliocentric model of the universe replace the geocentric model of the universe?   (1) The geocentric model no longer predicted the positions of the constellations.   (2) The geocentric model did not predict the phases of the moon.   (3) The heliocentric model provided a simpler explanation of the motions of the planets.   (4) The heliocentric model proved that the earth rotates.

53. In the geocentric model (the earth at the center of the universe), which motion would occur?   (1) The earth would revolve around the sun.   (2) The earth would rotate on its axis.   (3) The moon would revolve around the sun.   (4) The sun would revolve around the earth.

54. Which observation can *not* be explained by a geocentric model?   (1) Stars follow circular paths around Polaris.   (2) The sun's path through the sky is an arc.   (3) A planet's apparent diameter varies.   (4) A freely swinging pendulum appears to change direction.

ENERGY. All earth processes result from the transfer of energy. **Energy** is the ability to do work.

ELECTROMAGNETIC ENERGY

Electromagnetic energy is energy that is radiated in the form of waves. All matter gives off electromagnetic energy unless it is at **absolute zero,** which is theoretically the lowest possible temperature and one at which the particles of matter have no motion. Electromagnetic energy has **transverse wave** properties, which means that the waves vibrate at right angles to the direction in which they are moving (see Figure 5-1). As an example, when a rope tied to a solid object is shaken, the particles making up the rope move up and down, but a transverse wave travels along the length of the rope.

Rope particles move up and down

ONE WAVELENGTH

ONE WAVELENGTH

Wave moves horizontally

Figure 5-1. A transverse wave in a rope at two moments a short time apart. As the particles of the rope move up and down, the form of the wave moves to the right. In an electromagnetic wave, there are no moving particles. Instead, there are varying electric and magnetic forces at right angles to the direction of propagation of the wave.

The different types of electromagnetic energy are distinguished by their different *wavelengths*. The **wavelength** is the distance from one crest of the wave to the next crest or between corresponding points on successive cycles. Figure 5-2 lists various forms of electromagnetic energy in order of increasing wavelength. This group of electromagnetic radiations is known as the **electromagnetic spectrum.**

INTERACTION OF ELECTROMAGNETIC ENERGY WITH AN ENVIRONMENT. When electromagnetic energy interacts with a material, it can be   (1) **refracted,** or bent in its passage through the material; (2) **reflected,** or bounced off the material;   (3) **scattered,** or refracted and/or reflected in various directions; or   (4) **absorbed,** or taken into the material.

SURFACE PROPERTIES AND ABSORPTION. The characteristics of a surface determine the quantity and type of electromagnetic energy that can be absorbed. For example, the darker and rougher the surface of a material, the more visible light will be absorbed. The better a material is at absorbing electromagnetic energy, the better it also is at giving off or radiating electromagnetic energy. Thus a dark-colored object will heat up fast in sunlight but will also cool off fast after sunset. A material that does not absorb electromagnetic energy well may reflect it well. Light-colored smooth surfaces do not absorb visible light well, but they are good reflectors of visible light.

METHODS OF ENERGY TRANSFER

The three methods of energy transfer are *conduction, convection,* and *radiation.* Conduction and convection refer to the transfer of heat energy in matter (solids, liquids, and gases). Radiation refers to the transfer of energy by electromagnetic waves in space and in matter.

CONDUCTION. **Conduction** is the transfer of heat energy from atom to atom or molecule to molecule through contact when atoms or molecules collide. Conduction is most effective in solids, because the atoms or molecules are closer together than in gases and liquids.

CONVECTION. **Convection** is the transfer of heat by movements in fluids (gases and liquids) caused by *differences in density* within the fluid. Warmer portions of the fluid usually have lower density and tend to rise above cooler portions. The result is a circulatory motion called a **convection cell** or **convection current** which transfers heat energy from one place to another. (See Figure 5-2.) Convection currents transfer heat through the earth's atmosphere, hydrosphere, and perhaps in parts of the mantle zone below the lithosphere.

RADIATION. In **radiation,** no medium is needed to transfer the transverse waves that carry electromagnetic energy; such energy can radiate from its source across empty space. This is the method by which the sun's electromagnetic energy gets through space to the other objects in the solar system. The higher an object's temperature, the more electromagnetic energy it gives off. (See the diagram *Electromagnetic Spectrum* in the *Earth Science Reference Tables.*)

Figure 5-2. Heating a room by convection.

TRANSFER OF ENERGY WITHIN A CLOSED SYSTEM

SOURCE AND SINK. Energy moves away from an area of high concentration, called a **source,** to an area of low concentration, called a **sink.** The energy will continue to move from the source to the sink until their energies are equal, establishing a **dynamic equilibrium.** At dynamic equilibrium an object loses and gains equal amounts of energy. If the dynamic equilibrium is between all forms of energy, then the temperature of the object or system will remain constant.

CONSERVATION OF ENERGY. In any energy system that is closed, or isolated, the total amount of energy remains the same. Thus the amount of energy lost by a source must equal the amount of energy gained by a sink. This concept, that energy is not created or destroyed but stays the same in amount in a closed system, is called the principle of **conservation of energy*.**

KINETIC AND POTENTIAL ENERGY. An object in motion has a kind of energy called **kinetic energy.** Objects or systems can also have a kind of energy called **potential energy,** which is energy related to position or state. It may be thought of as "stored" energy. Either of these two kinds of energy can be transformed into the other. For example, water at the top of a waterfall has potential energy because of its position with respect to the earth's center of mass. As the water falls to a lower level, some of its potential energy is transformed to kinetic energy, resulting in an increase in speed. In a swinging pendulum, there is a cyclic exchange of kinetic and potential energy. At the top of its swing, the pendulum has zero kinetic energy and maximum potential energy. As it passes through the low point of its swing, it has its maximum kinetic energy and minimum potential energy.

FRICTION AT INTERFACES. Transformations of energy occur when there is *friction.* For example, as a stream flows, some of its kinetic energy is transformed into heat energy at the interface between the stream and its bed. This transformation occurs because of friction between the moving water and the bed.

WAVELENGTH CHANGE. A good absorber of electromagnetic energy is also a good radiator. Often when electromagnetic energy is absorbed by an object, it is reradiated at a longer wavelength. This is very common at the earth's surface, where the relatively short-wavelength ultraviolet and visible radiations from the sun are absorbed and reradiated as longer-wavelength infrared radiations.

---

*Einstein's theory of relativity states that mass (or matter) and energy are equivalent, and that one can be converted to the other. The release of energy by radioactivity is an example of the conversion of mass to energy. The energy radiated by the sun and the other stars is also generated by the conversion of mass to energy within the stars.

TEMPERATURE AND HEAT

TEMPERATURE.   According to the modern theory of matter, the particles of every material are in continuous, random motion. The particles therefore have kinetic energy. At any moment, some of the particles have large kinetic energies, some have small kinetic energies, and some have intermediate kinetic energies. **Temperature** is a measure of the *average kinetic energy* of the particles of a body of matter. The greater the average kinetic energy of the particles, the higher the temperature of the body. If two bodies have the same temperature, the average kinetic energy of their particles is also the same. This is true regardless of the substances in the bodies.

TEMPERATURE SCALES.   The human senses respond to temperature by the sensations called "hot" and "cold." Temperature can be measured more accurately by instruments called *thermometers*. Thermometers indicate temperature on a scale marked off in *degrees*. There are several different temperature scales in use, with different sizes of degrees and different zero points. Relationships among three common temperature scales are given in the *Earth Science Reference Tables*.

HEAT.   If two bodies at different temperatures are placed in contact, some of the kinetic energy of the particles of the hotter body will be transferred to the particles of the cooler body. As a result, the particles of the cooler body will acquire more kinetic energy on the average, and its temperature will therefore rise. The particles of the hotter body will lose kinetic energy and its temperature will fall. This transfer of energy will continue until both bodies have the same temperature.

Energy that is transferred from a hotter body to a cooler one because of the difference in temperature is called **heat energy** or **thermal energy,** or more simply **heat.** For example, if a stone at a temperature of 80°C is placed in a container of water at 20°C, heat will flow from the stone into the water until both arrive at the same temperature. The heat transfer in this example occurs by conduction and convection.

QUANTITY OF HEAT.   Since an increase in temperature requires an increase in kinetic energy of the particles of a body, it takes twice as much heat energy to raise the temperature of a body 2° as to raise it 1°. It also takes twice as much heat energy to raise the temperature of 2 grams of a substance 1° as to raise the temperature of 1 gram of the same substance by this amount. In general, the quantity of heat involved in a temperature change of a given substance is directly proportional to the amount of temperature change and the mass of the substance.

When a substance "cools off," that is, when its temperature decreases, it releases the same amount of heat energy that was needed to raise its temperature by the same number of degrees. This is an example of the conservation of energy as applied to heat.

THE CALORIE.   The relationship between quantity of heat, mass of material, and temperature change can be used to define a unit of heat called the *calorie*. For this purpose, water is used as the standard material. One **calorie** is defined as the quantity of heat needed to raise the temperature of one gram of liquid water by one degree Celsius. Since one calorie is needed for each gram of water and for each degree Celsius of temperature change, the number of calories needed to change the temperature of a given mass of water by a given number of degrees can be calculated by the following formula:

No. of calories =
mass of water in grams × temperature change in °C × 1 cal/g/°C

Example

How many calories of heat must be added to 10 grams of liquid water to raise its temperature 15°C?

Solution:

$$\text{No. of cal} = 10 \text{ g} \times 15°C \times 1 \text{ cal/g/°C}$$
$$= 150 \text{ cal}$$

SPECIFIC HEAT. It takes one calorie to raise the temperature of one gram of water one degree Celsius. It takes only about 0.2 calorie (⅕ as much) to raise the temperature of one gram of a typical rock one degree Celsius. The quantity of heat needed to raise the temperature of one gram of any substance one degree Celsius is called the **specific heat** of that substance. The specific heat of the rock is 0.2 cal/g/°C. The specific heat of water is 1.0 cal/g/°C. Liquid water has the highest specific heat of naturally occurring substances. All other naturally occurring substances have a specific heat less than 1 (see the *Earth Science Reference Tables*). Therefore, for equal masses, the same amount of heat causes them to heat up or cool off faster than water.

HEAT LOST OR GAINED. The amount of heat lost or gained by a substance (in calories) equals the mass (in grams) times the temperature change (in °C) times the specific heat of the substance. (See *Equations and Proportions* in the *Earth Science Reference Tables*.)

Example

How much heat is needed to heat 15 grams of granite from 15°C to 20°C if the specific heat of the granite is 0.19 cal/g/°C?

Solution:

$$\text{Temperature change} = 20°C - 15°C = 5°C$$
$$\text{No. of cal} = 15 \text{ g} \times 5°C \times 0.19 \text{ cal/g/°C}$$
$$= 14.25 \text{ cal}$$

HEAT ENERGY AND CHANGES OF PHASE

LATENT HEAT. Matter may exist in the solid, liquid, or gaseous phase. As long as a material is in a single one of these phases, its temperature rises as heat is added to it. If, however, the material begins to *change* phase, for example, from solid to liquid, its temperature *remains the same* as heat is added to it. During the phase change, the added heat energy is not increasing the kinetic energy of the molecules, and therefore the temperature does not change. The added heat energy is being converted to a kind of *potential energy* called **latent heat.**

HEAT LOST OR GAINED IN PHASE CHANGE.   When the change of phase is from a solid to a liquid or from a liquid to a gas, latent heat must be gained by the substance. When the phase change is from a gas to a liquid or from a liquid to a solid, latent heat must be lost by the substance. The heat gained (or lost) in a phase change is equal to the product of the mass times the latent heat (change in potential energy) per unit mass. The latent heat varies with the particular substance and type of phase change.

Figure 5-3. Heating curve for water. The graph shows the temperature change of one gram of water as heat is added at a constant rate (50 calories per minute). If read from right to left, the graph is the corresponding cooling curve.

LATENT HEAT AND PHASE CHANGE OF WATER.   Figure 5-3 shows how the temperature of a fixed amount of water changes as it is heated at a constant rate from ice at − 100°C to gaseous water (water vapor) at 200°C. The temperature is plotted against time in minutes (upper scale of the graph) and the corresponding amount of heat added (lower scale of the graph). It can be seen that the temperature remains constant at 0°C for almost 2 minutes while the water is changing from the solid phase (ice) to the liquid phase. There is another constant-temperature interval of more than 10 minutes at 100°C while the water is changing from the liquid phase to the gaseous phase. The reason for these intervals of constant temperature is that the heat being added at those times is being changed to latent heat (potential energy). The latent heat for the change from solid to liquid water (heat of fusion) is 80 calories per gram; for the change from liquid to gas, the latent heat (heat of vaporization) is 540 calories per gram.

THE EARTH'S ENERGY SUPPLY

SOLAR ENERGY.   Most of the energy of the earth comes from electromagnetic radiations from the sun. The sun gives off (radiates), and the earth receives, a wide range of electromagnetic energy radiations of various wavelengths. This solar electromagnetic spectrum includes X rays, ultraviolet rays, visible light, and infrared rays. Of all the types of electromagnetic radiations from the sun, the one of greatest intensity is visible light (see Figure 6-1 on page 65).

RADIOACTIVE DECAY.   The atoms of certain elements, such as uranium and radium, are unstable and tend to break down into more stable atoms of other elements. This natural, spontaneous breakdown of unstable atoms is called **radioactivity** or **radioactive decay.** It is a process that releases energy and that continues at a constant rate for any particular radioactive element, unaffected by changes in temperature, pressure, or other environmental conditions. Radioactive decay of elements within the earth is an additional source of energy for many earth processes, such as mountain building and volcanic activity.

VOCABULARY

energy	source
electromagnetic energy	sink
absolute zero	dynamic equilibrium
transverse wave	conservation of energy
wavelength	kinetic and potential energy
electromagnetic spectrum	dynamic equilibrium
refraction	temperature
reflection	heat energy
scattering	calorie
absorption	specific heat
conduction	phase change
convection cell or	latent heat
convection current	radioactivity or radioactive
radiation	decay

QUESTIONS ON TOPIC V—ENERGY IN EARTH PROCESSES

Questions in Recent Regents Exams (end of book)

June 1991:   15, 17, 66–70, 90, 103
June 1992:   11, 12, 66–70
June 1993:   12, 66–70
June 1994:   5, 11, 12, 29

Questions from Earlier Regents Exams

1. At which temperature would an object *not* radiate electromagnetic energy?   (1) 100°C   (2) 0° Fahrenheit   (3) 0° Celsius   (4) absolute zero

2. The various forms of electromagnetic energy are distinguished from one another by their   (1) temperature   (2) wavelengths   (3) longitudinal wave properties   (4) speed of travel

3. As electromagnetic energy from a heat source interacts with its surroundings, it is being absorbed and   (1) reflected, only   (2) refracted, only   (3) scattered, only   (4) reflected, refracted, and scattered

4. Which would absorb the most solar radiation, if you assume that each covers an equal geographic area?   (1) a freshwater lake   (2) a snow field   (3) a sandy beach   (4) a forest

5. Which type of surface would most likely be the best reflector of electromagnetic energy?   (1) dark-colored and rough   (2) dark-colored and smooth   (3) light-colored and rough   (4) light-colored and smooth

6. An object that is a good radiator of electromagnetic waves is also a good   (1) insulator from heat   (2) reflector of heat   (3) absorber of electromagnetic energy   (4) refractor of electromagnetic energy

7. Which process transfers heat from one part of a solid object to another part of the object by direct contact when molecules collide? (1) radiation   (2) advection   (3) conduction   (4) convection

8. By which method is energy transferred by density differences? (1) absorption   (2) conduction   (3) convection   (4) radiation

9. Water is being heated in a beaker as shown below.

Heat Source

Which drawing shows the most probable movement of water in the beaker due to the heating?

(1)   (2)   (3)   (4)

10. At which temperature will an object radiate the greatest amount of electromagnetic energy? [Refer to the *Earth Science Reference Tables.*] (1) 0° Fahrenheit   (2) 5° Celsius   (3) 10° Fahrenheit   (4) 230 Kelvins

11. What method of energy transfer requires no medium for transfer? (1) conduction   (2) convection   (3) advection   (4) radiation

12. An ice cube is placed in a glass of water at room temperature. Which heat exchange occurs between the ice and the water within the first minute?   (1) The ice cube gains heat and the water loses heat.   (2) The ice cube loses heat and the water gains heat.   (3) Both the ice cube and the water gain heat.   (4) Both the ice cube and the water lose heat.

13. An example of a heat sink is   (1) a glacier on a summer day   (2) magma from an erupting volcano   (3) steam from heated ground water (4) an ocean current beginning at the equator

14. The environment is in dynamic equilibrium when it is gaining (1) less energy than it is losing   (2) more energy than it is losing   (3) the same amount of energy as it is losing

15. In a closed system, the amount of energy lost by a heat source (1) is less than the amount of energy gained by heat sink   (2) is greater than the amount of energy gained by a heat sink   (3) equals the amount of energy gained by a heat sink

Questions 16–20 refer to the diagram below. A student is using the apparatus shown to perform an investigation. The two calorimeters contain equal amounts of water, and the metal bar is touching the water inside each calorimeter. At the beginning of the investigation, the temperature of the water was 100°C in calorimeter *A* and 20°C in calorimeter *B*. The room temperature is 20°C.

16. At the start of the investigation, which could be considered a heat source?   (1) the water in calorimeter *A*   (2) the water in calorimeter *B*   (3) the air surrounding the calorimeters   (4) the metal bar between the calorimeters

17. If this were a closed system, what would be the temperature when the system reaches equilibrium?   (1) 100°C   (2) 75°C   (3) 60°C   (4) 40°C

18. Which conclusion should the student make after actually performing this investigation?   (1) The energy gained by the cold water equaled the energy lost by the hot water.   (2) The energy gained by the cold water was less than the energy lost by the hot water.   (3) The change in temperature of the cold-water thermometer equaled the change in temperature of the hot-water thermometer.   (4) Energy was transferred between the two calorimeters primarily by radiation.

19. Which procedure would increase the amount of heat energy that is actually gained by calorimeter *B*?   (1) increasing the length of the metal bar   (2) increasing the thickness of the metal bar   (3) circulating air over the metal bar   (4) placing insulation around the metal bar

20. Which graph best represents the probable relationship between the temperatures of the two calorimeters and the time for this heat transfer investigation?

HOT-WATER CAL.
COOL-WATER CAL.

21. During a volcanic eruption, a rock is thrown upward into the air from point *A* to point *B* as shown in the diagram at the right. Which graph below best represents the relationship between the height of the rock and its potential energy (*PE*) as it rises?

VOLCANO

22. How do the wavelengths of electromagnetic energy absorbed by earth materials compare to the wavelengths reradiated by earth materials?   (1) The reradiated wavelengths are shorter.   (2) The reradiated wavelengths are longer.   (3) The absorbed and reradiated wavelengths are the same.

23. The temperature of an object is determined by the   (1) average kinetic energy of its molecules   (2) average potential energy of its molecules   (3) total kinetic energy of the object   (4) total potential energy of the object

24. According to the *Earth Science Reference Tables*, at which temperature will ice melt under normal conditions?   (1) 0 K   (2) 32 K (3) 212 K   (4) 273 K

25. According to the *Earth Science Reference Tables*, how many calories of heat energy must be added to 5 grams of liquid water to change its temperature from 10°C to 30°C?   (1) 5 cal   (2) 20 cal   (3) 100 cal (4) 150 cal

26. Equal masses of lead, granite, basalt, and water at 5°C are exposed to equal quantities of heat energy. Which would be the first to show a temperature rise of 10°C?   (1) lead   (2) granite   (3) basalt   (4) water

27. According to the *Earth Science Reference Tables*, how many calories of heat energy must be added to 10 grams of iron to raise its temperature 10°C?   (1) 0.11 cal   (2) 1.1 cal   (3) 11 cal   (4) 110 cal

28. Based on the *Earth Science Reference Tables*, what is the total amount of energy gained by a 100-gram piece of basalt when it is heated from 20.0°C to 60.0°C?   (1) 40.0 calories   (2) 800. calories   (3) 4,000 calories   (4) 6,000 calories

29. The change from the vapor phase to the liquid phase is called (1) evaporation   (2) condensation   (3) precipitation   (4) transpiration

30. Water vapor crystallizes in the atmosphere to form snowflakes. Which statement best describes the exchange of heat energy during this process?   (1) Heat energy is transferred from the atmosphere to the water vapor.   (2) Heat energy is released from the water vapor into the atmosphere.   (3) Heat energy is transferred equally to and from the water vapor.   (4) No heat energy is exchanged between the atmosphere and the water vapor.

31. Two identical towels are hanging on a clothesline in the sun. One towel is wet; the other is dry. The wet towel feels much cooler than the dry towel because the   (1) dry towel receives more heat energy from the sun   (2) dry towel has more room for heat storage than the wet towel   (3) presence of water in the wet towel requires an additional amount of heat energy to bring about a temperature change   (4) water in the wet towel prevents absorption of heat energy

32. Which process results in a release of latent heat energy? (1) melting of ice   (2) heating of liquid water   (3) condensation of water vapor   (4) evaporation of water

33. Water loses energy when it changes phase from   (1) liquid to solid   (2) solid to liquid   (3) liquid to gas   (4) solid to gas

Base your answers to question 34 through 40 on the *Earth Science Reference Tables* and the graph below. The graph shows the temperatures recorded when a sample of water was heated from −100°C to 200°C. The water received the same amount of heat every minute.

34. For the time on the graph represented by the line from point *B* to point *C*, the water was   (1) freezing   (2) melting   (3) condensing (4) boiling

35. At which point in time would most of the water be in the liquid phase?   (1) 1 minute   (2) 14 minutes   (3) 16 minutes   (4) 4 minutes

36. How many calories were required to change 10. grams of liquid water at point D to water vapor at point E?   (1) 500 cal   (2) 800 cal   (3) 1,000 cal   (4) 5,400 cal

37. What is the rate of temperature change between points C and D? (1) 10 C°/min   (2) 25 C°/min   (3) 50 C°/min   (4) 150 C°/min

38. The greatest amount of energy was absorbed by the water between points   (1) A and B (2) B and C (3) C and D (4) D and E

39. During which time interval was the rate of temperature change the greatest?   (1) A to B (2) B to C (3) C to D (4) D to E

40. What is the most probable explanation for the constant temperature between points D and E on the graph?   (1) The added heat was radiated as fast as it was absorbed.   (2) The added heat was lost to the surroundings.   (3) The added heat changed liquid water to water vapor. (4) The added heat changed water vapor to liquid water.

41. What is the major source of energy for the earth?   (1) electrical storms   (2) radioactive decay of earth materials   (3) the sun   (4) thermal currents in the mantle

42. The source of energy for the high temperatures found deep within the earth is   (1) tidal friction   (2) incoming solar radiation   (3) decay of radioactive materials   (4) meteorite bombardment of the earth

INSOLATION

SOLAR RADIATION. As stated on page 53, every body of matter that is not at absolute zero radiates electromagnetic energy. This energy is radiated over a portion of the electromagnetic spectrum, with more of the energy radiated at some wavelengths than at others. The rate at which energy is radiated is called the *intensity* of the radiation. The higher the temperature of the matter, the shorter the wavelength at which the maximum intensity of radiation occurs. At the temperature of the sun, the maximum intensity of radiation occurs in the range of visible wavelengths.

INSOLATION. Insolation (INcoming SOLar radiATION) is the portion of the sun's radiation that is received by the earth. Figure 6-1 shows how the intensity of insolation varies with wavelength. The maximum intensity occurs in the visible range, but about 50% of the total energy received is infrared, a type of long-wave radiation.

Figure 6-1. Intensity of insolation received and radiated by the earth's surface. Total amount of energy is proportional to the area under the curves. About 50% of the insolation received at the surface is in the infrared range of wavelengths, but 100% of the radiated energy is in this range. (The terrestrial radiation curve is not drawn to the same scale as the insolation curves. If drawn to the same scale, it would be much flatter and would extend much farther to the right.)

EFFECTS OF THE ATMOSPHERE ON INSOLATION. Figure 6-1 also shows that the insolation reaching the earth's surface is different from the insolation entering the earth's upper atmosphere because of *absorption, reflection,* and *scattering* by the atmosphere. Some of the specific effects of the atmosphere on insolation are as follows:

1. Nearly all the ultraviolet radiation is absorbed by the atmosphere.

2. Most of the visible light passes through the atmosphere because the atmosphere is transparent to it.

3. Much infrared radiation is absorbed by water vapor (gaseous water) and carbon dioxide.

4. When clouds are present, much of the incident (incoming) insolation is reflected. For the earth as a whole on a typical day, it is estimated that about 25% of incident insolation is reflected by the cloud cover.

5. *Aerosols* cause random reflection, or scattering, of insolation. **Aerosols** are finely dispersed solids and liquids suspended in air. The dispersed materials include dust, ice crystals, liquid water droplets, and various air pollutants. As the concentration of aerosols increases, the scattering of insolation also increases, thus reducing the amount of insolation that reaches the earth's surface.

ABSORPTION AND RADIATION OF INSOLATION. When insolation reaches the earth's surface, some of it is reflected and some is absorbed, as explained in the next section. Insolation that is absorbed by the earth's surface is converted to heat and tends to raise the temperature of the surface. However, since the earth's surface is not at absolute zero, it also radiates electromagnetic energy, thus tending to lower its temperature. This energy emitted at the earth's surface is called **terrestrial radiation,** or ground radiation. Over a period of time, the amount of energy absorbed from insolation is equal to terrestrial radiation, and a temperature (or radiative) balance exists (see page 72). Because the earth's temperature is much lower than the sun's, the earth radiates energy at much longer infrared wavelengths. Figure 6-1 indicates the relationship between the wavelengths of insolation and terrestrial radiation emitted from the earth's surface.

INTERACTION OF INSOLATION AT THE EARTH'S SURFACE. When insolation reaches the earth's surface, many factors affect what happens to it. Some of these are as follows:

1. The darker or rougher the surface, the more insolation is absorbed and the less is reflected.

2. Ice and snow reflect almost all of the insolation, keeping areas with ice and snow cooler than they would otherwise be.

3. The altitude of the sun in the sky determines the **angle of insolation,** that is, the angle at which insolation will hit the earth's surface. The lower the angle of insolation, the more insolation is reflected and the less is absorbed.

4. The evaporation of water and the melting of ice and snow transform insolation into latent potential energy which does not raise the temperature of the surface. The more evaporation or melting occurring in an area, the smaller will be the amount of insolation available to heat the area; thus the temperatures will be lower than would otherwise be the case.

LAND AND WATER HEATING.   With equal amounts of insolation, an area consisting largely of water will heat up and cool off more slowly than an equal area of land. There are several reasons for this:

1. Water has a much higher specific heat than land.

2. Water is highly transparent to insolation: therefore the insolation is absorbed to a greater depth.

3. Convection can occur in water, thus distributing the absorbed energy through a much larger volume than is the case with land.

THE GREENHOUSE EFFECT.   Although the atmosphere allows much of the insolation entering it to pass through to the earth's surface, it absorbs most of the energy radiated by the surface. The reason for this is that the longer infrared radiations are absorbed to a large extent by the carbon dioxide and water vapor in the atmosphere. This absorption warms the atmosphere and causes it to act as a heat "blanket," which reduces the loss of energy to outer space and makes the earth's surface warmer than it would otherwise be. This process by which the atmosphere transmits short-wave energy and absorbs radiated long-wave energy (preventing its immediate escape into space) is called the **greenhouse effect.**

In recent years there has been concern that the greenhouse effect may be causing an increase in earth temperatures. It is thought that release of carbon dioxide into the atmosphere (from the burning of fuels) is increasing the greenhouse effect and heating the planet. This heating could result in environmental problems such as rising sea levels caused by melting glaciers.

VARIATIONS OF INSOLATION

INTENSITY OF INSOLATION.   The rate at which solar energy is received by a given area per unit of time is the **intensity of insolation.** It can be measured in calories per square meter per second.

EFFECT OF ANGLE OF INSOLATION ON INTENSITY AND TEMPERATURE.   When insolation is perpendicular to a surface (that is, striking the surface at an angle of 90°) its intensity is a maximum, because the insolation is concentrated in the smallest possible area. As the angle of insolation decreases from 90° toward zero, the same amount of insolation is spread out over greater and greater areas, as shown by Figure 6-2 (page 68). Therefore the intensity of insolation becomes smaller as the angle becomes smaller. At a high angle of insolation (and therefore higher intensity of insolation), the heating effect of insolation is greater and temperatures are higher.

EARTH'S SHAPE AND INTENSITY OF INSOLATION. The sun's energy reaches the earth as a bundle of parallel rays. If the earth were flat and perpendicular to these rays, the intensity of insolation would be the same everywhere on the earth's surface. However, the earth's surface is nearly a sphere. As a result, at any given time there is just one place where the insolation is perpendicular to the surface; at all other places, the angle of insolation is less than 90°. Therefore the intensity of insolation varies over the earth because of the curvature of its surface.

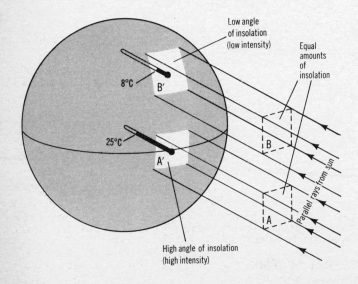

Figure 6-2. Because of the spherical shape of the earth, the parallel rays from the sun strike different parts of the surface at different angles. In high latitudes, where the angle is lower, the same amount of insolation spreads out over a larger area, thus resulting in a lower intensity than where the angle is higher.

INTENSITY OF INSOLATION IN RELATION TO LATITUDE. As shown in Fig. 6-3, insolation is perpendicular to the earth's surface at the equator at each of the **equinoxes** (March 21 and September 23). The rays of **perpendicular insolation** are known as **direct** or **vertical rays.** At each equinox, the intensity of insolation is maximum at the equator, where the direct rays strike, and it decreases with increasing latitude. At the **summer solstice** (June 21), the direct rays strike the earth at 23½°N latitude (the Tropic of Cancer). This is then the latitude of maximum intensity, and the intensity is less at any other latitude. At the **winter solstice** (December 21), the direct rays and the maximum intensity are at 23½°S latitude (the Tropic of Capricorn).

Figure 6-3. Intensity of insolation in relation to latitude. At any given time, intensity of insolation is a maximum at the latitude of the vertical rays, and is less at other latitudes.

INTENSITY OF INSOLATION IN RELATION TO SEASON. As the earth travels along its orbit around the sun, the angle of insolation at any given latitude varies with the seasons, depending on how far from the direct rays the given latitude is. The seasonal change in the maximum angle of insolation for a location at 42°N latitude is shown in Figure 6-4. For each degree of latitude a location is away from the position of 90° (perpendicular) insolation, the angle of insolation is one degree less. (See Table 6-1 on page 71.)

Figure 6-4. Maximum angle of insolation (at noon) at 42° north latitude at different seasons.

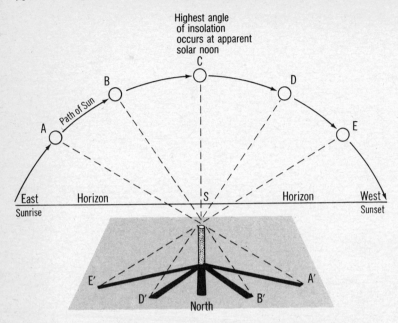

Figure 6-5. The shadow of a vertical post indicates how the angle of insolation varies during the day. The higher the angle of insolation, the shorter the shadow and the greater the intensity. Maximum angle and intensity occur at apparent solar noon.

INTENSITY OF INSOLATION IN RELATION TO TIME OF DAY.   The angle of insolation is the same as the altitude of the sun. On any given day, the altitude of the sun varies from zero at sunrise, to a maximum at apparent solar noon, and back to zero again at sunset. The angle of insolation, and hence the intensity of insolation, also vary during the day in the same way, as shown by the changing length of the shadow in Figure 6-5.

DURATION OF INSOLATION.   **Duration of insolation** is the length of time that insolation is received each day. That is, it is the number of hours that the sun is visible each day. The duration of insolation varies with latitude and with the seasons. Figure 4-6 on page 34 shows how the length of the sun's path through the sky varies during the year. The duration of insolation is proportional to the length of the path. There is one hour of insolation for each 15° of path. Thus, the longer the path, the greater the duration of insolation. Duration of insolation is greatest in the continental United States at the summer solstice (June 21), least at the winter solstice (December 21), and an average length, 12 hours, at the equinoxes (March 21 and September 23). See Table 6-1.

TEMPERATURES IN RELATION TO INSOLATION.   The surface of the earth continuously radiates energy, mostly in the infrared wave-

TABLE 6-1. ANGLE AND DURATION OF INSOLATION

Latitude	SUMMER SOLSTICE JUNE 21 Angle of Insolation at 12 Noon	Duration of Insolation	EQUINOXES MARCH 21 SEPTEMBER 23 Angle of Insolation at 12 Noon	Duration of Insolation	WINTER SOLSTICE DECEMBER 21 Angle of Insolation at 12 Noon	Duration of Insolation
90°N	23½°	24 Hours	0°	12 Hours	—	0 Hours
80°N	33⅓°	24	10°	12	—	0
70°N	43½°	24	20°	12	—	0
66½°N	47°	24	23½°	12	0°	0
60°N	53½°	18½	30°	12	6½°	5½
50°N	63½°	16¼	40°	12	16½°	7¾
40°N	73½°	15	50°	12	26½°	9
30°N	83½°	14	60°	12	36½°	10
23½°N	90°	13½	66½°	12	43°	10½
20°N	86½°	13¼	70°	12	46½°	10¾
10°N	76½°	12½	80°	12	56½°	11½
0°	66½°	12	90°	12	66½°	12
10°S	56½°	11½	80°	12	76½°	12½
20°S	46½°	10¾	70°	12	86½°	13¼
23½°S	43°	10½	66½°	12	90°	13½
30°S	36½°	10	60°	12	83½°	14
40°S	26½°	9	50°	12	73½°	15
50°S	16½°	7¾	40°	12	63½°	16¼
60°S	6½°	5½	30°	12	53½°	18½
66½°S	0°	0	23½°	12	47°	24
70°S	—	0	20°	12	43½°	24
80°S	—	0	10°	12	33½°	24
90°S	—	0	0°	12	23½°	24

lengths. The rate of radiation depends on the temperature, being greater when the temperature of the surface is higher, and less when it is lower. The temperature of the earth's surface at any particular location varies through the day, and the average daily temperature varies through the year. This variation depends on the balance between the energy being gained from insolation and the energy being lost by terrestrial radiation. When the energy is being gained at a greater rate than it is being lost, the temperature rises. When energy is being lost faster than it is being gained, the temperature falls. Temperatures are generally higher when the intensity of insolation is greater; they are also higher when the duration of insolation is longer.

TIMES OF MAXIMUM AND MINIMUM TEMPERATURES.
   1. During the year. It might be thought at first that the time of maximum temperature would occur at the time of maximum insolation, and the minimum temperature at the time of minimum insolation. This

is not the case, however. The times of maximum and minimum temperature occur somewhat later than the times of maximum and minimum insolation. In latitudes north of 23½°N, for example, the maximum intensity of insolation and the maximum duration of insolation occur on June 21, but the time of highest daily temperatures occurs toward the end of July or early in August. (See Figure 6-6.)

The reason for this is that as the intensity and duration of insolation increase during the spring, each day the surface receives more energy of insolation than it loses by radiation. Consequently, each day the average temperature goes up slightly. On June 21, more energy is gained than is lost; the temperature is still rising as a result. On June 22, a little less energy is received than on June 21. However, the amount received is still more than the amount lost. Therefore the temperature continues to go up. This continues until the rate of incoming energy finally drops below the rate of energy loss by radiation. At that time (usually in late July or early August) the surface temperature begins to drop.

Similarly, the earth north of 23½°N is not at its coolest during the time of minimum angle and duration of insolation on December 21. This occurs because the area continues to lose more energy than is gained by insolation until some time in January or February, when the region reaches its coolest temperature.

2. During the day. The hottest part of an average day is some time in midafternoon, not at apparent solar noon when insolation is greatest (see Figure 6-7). The coolest part of an average day is slightly after sunrise because the earth continues to lose heat during nighttime until after insolation begins at sunrise.

RADIATIVE BALANCE. If an object is in **radiative balance,** it gains the same amount of energy that it gives off, and average temperatures remain the same. Points X and Y in Figure 6-6 indicate the times when a given place on earth is in radiative balance. The graph (Figure 6-8)

Figure 6-6. Average daily temperatures, insolation, and terrestrial radiation for mid-latitudes of the Northern Hemisphere during a year.

Figure 6-7. Typical variation in air temperature just above surface, insolation, and terrestrial radiation in the course of one day.

can be used to illustrate average temperatures for the eastern United States, which we will assume reflect average temperature changes of the earth. This graph illustrates the following points:

1. Annual measurements of temperature indicate (by changing) that the earth is not in radiative balance on a yearly basis.

2. Intermediate measurements (decades) indicate little change in average decade temperatures; thus the earth is in radiative balance over periods of decades.

The graph in Figure 6-9 on page 74 illustrates that the earth is not in radiative balance over very large periods of time. At different times during the earth's history, the earth has cooled off and glaciers have covered large portions of the earth's surface.

Figure 6-8. Estimated annual temperatures of the eastern seaboard of the United States, centered on Philadelphia, for a period of several decades.

Figure 6-9. Estimated average temperature of the earth during the Pleistocene Ice Age.

SEASONS

The **seasons** are the four divisions of the year that are characterized by different types of weather conditions. For most of the earth, the major difference in the seasons is difference in temperature.

DIRECT CAUSE OF THE SEASONS. The seasonal changes in temperature and other weather conditions are the *direct* result of the cyclic variations in intensity and duration of insolation that occur during the year. These variations were described on pages 68–70.

INDIRECT CAUSES OF THE SEASONS. The variations in insolation that cause the seasons are themselves the result of factors that may be called the *indirect* causes of the seasons. These indirect causes are the following:

   1. **Tilt of the earth's axis.** As Figure 6-10 (page 75) shows, the earth's axis is inclined at an angle of 23½° with respect to a line perpendicular to the plane of its orbit.

   2. **Parallelism of the earth's axis.** Regardless of the position of the earth in its orbit, its axis always points in the same direction in space. The direction of the axis at any given time is always parallel to its direction at any other time.

   3. **Revolution of the earth.** As the earth revolves around the sun, the direction of the axis with respect to the sun varies, because of the first two factors described above. For example, on June 21 the North Pole is inclined *toward* the sun at an angle of 23½° from the perpendicular. On December 21, the North Pole is inclined *away* from the sun at this angle. On March 21 and September 23, the axis is still inclined 23½° from the perpendicular, but *neither* toward *nor* away from the sun. This cycle of variations causes the variations in angle and duration of insolation through the year.

SMALL EFFECT OF ELLIPTICAL ORBIT. The variation in distance between the earth and the sun as the earth travels along its orbit is too small to have a significant effect on the seasons. For example, winter in the Northern Hemisphere occurs at a time when the earth is actually nearest the sun.

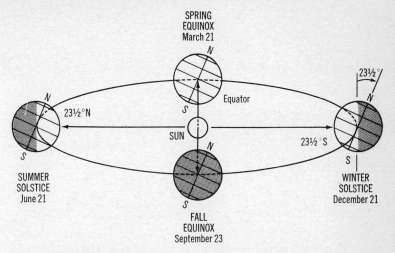

Figure 6-10. Causes of the seasons. The tilt of the earth's axis and parallelism of the axis result in varying angles and duration of insolation through the year.

VOCABULARY	
insolation	perpendicular insolation (direct or
aerosols	vertical rays)
terrestrial radiation	solstice
angle of insolation	duration of insolation
greenhouse effect	radiative balance
intensity of insolation	seasons
equinox	

QUESTIONS ON TOPIC VI—INSOLATION AND THE SEASONS
Questions in Recent Regents Exams (end of book)

Questions from Earlier Regents Exams

1. Electromagnetic energy that reaches the earth from the sun is called   (1) insolation   (2) conduction   (3) specific heat   (4) terrestrial radiation

2. The radiation that passes through the atmosphere and reaches the earth's surface has the greatest intensity in the form of   (1) visible-light radiation   (2) infrared radiation   (3) ultraviolet radiation   (4) radio-wave radiation

3. The graph below represents the relationship between the intensity and wavelength of the sun's electromagnetic radiation. Which statement is best supported by the graph?   (1) The infrared radiation given off by the sun occurs at a wavelength of 2000 angstroms.   (2) The maximum intensity of radiation given off by the sun occurs in the visible region.   (3) The infrared radiation given off by the sun has a shorter wavelength than ultraviolet radiation.   (4) The electromagnetic energy given off by the sun consists of a single wavelength.

4. Water vapor and carbon dioxide in the earth's atmosphere are good absorbers of   (1) visible radiation   (2) infrared radiation   (3) ultraviolet radiation   (4) x rays

Base your answers to questions 5 and 6 on the diagram below, which represents a field showing the amount of insolation received at the earth's surface in calories per square centimeter per minute on a clear day in the morning.

5. If the insolation value at the outer edge of the earth's atmosphere over New York State equals 1.85 calories per square centimeter per minute, which best explains why the values are lower at the surface in New York State?   (1) The angle of insolation is greater in New York State than at the equator.   (2) Insolation decreases with decreased latitude.   (3) The energy is used to evaporate water.   (4) Insolation is absorbed and reflected by the atmosphere.

6. Which change in atmospheric conditions within the dashed circle could cause the different pattern of isolines as indicated in that area in the accompanying diagram?

(1) decreasing dew point temperatures   (2) decreasing velocity of a north wind   (3) increasing cloud cover   (4) increasing air pressure

7. Which form of electromagnetic energy is radiated from the earth's surface with the greatest intensity?   (1) x rays   (2) infrared rays   (3) ultraviolet rays   (4) visible light rays

8. Electromagnetic energy that is being given off by the surface of the earth is called   (1) convection   (2) insolation   (3) specific heat   (4) terrestrial radiation

9. Which statement best explains why, at high latitudes, reflectivity of insolation is greater in winter than in summer?   (1) The North Pole is tilted toward the sun in winter.   (2) Snow and ice reflect almost all insolation.   (3) The colder air holds much more moisture.   (4) Dust settles quickly in cold air.

10. Adding more carbon dioxide to the atmosphere increases the amount of   (1) radiant energy reflected by the earth   (2) radiation from the sun absorbed by the oceans   (3) radiation from the earth absorbed by the atmosphere   (4) ultraviolet rays striking the earth

11. Some scientists predict that the increase in atmospheric carbon dioxide will cause a worldwide increase in temperature. Which could result from this increase in temperature?   (1) Continental drift will increase.   (2) Isotherms will shift toward the equator.   (3) Additional landmasses will form.   (4) Ice caps at the earth's poles will melt.

12. Which model best represents how a greenhouse remains warm as a result of insolation from the sun?

13. Compared to polar areas, why are equatorial areas of equal size heated much more intensely by the sun?   (1) The sun's rays are more nearly perpendicular at the equator than at the poles.   (2) The equatorial areas contain more water than the polar areas do.   (3) More hours of daylight occur at the equator than at the poles.   (4) The equatorial areas are nearer to the sun than the polar areas are.

14. In which diagram does the incoming solar radiation reaching the earth's surface have the greatest intensity?

15. The most logical conclusion that can be made from the relationship between the altitude of the sun throughout the day and the amount of insolation is that, as the sun's altitude   (1) increases, the insolation increases   (2) increases, the insolation decreases   (3) decreases, the insolation increases   (4) decreases, the insolation remains the same

16. In New York State at 3 P.M. on September 21, the vertical pole shown in the diagram casts a shadow. Which line best approximates the position of that shadow?

(1) OA   (2) OB   (3) OC   (4) OD

17. At the time of the fall equinox, the number of hours of daylight in New York City is generally about   (1) nine   (2) twelve   (3) fifteen   (4) eighteen

Base your answers to questions 18 through 21 on the diagrams below. The diagrams represent models of the apparent path of the sun across the sky for observers at four different locations *A* through *D* on the earth's surface.

18. At location *A*, on which side of an observer would his shadow fall at local noon?   (1) south side   (2) north side   (3) east side   (4) west side

19. If the model of location *B* represents the apparent path of the sun observed at the equator, what is the date at location *B?*   (1) March 21   (2) June 21   (3) October 21   (4) December 21

20. If the model of location *D* represents the apparent path of the sun on December 21, where is location *D?*   (1) the North Pole   (2) 45° N latitude   (3) the equator   (4) 45° S latitude

21. At location *B* three months later, how would the altitude of the noon sun compare to its present altitude?   (1) The altitude would be less than shown.   (2) The altitude would be greater than shown.   (3) The altitude would be the same as shown.

22. In New York State, summer is warmer than winter because in summer, New York State has   (1) more hours of daylight and is closer to the sun   (2) more hours of daylight and receives more direct insolation   (3) fewer hours of daylight but is closer to the sun   (4) fewer hours of daylight but receives more direct insolation

23. The diagram below represents a model of the sun's apparent path across the sky in New York State for selected dates.

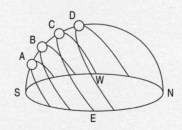

For which path would the duration of insolation be greatest?   (1) *A*   (2) *B*   (3) *C*   (4) *D*

Base your answers to questions 24 through 28 on the diagram below. The diagram represents the earth at a specific time in its orbit. The dashed lines indicate radiation from the sun. Points *A* through *H* are locations on the earth's surface.

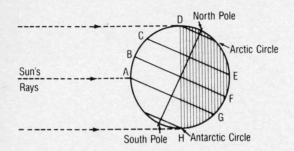

24. Which line represents the equator?   (1) *AG*   (2) *BF*   (3) *CE*   (4) *DH*

25. What is the season in the Northern Hemisphere when the earth is in the position shown in the diagram?   (1) spring   (2) summer   (3) fall   (4) winter

26. When the sun is in the position shown in the diagram, how many hours of daylight would occur at the North Pole during one complete rotation?   (1) 0   (2) 8   (3) 12   (4) 24

27. In which direction would a person located at position *H* have to look to see the sun at the time shown in the diagram?   (1) north   (2) east   (3) south   (4) west

28. Six months after the date indicated by the diagram, which point would receive the sun's vertical rays at noon?   (1) *A*   (2) *B*   (3) *C*   (4) *D*

29. Which two factors determine the number of hours of daylight at a particular location?   (1) longitude and season   (2) longitude and the earth's average diameter   (3) latitude and season   (4) latitude and the earth's average diameter

30. What is the primary reason New York State is warmer in July than in February?   (1) The earth is traveling faster in its orbit in February.   (2) The altitude of the noon sun is greater in February.   (3) The insolation in New York is greater in July.   (4) The earth is closer to the sun in July.

31. What is the usual cause of the drop in temperature that occurs between sunset and sunrise at most New York State locations?   (1) strong winds   (2) ground radiation   (3) cloud formation   (4) heavy precipitation

32. In New York State, the maximum total daily insolation occurs during June. Which statement best explains why the maximum annual temperature is usually observed about a month later, in July? (1) The earth is closer to the sun in June than it is in July. (2) The earth is farther from the sun in June than it is in July. (3) New York State loses more energy than it receives during most of July. (4) New York State receives more energy than it loses during most of July.

33. Between the years 1850 and 1900, records indicate that the earth's mean surface temperatures showed little variation. This would support the inference that (1) the earth was in radiative balance (2) another ice age was approaching (3) more energy was coming in than was going out from the earth (4) the sun was emitting more energy

34. Which is the main cause of seasons on the earth? (1) difference in the earth-sun distance at perihelion and aphelion (2) inclination of the earth's axis of rotation to the plane of its orbit (3) change of inclination of the earth's axis of rotation in relation to the plane of its orbit (4) increase in velocity of the earth as it approaches the sun

35. Which position in the diagram below best represents the earth on the first day of summer in the Northern Hemisphere?

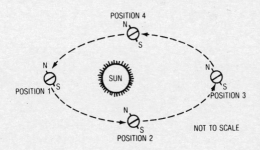

(1) 1   (2) 2   (3) 3   (4) 4

36. Which change would occur if the earth's axis were inclined at an angle of 33½° instead of 23½°? (1) The equator would receive fewer hours of daylight on June 21. (2) The sun's direct ray would move over a larger area of the earth's surface. (3) The celestial equator would be farther from the zenith.

37. Which is *not* a cause of our change of seasons? (1) revolution of the earth (2) inclination of the earth's axis (3) variation of the distance to the sun (4) parallelism of the earth's axis

Energy Exchanges in the Atmosphere—Weather

Variations in insolation (discussed in Topic VI) cause heat energy to be unevenly distributed in the atmosphere. This heat energy tends to move toward a condition of more uniform distribution. That movement of heat energy results in the constant changes in the atmosphere that are a major cause of *weather*.

Weather is the state or condition of the variables of the atmosphere at a location for any given short period of time. **Atmospheric variables** include temperature, pressure, wind, and moisture. Most of the weather changes occur in the troposphere, the part of the atmosphere immediately above the earth's surface. (For the location of the divisions of the atmosphere, see Figure 3-6, page 16.)

ATMOSPHERIC TEMPERATURE

Temperature data is often shown on maps by the use of isolines called **isotherms.**

HEATING OF THE ATMOSPHERE.   The sun is the original source of heat for the atmosphere. Generally, the more insolation at a location, the warmer will be the earth's surface and the atmosphere above it. The atmosphere acquires much of its heat directly from the earth's surface, but it also gains energy in other ways. The many ways in which the atmosphere is heated (gains energy) include the following:

1. Conduction by contact with the earth's surface.

2. Direct absorption of insolation from the sun.

3. Absorption of radiations from the earth's surface. (Much of the heat absorption by the atmosphere is due to the presence of water vapor and carbon dioxide; the larger the amounts of water vapor and carbon dioxide, the more heat is absorbed by the atmosphere.)

4. **Condensation** (change of water vapor to liquid water) and **sublimation** (change of water vapor directly to ice) release large amounts of latent heat, directly heating the atmosphere.

5. The Coriolis effect, resulting from the rotation of the earth, causes a **frictional drag** at the interface of the atmosphere and the earth's surface; this friction produces heat, some of which is added to the atmosphere.

TRANSFER OF HEAT IN THE ATMOSPHERE.   Differences in air density cause differences in air pressure. Air pressure differences in turn cause air to move parallel to the earth's surface *(wind)* and in vertical circular patterns called *convection cells* or *currents.* These air movements transfer heat energy within the atmosphere.

ADIABATIC HEATING AND COOLING. When a gas expands, its temperature decreases; when a gas is compressed, its temperature increases. This automatic change in the temperature of a gas due to expansion or compression is called an **adiabatic temperature change.** Thus when air rises in the atmosphere, it expands and its temperature decreases adiabatically; similarly, when it descends, it is compressed and its temperature increases. In the troposphere, temperatures generally decrease with altitude as a result of adiabatic processes. (See *Selected Properties of Earth's Atmosphere* in the *Earth Science Reference Tables*.)

ATMOSPHERIC PRESSURE AND DENSITY

The more dense the atmosphere, the greater the weight of a given volume and therefore the greater the air pressure exerted by it; thus air pressure and density are directly related. **Atmospheric pressure,** also called **barometric pressure** and **air pressure,** is the pressure due to the weight of the overlying atmosphere pushing down on any given area. Standard air pressure (one atmosphere) at sea level is 29.92 inches of mercury or 1013.2 millibars. Barometric pressure in millibars can be converted to inches of mercury using the scale in the *Earth Science Reference Tables*. Air pressure is measured by an instrument called a barometer. Air pressure is often shown on weather maps by the use of isolines called **isobars.**

EFFECT OF TEMPERATURE ON PRESSURE. Changes in the temperature of the air cause changes in air pressure. As the temperature of air increases, the air expands, so that its density and pressure decrease. Decreasing temperature has the reverse effect.

EFFECT OF MOISTURE ON PRESSURE. The greater the amount of water vapor in the air (called **moisture** content, absolute humidity, and vapor pressure), the lower the air density and pressure. The reason for this is that each water molecule in the atmosphere *replaces* a molecule of air, usually oxygen or nitrogen. Since a water molecule weighs less than either an oxygen or a nitrogen molecule, the greater the amount of water vapor in the air, the less dense the air as a whole becomes.

EFFECT OF ALTITUDE ON PRESSURE. As altitude increases, atmospheric density and pressure decrease. (See *Selected Properties of Earth's Atmosphere* in the *Earth Science Reference Tables.*)

To summarize, as either altitude, temperature, or moisture content in the atmosphere increases, air density and air pressure decrease.

WIND

Horizontal movement of air parallel to the earth's surface is called **wind.** Wind is a vector field, because it requires a magnitude and direction to describe it.

WIND SPEED.   Winds are caused by differences in air pressure. The difference in air pressure for a specific distance is called the **pressure gradient.** The closer together the isobars on a weather map are, the greater (steeper) the pressure gradient. The greater the pressure gradient is, the greater the wind speed (see Figure 7-1).

Figure 7-1. Pressure gradient as indicated by closeness of isobars on a weather map. The greater the pressure gradient, the greater the wind speed.

WIND DIRECTION.   Air (wind) moves from areas of high pressure to areas of low pressure. However, the Coriolis effect (caused by the earth's rotation) modifies that pattern of movement, deflecting winds to the right in the Northern Hemisphere and to the left in the Southern Hemisphere. Figure 7-2 illustrates how the wind directions are modified by the Coriolis effect.

A wind is named for the direction from which it comes; for example, a wind blowing *from* the south *toward* the north is called a *south* wind.

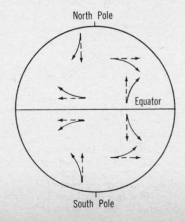

Figure 7-2. Deflection of winds by the Coriolis effect. The dashed arrow in each case shows the direction the wind would flow if there were no Coriolis effect. The solid arrow shows the actual path of the wind. If you face with the wind, it is always deflected to the right in the Northern Hemisphere and to the left in the Southern Hemisphere.

CIRCULATION OF THE ATMOSPHERE

CONVECTION CELLS. The unequal distribution of insolation on the earth results in unequal heating and differences in air pressure. Cooler air, being denser, sinks toward the earth under the influence of gravity, causing the less dense warmer air to rise. The result is a series of convection cells around the earth at various latitudes, as shown in Figure 7-3. As indicated by the solid arrows, there are upward currents in the vicinity of 0° latitude (the equator) and 60° north and south latitudes. Downward currents exist near 30° and 90° north and south latitudes. Regions where air comes together to form vertical currents are regions of **convergence** (labeled "C"). Regions where air spreads out from the vertical currents are regions of **divergence** (labeled "D").

PLANETARY WINDS. At the earth's surface, winds flow horizontally away from regions of divergence and toward regions of convergence. Because of the Coriolis effect, these winds are deflected to the right in the Northern Hemisphere and to the left in the Southern Hemisphere, as indicated by the dashed arrows in Figure 7-3. The result is a series of **planetary wind belts** within which the winds move generally in a specific direction much of the time. The *jet streams* are wavy bands of high-speed winds located near the top of the troposphere.

Figure 7-3. Planetary wind and pressure belts in the troposphere. The drawing shows the locations of the belts near the time of an equinox. The locations shift somewhat with the changing latitude of the sun's vertical ray. In the Northern Hemisphere the belts shift northward in summer and southward in winter. (Also see *Planetary Winds and Moisture Belts in the Troposphere* in the *Earth Science Reference Tables*.)

WEATHER MOVEMENT.   Much of the continental United States is affected by planetary winds that blow from the southwest. Therefore, weather changes in the United States move generally from a southwesterly direction to a northeasterly direction (see Figure 8-11).

SURFACE OCEAN CURRENTS.   The surface ocean currents are caused by wind blowing over the oceans and transferring energy to the water. The direction of these currents is affected by the direction of the planetary winds. Compare *Surface Ocean Currents* with *Planetary Winds and Moisture Belts in the Troposphere* in the *Earth Science Reference Tables*.

ATMOSPHERIC MOISTURE

Atmospheric moisture exists in three states of matter: liquid, solid, and gas. Gaseous water in the atmosphere is called **water vapor**.

SOURCES OF ATMOSPHERIC MOISTURE.   Moisture in the form of water vapor enters the atmosphere by *evaporation*, *sublimation*, and *transpiration*. **Evaporation** is the process by which a liquid changes to a gas; **transpiration** is the process by which plants release water vapor as part of their life functions. Collectively, evaporation and transpiration are called **evapotranspiration**. The oceans, which cover about 70% of the earth's surface, are the source of most atmospheric moisture.

ENERGY OF EVAPORATION AND TRANSPIRATION.   Large amounts of energy (approximately 540 calories/gram) are required to change liquid water into water vapor during processes of evaporation and transpiration. When evapotranspiration occurs, the more energetic water molecules leave the liquid and form water vapor. Since the molecules leaving the liquid are the more energetic ones, the average kinetic energy of the molecules remaining in the liquid decreases. As a result, the temperature of an evaporating liquid is somewhat lower than its surroundings.

FACTORS AFFECTING EVAPORATION RATE.   The net evaporation rate at a location is determined by (1) *the amount of energy available*— the more energy available, that is, the higher the temperature, the faster the evaporation of available water; (2) *surface area of the water*—the more spread out the water, the greater the air-water interface and the faster the evaporation; (3) *degree of saturation of the air with water vapor*— the higher the vapor pressure (moisture content), the closer the air is to being saturated and the slower the net evaporation rate.

PROCESS OF EVAPORATION.   Figure 7-4 helps to explain what happens when water—or any other liquid—evaporates. Diagram A shows a closed container of air into which some water has just been added. We assume there are no water vapor molecules in the air at this moment. However, as soon as water is placed in the container, some of its more energetic molecules begin to escape into the air above and mingle with the other gas molecules that are present. Diagram B shows the situation a short time later. There are now some water molecules in the air, represented by the four molecules shown. We see two more molecules in the process of leaving the water. However, one of the other four is about to enter the water, so that there will be five molecules in the air after this happens. Diagram C shows the situation some time later. There are now eight water molecules in the air. Again, two more water molecules are about to leave the water. But now *two* of the eight molecules in the air are about to return to the water. The net result wil be eight molecules in the air—the same number as before. We have a condition of *dynamic equilibrium*, in which the rate at which water is entering the gaseous state (evaporation) equals the rate at which water vapor is returning to the liquid state (condensation).

o = Air molecule   ● = Water molecule

Figure 7-4. The saturation of the air over an evaporating liquid. At A, no evaporation has occurred. At B, evaporation is proceeding faster than condensation. At C, equilibrium has been reached. The air is **saturated** with vapor, and evaporation and condensation are occurring at the same rate. The pressure of the vapor under these conditions is called the **saturation vapor pressure**. The higher the temperature, the greater the saturation vapor pressure.

SATURATION VAPOR PRESSURE. In the equilibrium condition described above, the air contains the maximum amount of water vapor it can hold (represented by eight molecules). This conditions is called **saturation**. Water vapor, being a gas, exerts a pressure, which is called **vapor pressure**. When the air is saturated with water vapor (at capacity), the vapor pressure is called the **saturation vapor pressure**.

ABSOLUTE HUMIDITY. Humidity, like moisture, is a general term that refers to the water vapor content of the atmosphere. The amount of water vapor in each unit volume of air is called the **absolute humidity**. There is a definite vapor pressure corresponding to each value of absolute humidity. The vapor pressure increases in direct proportion to the absolute humidity, so that vapor pressure can be used as a measure of absolute humidity.

ABSOLUTE HUMIDITY AND TEMPERATURE. The maximum absolute humidity and saturation vapor pressure (and capacity) increase rapidly with an increase in temperature, as shown in the graph in Figure 7-5. This means that the moisture capacity of the air increases with an increase in temperature.

Figure 7-5. Relationship between air's capacity for water vapor and temperature. Note that air with a temperature of 35°C can hold about four times more water vapor than can air at 10°C.

RELATIVE HUMIDITY.   **Relative humidity** is the ratio of the amount of water vapor in the air to the maximum amount it can hold (its **moisture capacity**). It is also the ratio of the absolute humidity/maximum absolute humidity (capacity). The closer the absolute humidity is to the maximum absolute humidity, the higher the relative humidity. (Be sure to understand that relative humidity is a percentage of saturation, *not* a percentage of the volume of air present.)

RELATIVE HUMIDITY AND TEMPERATURE.   At any given time and place, the air has a certain amount of water vapor (humidity), with a corresponding absolute humidity. If the temperature of the air changes, but the amount of water vapor (that is, the absolute humidity) remains the same, the relative humidity will change. For example, if the temperature increases, the relative humidity will decrease. This occurs because the capacity increases with the increase in temperature, while the absolute humidity remains the same. On the other hand, if the temperature decreases while the absolute humidity remains the same, the relative humidity will increase.

RELATIVE HUMIDITY AND ABSOLUTE HUMIDITY. If the temperature of the air remains constant, but more water vapor is added to it (for example, by evapotranspiration), the absolute humidity, the vapor pressure, and the relative humidity will all increase.

DEW POINT TEMPERATURE. If the temperature of the air decreases while the absolute humidity remains the same, the temperature will eventually reach a point at which the absolute humidity equals the maximum absolute humidity. At this temperature, the relative humidity will be 100%, that is, the air will be saturated. This temperature is called the **dew point temperature**, or simply the **dew point**. Any further drop in temperature will result in condensation or sublimation of water, since there would then be more water vapor in the air than it can hold.

DEW POINT AND ABSOLUTE HUMIDITY. The dew point temperature depends only on the absolute humidity or vapor pressure of the air, and not on the relative humidity. As the vapor pressure or the amount of water vapor in the air increases, the dew point rises.

RELATIVE HUMIDITY. It is difficult to measure absolute humidity or determine the air's capacity to hold water vapor directly. Relative humidity is therefore measured by indirect methods. One such method uses an instrument called a *sling psychrometer*, as shown in Figure 7-6. This instrument contains an ordinary thermometer called the **dry-bulb thermometer,** and another thermometer with a wick around its bulb, called the **wet-bulb thermometer.** When the wick is moistened and the thermometers are whirled in the air, the temperature of the wet-bulb drops because of the cooling effect of the evaporation of the water. The amount of cooling depends on the rate of evaporation, and is therefore related to the relative humidity.

Figure 7-6. Sling psychrometer. The difference between the two temperature readings is used to find the relative humidity.

MEASURING DEWPOINT TEMPERATURE. To determine the dewpoint temperature, you need the dry-bulb and wet-bulb readings from a sling psychrometer and the *Dewpoint Temperatures* chart in the *Earth Science Reference Tables*.

1. Locate the dry-bulb reading on the left-hand side of the chart. (Note that the dry-bulb reading is the same as a regular temperature reading.)

2. Subtract the wet-bulb reading from the dry-bulb reading.

3. Locate the difference between the wet-bulb and dry-bulb readings across the top of the chart.

4. Follow the horizontal row for the dry-bulb reading to the right until it meets the vertical column running down from the difference between the wet-bulb and dry-bulb readings. This number is the dewpoint temperature.

As an example, suppose the dry-bulb reading is 8°C and the wet-bulb reading is 6°C. The difference is 2°C. Reading across from 8°C and down from 2°C, you find a dewpoint temperature of 3°C.

MEASURING RELATIVE HUMIDITY (%).   Determining the percent relative humidity is similar to determining the dewpoint temperature.

1. Locate the dry-bulb reading on the left-hand side of the *Relative Humidity (%)* chart in the *Earth Science Reference Tables*.

2. Subtract the wet-bulb reading from the dry-bulb reading.

3. Locate the difference between the wet-bulb and dry-bulb readings across the top of the chart.

4. Follow the horizontal row for the dry-bulb reading to the right until it meets the vertical column running down from the difference between the wet-bulb and dry-bulb readings. This number is the relative humidity.

As an example, suppose the dry-bulb reading is 4°C and the wet-bulb reading is −2°C. The difference is 6°C. Reading across from 4°C and down from 6°C, you find a relative humidity of 14%.

CONDENSATION, SUBLIMATION, AND CLOUDS.   If the temperature of the air cools (often adiabatically) below the dewpoint, the water vapor will usually condense or sublime to a solid, changing to microscopic liquid water droplets or ice crystals. In the atmosphere, if the temperature is above 0°C, condensation produces water droplets which as a group appear as a *cloud*. Some clouds are composed of ice crystals, which form when water vapor sublimates to a solid. A **cloud** is therefore a collection of liquid water droplets and/or ice crystals suspended in the atmosphere. This condensation or sublimation to form clouds releases tremendous amounts of energy to the troposphere. At the earth's surface, condensation produces dew and sublimation produces frost.

Since temperature and dewpoint temperature both decrease with elevation in the troposphere, the altitude where temperature and dewpoint are the same is the level where clouds form by condensation or sublimation. This is often illustrated by a lapse rate (change rate) chart like the *Lapse Rate* chart in the *Earth Science Reference Tables*.

Refer to the *Lapse Rate* chart. On this chart, the dashed lines represent the decrease in dewpoint with increasing altitude (2C°/km). The solid diagonal lines represent the decrease in temperature with increasing altitude (10C°/km) above the earth's surface. If you know the temperature and dewpoint at the earth's surface, such as from using a sling psychrometer, you can determine the altitude of the condensation (sublimation) level and therefore the altitude of the bottom of the clouds above a location.

Suppose the surface temperature is 20°C and the surface dewpoint is 10°C. Follow these steps to find the level at which clouds will form.

1. Find the 20°C mark and the 10°C mark along the bottom edge of the chart.

2. From the 20°C mark, follow the solid diagonal line upward and to the left.

3. From the 10°C mark, follow the dashed line upward.

4. The place where the two lines intersect represents the altitude at which clouds will form, in this case, about 1,200 km above the surface.

CONDENSATION SURFACE.   Besides needing saturated air, condensation requires a surface upon which the vapor can condense. This is called the **condensation surface**. In the formation of clouds, the condensation surfaces are aerosols such as dust and volcanic ash.

PRECIPITATION.   **Precipitation** is the falling of liquid or solid water from clouds toward the surface of the earth. The forms in which precipitation occurs are rain, snow, sleet, drizzle, freezing rain, and hail. For precipitation to occur, the ice crystals or water droplets in clouds must become big enough so that they will fall.

ATMOSPHERIC TRANSPARENCY AND PRECIPITATION.   The more pollutants added to the atmosphere by the activities of nature and people, the more aerosols are present. The more aerosols in the air, the less transparent the atmosphere is to insolation. "Less transparent" means that more energy from the sun is absorbed or reflected by the atmosphere, resulting in less insolation reaching the earth's surface. When the atmosphere has a high enough aerosol content so that distant images are blurred and a cloudless sky does not appear clear blue, the condition is called *haze*. Condensation in cloud formation incorporates some of the aerosols, and these aerosols are removed from the atmosphere during precipitation. The falling liquid or solid water also collects other aerosols on the way down, thus lowering air pollution levels and cleaning the atmosphere.

AIR MASSES AND FRONTS

Much of the weather of the continental United States is the result of the invasion of *air masses* and their interactions. An **air mass** is a large body of air in the troposphere with similar characteristics of pressure, moisture, and temperature.

SOURCE REGIONS.   An air mass forms when a large mass of air stagnates over a part of the earth's surface for a period of time and thus acquires some of the characteristics of that surface. The geographic regions in which air masses are formed are called **source regions.** The source regions for the air masses that invade the United States are shown in Figure 7-7.

If the source region is at a high latitude, the air mass will have a low temperature; if the source region is at a low latitude, the air mass will have a high temperature. If the source region is land, the air mass will be dry; if the source region is water, the air mass will be moist. Air masses are described as arctic (A), polar (P), or tropical (T), depending on whether they originate at high or low latitudes. Air masses are also described as either continental (c) or maritime (m), depending on whether they originate over land or water. These air mass symbols are found in the *Earth Science Reference Tables.* When an air mass remains stationary over its source region for a period of time, it tends to acquire relatively uniform temperature and moisture conditions at any one altitude within it.

Figure 7-7. Source regions and tracks of air masses that affect the weather of the continental United States.

LOWS AND HIGHS.   Portions of the troposphere are divided into two types according to pressure and direction of circulation of winds. **LOWS,** also called **cyclones,** have low pressure. The pressure in a LOW is lowest at its center, and thus winds blow toward the center. The winds are deflected by the Coriolis effect, so that in the Northern Hemisphere a counterclockwise circulation occurs within LOWS, as shown in Figure 7-8. **HIGHS,** or **anticyclones,** have high pressure. The pressure in a HIGH is greatest at its center, and thus winds blow out from the center. The general circulation around HIGHS is clockwise in the Northern Hemisphere.

FRONTS.   Where two air masses of different characteristics meet, an interface called a **front** develops (see Figure 7-9 on page 94). A **cold front** is the interface between an advancing cold air mass and a warmer air mass, where the underlying cold air pushes forward like a wedge. A **warm front** is a front between an advancing warm air mass and a retreating wedge of a cooler air mass; because the cool air is heavier, the warm air mass is forced to rise as it advances. An **occluded front** is the interface between opposing wedges of cold air masses formed when a cold front overtakes a warm front, lifting the warm air mass off the ground. Occluded fronts are important because they are associated with the formation of mid-latitude cyclones (LOWS), as shown in Figure 7-8. When two adjacent air masses of different characteristics remain in the same positions, they form a **stationary front**.

At fronts between air masses of different temperatures the warmer air, being less dense, is forced to rise. This results in the unstable conditions that are characteristic of fronts and that produce much of the precipitation of the continental United States.

FRONTS AND WEATHER MAPS.   On weather maps half-circles and/ or triangles are used on the lines representing fronts to indicate the type of front. See Figure 7-8 for specific front symbols. The triangles and half-circles point in the direction the fronts and associated air masses are moving.

Figure 7-8. Circulation of winds and interaction of high and low pressure air masses in the Northern Hemisphere. Air circulates clockwise in a HIGH and counterclockwise in a LOW.

●●● WARM FRONTAL SURFACE
▲▲▲ COLD FRONTAL SURFACE
////// PRECIPITATION

Figure 7-9. Cross-sectional view of the ---- line in Figure 7-8. The conditions of the cold front at left are: steep slope, cumulo (puffy) clouds, and precipitation just before and after the point where the front meets the earth's surface. The conditions of the warm front at right are: gentle frontal surface, strato (layered) clouds, and a broad band of precipitation preceding the point where the front meets the earth's surface.

TRACKS OF AIR MASSES AND FRONTS. In the United States, the **tracks** (paths) and rate of movement of air masses and fronts can be predicted on the basis of past observations. Thus, the succession of weather changes that accompanies such movements can be reasonably forecasted. The direction of some of these tracks is indicated by the arrows in Figure 7-7. Most of the tracks follow a westerly to easterly route in the United States because of our location in the southwest planetary winds.

WEATHER PREDICTION AND PROBABILITY

Most weather predictions, or forecasts, are based on the **probability** (chance) of occurrence of weather variables based on relationships between weather variables. As an example, suppose that in a twenty-day period the air pressure drops on ten days and that the air temperature increases on eight of those ten days. What is the probability that air temperature will increase if air pressure is decreasing? Based on the data above, there is an 8/10 or 80% chance of increasing temperature. In actual cases of computing probability, the Weather Service uses large amounts of data collected over many years on which to base predictions.

Probabilities have been worked out for a vast number of possible relationships between variables. Many of the relationships are very complex, but some of them are simple direct or inverse relationships. Some of the simple relationships are listed below:

1. Air pressure is related to temperature changes: As temperature increases, pressure decreases, and vice versa.

2. The chance of precipitation increases as the air temperature gets closer to the dew point temperature. This is the case because the smaller the difference between the air temperature and the dew point temperature, the nearer the air is to saturation, condensation, and precipitation.

3. The greater the pressure gradient in an area, the faster is the speed of the winds.

STATION MODELS. On weather maps the weather conditions for each weather station are shown by symbols arranged in order around a small circle. These symbols and the circle make up a **station model,** which gives the latest readings for all the weather variables. For a sample of a station model see Figure 7-10 below.

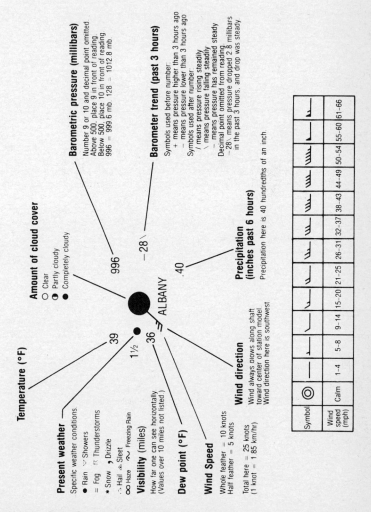

Figure 7-10. Sample Station Model For Weather Map. (Also see the charts of weather map symbols in the *Earth Science Reference Tables.*)

VOCABULARY

weather	relative humidity
atmospheric variables	moisture capacity
isotherm	dew point temperature
condensation	cloud
sublimation	condensation surface
frictional drag	precipitation
adiabatic temperature change	air mass
atmospheric pressure	continental polar air mass (cP)
barometric pressure	continental tropical air mass (cT)
air pressure	maritime tropical air mass (mT)
isobar	maritime polar air mass (mP)
moisture	source region
wind	LOW
pressure gradient	cyclone
convergence	HIGH
divergence	anticyclone
planetary wind belts	front
water vapor	cold front
evaporation	warm front
transpiration	occluded front
evapotranspiration	stationary front
saturation	track
vapor pressure	probability
saturation vapor pressure	visibility
absolute humidity	present weather

QUESTIONS ON TOPIC VII—ENERGY EXCHANGES IN THE ATMOSPHERE AND WEATHER

Questions in Recent Regents Exams (end of book)

June 1991: 16, 18–22, 24, 29, 54, 71–75
June 1992: 12, 14, 18–21, 23, 38, 71–73, 75–80, 103,104
June 1993: 3, 7, 11, 15–17, 19, 20, 54, 76–80, 101, 104
June 1994: 9, 13, 14, 18, 19, 20, 22, 23, 66–70, 104

Questions from Earlier Regents Exams

1. A balloon carrying weather instruments is released at the earth's surface and rises through the troposphere. As the balloon rises, what will the instruments generally indicate? [Refer to the *Earth Science Reference Tables*.]   (1) a decrease in both air temperature and air pressure   (2) an increase in both air temperature and air pressure   (3) an increase in air temperature and a decrease in air pressure   (4) a decrease in air temperature and an increase in air pressure

2. As a parcel of air rises, its temperature will   (1) decrease due to expansion   (2) decrease due to compression   (3) increase due to expansion   (4) increase due to compression

3. The diagram below shows the direction of movement of air over a mountain.

As the air moves down the leeward side of the mountain, the air will (1) warm due to compression   (2) warm due to expansion   (3) cool due to compression   (4) cool due to expansion

4. On a clear, dry day an air mass has a temperature of 20°C and a dewpoint temperature of 10°C. According to the graph, about how high must this air mass rise before a cloud can form?   (1) 1.6 km   (2) 2.4 km (3) 3.0 km   (4) 2.8 km

5. According to the graph below, what happens to the density of a mass of air when its water vapor content increases?   (1) density decreases (2) density increases   (3) density remains the same

6. At sea level, as the temperature of the atmosphere decreases, the air pressure usually   (1) decreases   (2) increases   (3) remains the same

7. An air pressure of 1023 millibars is equal to how many inches of mercury?   (1) 30.10   (2) 30.15   (3) 30.19   (4) 30.21

8. According to the *Earth Science Reference Tables*, an air pressure of 30.15 inches of mercury is equal to   (1) 1017 mb   (2) 1019 mb (3) 1021 mb   (4) 1023 mb

9. As the pressure gradient increases, wind velocity   (1) decreases (2) increases   (3) remains the same

10. The map below represents a portion of an air-pressure field at the earth's surface. At which position is wind speed *lowest*?   (1) A (2) B   (3) C   (4) D

11. Winds blow from regions of   (1) high air temperature to regions of low air temperature   (2) high air pressure to regions of low air pressure   (3) high precipitation to regions of low precipitation (4) convergence to regions of divergence

12. In the Northern Hemisphere, a wind blowing from the south will be deflected toward the   (1) northwest   (2) northeast   (3) southwest (4) southeast

13. Which diagram shows the *usual* path followed by low-pressure storm centers as they pass across the United States?

| (1) | (2) | (3) | (4) |

14. Which is the primary source of energy for ocean currents and waves?   (1) the moon   (2) the atmosphere   (3) the continents   (4) the sun

15. What is the most direct cause of major surface ocean currents? (1) wind   (2) gravity   (3) tides   (4) pollution

To answer questions 16 through 21 refer to the adjoining diagram, which shows movement of air in the lower part of the atmosphere around the time of an equinox.

16. The movement of air from 1 to 2 to 3 to 4 to 1 would be called a(n) (1) advection cell   (2) adiabatic cell (3) convection cell   (4) Coriolis cell

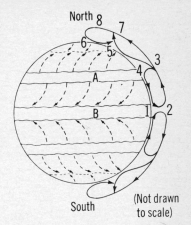

(Not drawn to scale)

17. What is the basic underlying reason for the movement of air shown?   (1) differences in gravity   (2) differences in air density (3) differences in pressure gradient   (4) differences in magnetism

18. How does the movement of air at position 2 compare to the movement of air at position 4?   (1) They both have converging air. (2) They both have diverging air.   (3) Position 2 is diverging and position 4 is converging.   (4) Position 2 is converging and position 4 is diverging.

19. What would be the most likely cause of the movement of air at position 1?   (1) low moisture content and low temperature   (2) high moisture content and high temperature   (3) low moisture content and high temperature   (4) high moisture content and low temperature

20. The air moves at the surface of the earth, from position A to position B, because   (1) positions A and B have low pressure (2) positions A and B have high pressure   (3) position A has low pressure and position B has high pressure   (4) position A has high pressure and position B has low pressure

21. Condensation would most likely occur at position   (1) 3   (2) 4 (3) 6   (4) 7

22. By which process does moisture leave green plants?   (1) convection   (2) condensation   (3) transpiration   (4) radiation

23. Most moisture enters the atmosphere by the processes of (1) convection and conduction   (2) condensation and radiation (3) reflection and absorption   (4) transpiration and evaporation

24. The primary source of most of the moisture for the earth's atmosphere is   (1) soil-moisture storage   (2) rivers and lakes (3) melting glaciers   (4) oceans

25. As the exposed area of a moist object decreases, the rate of evaporation of the liquid from that object   (1) decreases   (2) increases (3) remains the same

26. As the amount of light energy striking a moist object increases, the rate of evaporation of the liquid from that object   (1) decreases   (2) increases   (3) remains the same

27. As the amount of water vapor in a given volume of air increases, the rate of evaporation from a moist object   (1) decreases   (2) increases   (3) remains the same

28. As the rate of molecular activity of a liquid increases, the rate of evaporation of that liquid   (1) decreases   (2) increases   (3) remains the same

29. In the diagram below, at which location would the vapor pressure of the air most likely be greatest?   (1) A   (2) B   (3) C   (4) D

30. Which graph best represents the relationship between the moisture-holding capacity (ability to hold moisture) of the atmosphere and atmospheric temperature?

31. To say that the relative humidity of a given day is 70 percent means that the air   (1) is composed of 70 percent water vapor   (2) holds 70 percent of its water vapor capacity   (3) contains 70 parts of water to 100 parts of dry air   (4) contains the same amount of water that it would contain at 70°F

32. During which part of the day is the relative humidity usually *lowest*?   (1) morning   (2) midafternoon   (3) evening   (4) late night

33. Air at a temperature of 60°F and a relative humidity of 51% was warmed to a temperature of 70°F, but the relative humidity remained at 51%. What change occurred in the moisture content?   (1) the moisture content decreased   (2) the moisture content increased   (3) the moisture content remained the same

34. If the amount of water vapor in the air increases, then the dewpoint temperature of the air will   (1) decrease   (2) increase   (3) remain the same

35. The dry-bulb temperature is 20°C. The wet-bulb temperature is 17°C. What is the dewpoint?   (1) 12°C   (2) 13°C   (3) 14°C   (4) 15°C

36. Which statement best explains why the wet-bulb thermometer of a sling psychrometer usually shows a lower temperature than the dry-bulb thermometer?   (1) Water evaporates from the wet-bulb thermometer. (2) Water vapor condenses on the wet-bulb thermometer.   (3) The air around the wet-bulb prevents absorption of heat.   (4) The air around the dry bulb prevents absorption of heat.

To answer questions 37 through 41, refer to the graph below, which shows the hourly surface air temperature, dew point, and relative humidity for a 24-hour period during the month of May at Washington, DC.

37. The greatest net change in air temperature occurred during the period from   (1) midnight to 6 A.M.   (2) 6 A.M. to noon   (3) noon to 6 P.M.   (4) 6 P.M. to midnight

38. Which conclusion concerning the relationship between the dew point and air temperature is best justified by the data shown? (1) Changes in dew point do not necessarily occur when air temperature changes.   (2) The dew point increases in proportion to an increase in air temperature.   (3) The dew point increases in proportion to a decrease in air temperature.   (4) Changes in dew point are caused by air temperature changes but not in proportion to these changes.

39. The graph indicates that as the air temperature increases, the relative humidity   (1) increases   (2) decreases   (3) sometimes increases and sometimes decreases   (4) remains the same

40. Condensation is most likely to occur at approximately   (1) 6 A.M. (2) 9 A.M.   (3) 7 P.M.   (4) 10 P.M.

41. The energy supply of a hurricane comes from   (1) heat released by condensation   (2) evaporation of tropical waters   (3) the trade winds   (4) discharge of lightning

42. Why do clouds usually form at the leading edge of a cold air mass?   (1) Cold air contains more water vapor than warm air does. (2) Cold air contains more dust particles than warm air does.   (3) Cold air flows over warm air, causing the warm air to descend and cool. (4) Cool air flows under warm air, causing the warm air to rise and cool.

43. Which process most directly results in cloud formation? (1) condensation   (2) transpiration   (3) precipitation   (4) radiation

44. At which temperature could water vapor in the atmosphere change directly into solid ice crystals?   (1) 20°F   (2) 40°F   (3) 10°C (4) 100°C

45. Which graph best represents the relationship between water droplet size and the chance of precipitation?

46. Which process is most likely to remove pollutants from the air? (1) precipitation   (2) evaporation   (3) transpiration   (4) runoff

47. Which statement best explains how atmospheric dust particles influence the water cycle?   (1) Dust particles are the main source of dissolved salts in the sea.   (2) Dust particles increase the capacity of the atmosphere to hold water vapor.   (3) Dust particles increase the amount of evaporation that takes place.   (4) Dust particles provide surfaces on which water vapor can condense.

48. Which graph best shows the relationship between atmospheric transparency and the concentration of pollution particles in the air?

49. The original characteristics of an air mass are determined by the   (1) surface over which it is formed   (2) pressure of the air mass   (3) insolation it receives   (4) rotation of the earth

50. In order for a large mass of air to acquire uniform characteristics, it must   (1) stagnate over a large land or water surface   (2) descend from the upper troposphere   (3) move rapidly with the prevailing westerlies   (4) move in the general planetary circulation

51. During the summer a warm, moist air mass moved over Texas. This air mass probably originated over   (1) northern Canada   (2) the Pacific Ocean   (3) southern Arizona   (4) the Gulf of Mexico

52. Which best describes the movement of air in a high pressure air mass (anticyclone) in the Northern Hemisphere?   (1) clockwise and away from the center   (2) clockwise and toward the center   (3) counterclockwise and away from the center   (4) counterclockwise and toward the center

53. In approaching the center of a cyclone on a weather map, the numerical values of the isobars   (1) increase   (2) may increase or decrease   (3) decrease   (4) remain the same

54. A high-pressure center is generally characterized by   (1) cool, wet weather   (2) cool, dry weather   (3) warm, wet weather   (4) warm, dry weather

55. The diagram below shows four points on a map with their positions relative to a low-pressure weather system. Which point is most likely having heavy precipitation?

(1) 1   (2) 3   (3) 3   (4) 4

56. The station model below represents atmospheric conditions at a location in New York at noon on a day in January. What is the air pressure indicated on the station model?   (1) 900.3 mb   (2) 1000.3 mb   (3) 1003.0 mb   (4) 9000.3 mb

Refer to the weather map below to answer questions 57 through 67.

57. Which of the following locations has the highest wind velocity?
(1) Jacksonville   (2) Charlotte   ((3) Indianapolis   (4) Jackson

58. What type of front is found between Montgomery and Jacksonville?   (1) cold   (2) warm   (3) stationary   (4) occluded

59. The barometric reading in millibars of the isobar that passes through Jackson, Miss., is   (1) 160   (2) 1016   (3) 1060   (4) 1600

60. Which station has the highest relative humidity?   (1) Montgomery   (2) Jackson   (3) Bristol   (4) Richmond

61. Which is characteristic of most weather stations within the closed isobar?   (1) low velocity wind   (2) overcast skies   (3) a barometer now lower than three hours ago   (4) poor visibility

62. At which location is visibility the lowest?   (1) Charleston (2) Jacksonville   (3) Montgomery   (4) Bristol

63. If the front started moving in a northwesterly direction, in a few hours temperatures at Montgomery would most likely   (1) increase (2) decrease   (3) remain the same

64. At Charlotte, wind is blowing from what compass direction?
(1) South   (2) Northeast   (3) Northwest   (4) Southeast

65. The most precipitation in the six hours before the time of the map was reported at which station?   (1) Memphis   (2) Charleston (3) Jacksonville   (4) Richmond

66. The air mass found south and east of the front would most likely be classified as a(n)   (1) cP   (2) cT   (3) mT   (4) mP

67. What was the barometric pressure at Indianapolis 3 hours before the time of the map?   (1) 1014.6 mb   (2) 1015.8 mb (3) 1013.4 mb   (4) 1026.6 mb

Additional Questions

1. Which is *not* true about wind?   (1) Wind direction is named for the direction toward which the wind blows.   (2) Wind moves from regions of higher pressure to lower pressure.   (3) The steeper the gradient, the greater the wind speed.   (4) Wind is horizontal movement of air.

2. When the dry-bulb temperature is 20°C and the wet-bulb temperature is 16°C, the percent relative humidity is   (1) 42%   (2) 62%   (3) 66%   (4) 69%

3. When the dry-bulb temperature is 24°C and the difference between the wet-bulb and dry-bulb temperatures is 10°C, the percent relative humidity is   (1) 8%   (2) 9%   (3) 30%   (4) 54%

4. If at sea level the temperature is 20°C and the dewpoint is 16°C, what is the most likely altitude of the bottom of the local clouds?   (1) 0.5 km   (2) 1 km   (3) 1.8 km   (4) 3 km

5. If at an altitude of 1 km the temperature is 10°C, what would be the temperature of the troposphere at 2 km assuming that no condensation of water occurred?   (1) −10°C   (2) 0°C   (3) 10°C   (4) 20°C

To answer questions 6–13 use the diagram below, which shows four station models, at the same instant in time, identified by letters _A–D_. The stations are located on a west-end line at fifty-mile intervals in the United States.

6. The strongest wind is reported at station   (1) *A*   (2) *B*   (3) *C* (4) *D*

7. Station *B* has just experienced the passage of a   (1) warm front (2) cold front   (3) stationary front   (4) hurricane

8. At station *D* the wind is blowing from the   (1) northeast (2) northwest   (3) southeast   (4) southwest

9. The temperature at station *A* is   (1) 6°F   (2) 16°F   (3) 32°F (4) 38°F

10. The relative humidity at station *C* is   (1) 0%   (2) 25%   (3) 70% (4) 100%

11. Heaviest rainfall in the past 6 hours was reported from station (1) *A*   (2) *B*   (3) *C*   (4) *D*

12. Clear skies are reported from station   (1) *A*   (2) *B*   (3) *C* (4) *D*

13. What is the wind speed at station *B* in km/h?   (1) 3 km/h (2) 5.5 km/h   (3) 30 km/h   (4) 55.5 km/h

THE WATER CYCLE

The **water cycle** is a model used to illustrate the movement and the phase changes of water at and near the earth's surface (see Figure 8-1). Below are some of the important aspects of the water cycle:

1. The ultimate source of most water on land is the oceans.

2. The moisture gets to the land from the oceans by way of the atmosphere.

3. When precipitation falls on the land, four things can happen to it:

a. Storage. It can be stored on the land surface as ice or snow.

b. Infiltration. It can infiltrate, or seep into, the earth. The water beneath the earth's surface is called **subsurface water.**

c. Runoff. It can flow on the surface of the land, and is then called **runoff.**

d. Evapotranspiration. Usually a large percentage of precipitation is evaporated or transpired back into the atmosphere.

Figure 8-1. The water cycle: a model of the movement and phase changes of water at and near the earth's surface. The water table is an interface of changing position between the zone of saturation, where the pores of the regolith are filled with water (ground water), and the zone of aeration, where the pores are only partly filled with water (capillary water).

FACTORS AFFECTING INFILTRATION. Most infiltration occurs in the *regolith*, which is the unconsolidated material (including soil) at the earth's surface. The amount of water that can infiltrate when precipitation occurs depends on several variables:

1. *The slope of the land.* The steeper the slope (gradient), the less the infiltration.

2. *The degree of saturation of the regolith.* The more saturated the regolith, the less the infiltration. Figure 8-1 shows that the regolith is divided into two zones: the **zone of saturation,** where the pores between solid particles are filled with water; and the **zone of aeration,** where the air spaces are partly filled with water (capillary water). Water infiltrates until it meets the interface between the zone of saturation and the zone of aeration. This interface is called the **water table.** The height of the water table varies with the amount of infiltration. The portion of the subsurface water below the water table is called **ground water.**

3. *The porosity of the regolith.* **Porosity** is the percentage of open space (pores) in a material compared to its total volume. Generally, the greater the porosity of the regolith, the greater the amount of infiltration that can occur.

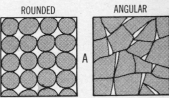

Well-rounded particles have more porosity than particles with angular shapes.

The porosity of a material is determined by the *shape, packing,* and *sorting* of the particles composing it. (See Figure 8-2.)

a. *Shape.* Well-rounded particles have greater porosity than particles with angular shapes, because the round ones do not fit together so well.

b. *Packing.* The more closely packed the particles, the lower the porosity.

Loosely packed particles have more porosity than closely packed particles.

c. *Sorting.* If all the particles in a material are about the same size, they are called **sorted;** if the particles are of mixed sizes, they are **unsorted.** The more unsorted the particles, the lower the porosity, because the small particles can fit into the spaces between the larger particles. It should be noted that size by itself does not affect porosity. For example, a material with large particles may have about the same porosity as one with smaller particles if the shape, packing, and sorting of both particle sizes are about equal.

Sorted particles have more porosity than unsorted particles.

Figure 8-2. Effect of particle or sediment shape, packing, and sorting on porosity of the regolith.

4. *The permeability of the regolith.* **Permeability** is the ability of a material to allow fluids such as water to pass through it. The **permeability rate** is the speed at which fluids will flow through a material. A material can be porous and yet impermeable (not permeable). Impermeability may be due to tight packing or cementing of particles, which seals off the pores from one another so that water cannot enter them. In the winter the cementing is often due to ice. In loose particles, the larger the particle size, the faster the permeability rate. The reason is that the size of the pores increases with the size of the particles, thus reducing the amount of friction.

5. *Capillarity.* During infiltration, some water is stopped from moving downward by the attractive force between water molecules and the surrounding earth materials. This attractive force is called **capillarity.** The water that is thus stored in small openings in the zone of aeration is called **capillary water.**

Capillarity also causes water to move up from the water table toward the earth's surface in the zone of aeration. This upward movement is called **capillary migration.**

When the particle size of loose particles becomes smaller, the capillarity becomes greater.

FACTORS AFFECTING RUNOFF AND STREAM DISCHARGE. Surface runoff can occur when (1) rate of precipitation exceeds the permeability rate (or infiltration rate) of the earth's surface, (2) the regolith pore space is saturated, or (3) the slope of the surface is too great to allow infiltration to occur.

Most runoff gets to streams, which eventually carry the water to the oceans. The greater the runoff, the greater the amount of *stream discharge* in local streams. **Stream discharge** is the volume of water flowing past a certain spot in a stream in a specific amount of time, and is expressed in such units as cubic meters/second.

WATER, OR HYDROSPHERIC, POLLUTION

SOURCES OF WATER POLLUTANTS. Pollutants are added to the hydrosphere by individuals, community action, and industrial processes. Generally, as the population density of an area increases, the concentration of pollutants in local lakes, streams (rivers), and ground water increases.

TYPES OF POLLUTANTS IN THE HYDROSPHERE. Water pollutants include dissolved and suspended materials, organic and inorganic wastes, outflow from industrial processes, radioactive substances, larger than normal concentrations of certain life forms, and thermal (heat) energy.

Excessive heat energy is considered a source of pollution because of its effects on oxygen content of water. The higher the temperature of water, the less the amount of dissolved oxygen it can hold. Furthermore, high temperatures increase the activity of the **aerobic bacteria** that are normally present. These bacteria use oxygen for their life processes, and their increased activity reduces the oxygen content of the water still further, thus killing many of the other forms of life that are present. Eventually, the aerobic bacteria are replaced by **anaerobic** varieties (types of bacteria that live without free oxygen). These bacteria and their wastes then become pollutants.

Power generating plants, including nuclear reactor types, are a major source of *thermal* (heat) pollution of bodies of water.

LONG-RANGE EFFECTS OF WATER POLLUTION. As water pollution increases, more and more water becomes unfit for human use. Purification of unfit water is a very complex and costly process.

LOCAL WATER BUDGET

The **local water budget** is a numerical model of a local area's water supply by months during a year. The water budget is useful to help determine an area's climate type and has practical applications in flood and irrigation control.

SYMBOLS AND MEANING OF TERMS IN LOCAL WATER BUDGET. To understand the local water budget, one must know the meaning of the terms used and how they relate to one another. The list below shows the symbols and the meaning of each of the terms used in the local water budget. Quantities of water per unit of area are expressed in millimeters. This is the depth to which the water would fill a pan covering the area involved.

1. Precipitation *(P)*. The moisture source for the local water budget is precipitation.

2. Potential evapotranspiration (E_p) is the amount of water that would evapotranspirate if the water were available. The E_p of an area is directly related *(a)* to the amount of energy (heat) available to the area (which for most places is largely determined by the amount of insolation—thus E_p generally decreases as latitude increases), and *(b)* the amount of evaporation surface area. An area of forest has more evaporation surface area for evapotranspiration, thus it has a higher E_p than an equal area of lawn receiving the same insolation. Figures 8-3 and 8-4 on page 110 show the relationships between insolation and latitude and between insolation and potential evapotranspiration.

3. The difference between precipitation and potential evapotranspiration $(P - E_p)$. Its value can be negative, positive, or zero.

4. The amount of change in the water stored in the ground (ΔSt). Its value can be negative, positive, or zero. If ΔSt is positive, it is called **recharge.** Recharge occurs when the soil is not saturated and P is greater than E_p. Negative ΔSt is called **usage.** Water usage occurs when E_p is greater than P and soil storage is greater than zero.

5. Soil storage *(St)* is the amount of water stored in the soil. Each area has a specific maximum amount of soil storage, but for most areas it is assumed to be 100 millimeters.

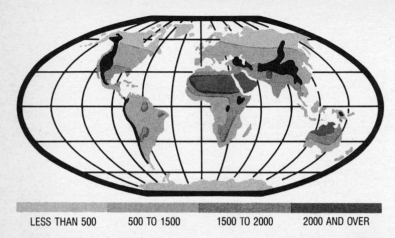

LESS THAN 500   500 TO 1500   1500 TO 2000   2000 AND OVER

Figure 8-3. World map of insolation at the earth's surface in thousands of calories/cm²/year. Note how yearly insolation generally increases with decreasing latitude. Due to many factors, however, especially differences in cloud coverage, it is not a perfect correlation. (Darkest areas have very high elevation.)

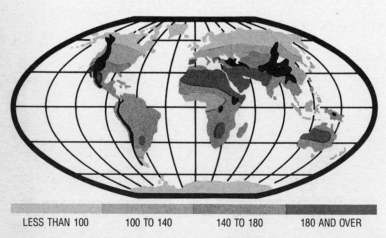

LESS THAN 100   100 TO 140   140 TO 180   180 AND OVER

Figure 8-4. World map of potential evapotranspiration in centimeters per year. Note the very good comparison to the yearly insolation map above. It is not a perfect correlation, because local heat values are affected by many other factors such as surface ocean currents and tropospheric convection currents. (Darkest areas have very high elevation.)

6. Actual evapotranspiration (E_a). E_a can never be greater than E_p. When there is a deficit, E_a is less than E_p, and at all other times E_a equals E_p.

7. Water deficit (D). A water deficit exists when E_a does not equal E_p because there is not enough water in the combination of P and St. The deficit is the amount of water that would be necessary for E_a to equal E_p, that is, it is E_p minus E_a. A deficit can occur only when the combined St and P are not as great as E_p.

8. Water surplus (S). There is a surplus when the soil is saturated (maximum St) and P is greater than E_p. Surplus water eventually becomes runoff.

EXAMPLES OF LOCAL WATER BUDGETS. To understand how a water budget is worked out, study the procedure that is described for the water budget of Syracuse, New York (Figure 8-6 on page 112). Then use the procedure to complete the water budget for El Paso, Texas (Figure 8-7 on page 113). Graph your results and see if they agree with the graph in Figure 8-7.

STREAM DISCHARGE AND WATER BUDGET. The discharge of a local stream is usually a measure of the amount of surplus water in the local drainage area of the stream. Figure 8-5 shows the discharge of a stream in Syracuse, New York. Comparison of this data with the water budget of Syracuse shows that the stream discharge is greatest when the surplus is the largest and least when the surplus is smallest.

Figure 8-5. Discharge of a stream in Syracuse, New York, which is dependent on local precipitation. Compare with the water budget of Syracuse (Fig. 8-6). Much of the surplus in the winter months is stored temporarily as snow and ice, and does not contribute to stream discharge until early spring. The discharge during the period of deficit (August and September) is due to depletion of ground water at levels too deep to be available to plants.

Note that the stream is still flowing when Syracuse has a deficit in the water budget. If a local stream is still flowing during a deficit period, the source of the water is ground water depletion.

	J	F	M	A	M	J	J	A	S	O	N	D	Totals
P	72	68	81	75	74	87	84	82	72	76	68	72	911
E_p	0	0	3	34	83	115	134	122	84	46	15	0	636
$P-E_p$	72	68	78	41	−9	−28	−50	−40	−12	30	53	72	
ΔSt	0	0	0	0	−9	−28	−50	−13	0	30	53	17	
St	100	100	100	100	91	63	13	0	0	30	83	100	
E_a	0	0	3	34	83	115	134	95	72	46	15	0	597
D	0	0	0	0	0	0	0	27	12	0	0	0	39
S	72	68	78	41	0	0	0	0	0	0	0	55	314

Figure 8-6. The water budget for Syracuse, New York. The data for P and E_p in the first two rows of the table are given. To complete the table, first enter all the values of P − E_p in the third row. This is done by simple subtraction. If E_p is greater than P, the result is entered with a minus sign. The next step is to find a month in which storage (St) is either 0 or 100. When the total P is greater than the total E_p (a humid climate), look for a storage of 100. This will occur whenever there is a series of months in which positive values of P − E_p add to more than 100. This happens in October to December (30 + 53 + 72 = 155). Therefore, St for December must be 100 (the assumed maximum storage). We now go on to the next month, January. Since storage is full, and P − E_p is positive, there is no change in storage (ΔSt = 0), and all of P − E_p (72 mm) is surplus. We also make E_a equal to E_p. (It is zero in this month because the ground is frozen and plants are dormant.) For the next three months, St remains at 100, E_a = E_p, and all of P − E_p is surplus.

In May, P − E_p is negative. However, the difference can come out of storage. Thus, ΔSt = −9, St becomes 91, and E_a = E_p because there is enough water available. But there is no surplus this month. This continues until August. In August, P − E_p = −40, but there is only 13 mm in storage. Therefore E_a is only 95 (P of 82 plus 13 from St). St drops to zero, and there is a deficit of 27 (E_p − E_a). In September there is another deficit. E_a equals P, because there is no water in storage. In October, P − E_p becomes positive, and recharge begins (ΔSt = 30). In November, ΔSt = 53, bringing St up to 83. In December, St becomes 100 (as already noted), and there is a surplus of 55.

	J	F	M	A	M	J	J	A	S	O	N	D	Totals
P	10	11	8	7	8	18	40	41	33	17	13	12	218
E_p	11	18	37	75	117	163	171	152	111	62	24	10	951
$P-E_p$	-1	-7	-29	-68	-109	-145	-131	-111	-78	-45	-11	2	
ΔSt													
St				0									
E_a													
D													
S													

Figure 8-7. The water budget for El Paso, Texas. Since P is less than E_p, this is an arid climate. To complete the table, look for a series of months in which negative values of P − E_p add to −100. From January to April, the total is −105. Therefore, St for April must be 0. This can be your starting point.

CLIMATE

Climate is the overall view of weather conditions of a region over a long period of time. The two major aspects of climate are *temperature* and *moisture conditions*. The factors that determine climate include latitude, planetary wind and pressure belts, oceans and other large bodies of water, ocean currents, mountains, and elevation.

TEMPERATURE AND CLIMATE. In terms of climate, two characteristics of the temperatures of a region are important: (1) the average temperature over the year, and (2) the range of average monthly temperatures from lowest to highest during the year.

MOISTURE AND CLIMATE. A climate is called **arid,** or dry, if the total precipitation during the year is less than the potential evapotranspiration, that is, if P is less than E_p. A climate is called **humid** if P is greater than E_p. Thus, whether a climate is said to be arid or humid depends not on the amount of precipitation but on the difference between the amount of moisture available and the potential need. As illustrated in Figure 8-8 on page 114, a region can have very little precipitation and still have a humid climate.

Figure 8-8. Examples of an arid and a humid climate. Graph A shows the relationship between P and E_p for a region of moderate rainfall but high values of E_p. Since there is a net moisture deficit for the year, the region has an arid climate. Some regions around 30° latitude have climates of this type. Graph B represents a climate in which there is little precipitation, but even smaller values of E_p. Since there is a moisture surplus for the year, the climate is humid. Many polar regions have climates of this type.

Regions with extreme moisture deficits (large yearly negative values of $P - E_p$) are called **deserts.** The term *semi-arid* is sometimes used to describe the moisture conditions of a region with a moderate deficit.

LATITUDE AND TEMPERATURE.   Latitude is a major factor in determining climates because of its influence on both temperature and moisture conditions. Temperature characteristics vary with latitude because of the relationships between insolation and latitude discussed in Topic VI. At low latitudes, where the maximum angle of insolation is always high, average temperatures are high throughout the year. Because the duration of insolation is fairly constant at about 12 hours per day, there is little temperature variation during the year. At high latitudes, where the maximum angle of insolation is never large and in some months remains zero, average temperatures are low. Since the duration of insolation varies from zero to 24 hours a day, and is longest at the times of greatest angle of insolation, temperatures vary over a wide range from winter lows to summer highs.

LATITUDE AND MOISTURE.   Moisture conditions vary with latitude because of the location of the planetary wind and pressure belts (see page 85). Where there is low pressure, such as near the equator and in mid-latitudes, the air rises. The cooling of that rising air results in large amounts of precipitation and humid climates. When air falls in high-pressure belts, such as around 30° latitude, it warms and there is little precipitation. Such areas have arid climates.

LATITUDINAL CLIMATE PATTERNS.   The combination of the temperature and moisture effects of latitude results in a basic distribution of climate types around the world, called **latitudinal climate patterns** (see Figure 8-9).

Zones	Climate Types
1,8	POLAR Cold, humid to semi-arid, with large temperature variation
2,7	TEMPERATE Moderate temperatures, humid, with moderate temperature variation
3,6	DESERT Hot, arid
4,5	TROPICAL Hot, humid, with little temperature variation

M—Marine climate   C—Continental climate

Figure 8-9. Basic latitudinal climate pattern on an imaginary continent. The arid belts around 30° latitude are the result of descending air in the atmospheric circulation at that latitude (see Figure 7-3). The modification of this basic pattern by prevailing winds and distance from oceans is illustrated in Figure 8-10.

EFFECT OF LARGE BODIES OF WATER ON CLIMATE.   Large bodies of water serve to modify the latitudinal climate patterns. If an area is near the ocean or a large lake, its temperatures will be moderated by the slow heating up and cooling off of the water body. An area with these moderated temperatures is said to have a **marine climate.** Marine climates have cooler summers and warmer winters, thus a small annual range of temperatures compared to inland areas at the same latitude. Inland areas away from large bodies of water have cooler winters and warmer summers and a large annual range of temperatures. Such areas are said to have a **continental climate.**

EFFECT OF LARGE LANDMASSES ON CLIMATE.   As explained on page 67, bodies of land heat up and cool off more rapidly than bodies of water. As a result, the temperatures over a continent in the mid-latitudes are higher than the adjacent oceans in summer and lower in winter. These temperature differences produce convection currents that modify the planetary wind patterns and thus modify the latitudinal climate patterns. The general effect on the basic climate patterns of a continent is illustrated in Figure 8-10.

Figure 8-10. Modification of basic climate patterns by prevailing winds.

Notice in Figure 8-10 that the arid belt around 30° latitude does not extend across the eastern portion of the continent. The reason for this is that in the summer months the land temperatures are higher than the ocean temperatures, causing air to rise over the land and resulting in prevailing winds carrying moisture inland from the oceans on the east. The eastern regions of the continent therefore have much more precipitation than they would have if the planetary wind pattern remained unchanged.

A second effect is the arid region in the central portion of the continent at the mid-latitudes (40° to 50°). The reason for this is that the prevailing winds from the western oceans lose their moisture by precipitation and become increasingly dry as they blow inland.

STORM TRACKS AND CLIMATE.   In the mid-latitudes, such as the continental United States, temperature and moisture are greatly affected by a succession of low-pressure systems. Major tracks of low-pressure storm systems are shown in Figure 8-11.

OCEAN CURRENTS AND CLIMATE.   Coastal climate patterns are modified by ocean currents. Currents flowing away from the equator carry warm water to higher latitudes, while currents flowing toward the

Figure 8-11. The usual paths followed by low-pressure storm centers as they pass across the United States.

equator carry cool water to lower latitudes. A cool ocean current will cause a coastal area to have cooler temperatures and less precipitation. One reason there is low precipitation is that cool water results in cool air, which has a low saturation vapor pressure and thus cannot hold much water vapor. The locations of the warm and cool ocean currents are shown on the *Surface Ocean Currents* map in the *Earth Science Reference Tables*.

ELEVATION AND CLIMATE.   The elevation of an area above sea level modifies the latitudinal climate pattern, because as air rises, it expands and cools (at the rate of 10°C/km; see *Lapse Rate* in the *Earth Science Reference Tables*). Thus the higher the altitude at any given latitude, the cooler it is. Elevation also affects precipitation. As the elevation increases, the temperature and saturation vapor pressure decrease; the air thus approaches the dew point. Therefore, areas at higher altitudes generally have more precipitation than lower areas.

MOUNTAINS AND CLIMATE—OROGRAPHIC EFFECT.   Mountains that intersect prevailing winds, such as those associated with the planetary wind belts, can modify the latitudinal climate pattern in the following manner. Figure 8-12 on page 118 shows a cross section of a mountain against which the prevailing winds blow from the left. This side is called the *windward side*. As the wind strikes the windward side of the mountain, the air is forced to rise. As it does so, it cools adiabatically. As long as the air temperature is above the dew point, the dry adiabatic cooling rate is about 10°C per kilometer. If the cooling continues until the dew point is reached, condensation will occur above this altitude. Since large amounts of latent heat are released during condensation, the temperature of the rising air does not drop as rapidly as before. The adiabatic cooling rate during condensation is only 6°C per kilometer.

On the opposite side of the mountain, called the *leeward side*, the air begins to descend. It therefore begins to warm adiabatically. Since condensation immediately stops, the warming rate is constant at the dry rate of 10°C per kilometer all the way down. As a result, the leeward side is warmer than the windward side at any given altitude. The leeward side also has much less precipitation, because the air has lost much of its moisture on the windward side, and its saturation vapor pressure rises as its temperature increases. Both of these factors make condensation and precipitation unlikely.

Another way that mountains modify climate is by acting as barriers to moving air masses, preventing cold air or warm air from crossing the mountain to the other side. As a result, opposite sides of a mountain can have different temperature patterns.

The effects of mountains on climate are called the **orographic effect.**

Figure 8-12. Orographic climate effect of mountains that intersect prevailing moist winds (such as those on the northwest coast of the United States). Compare the temperature at the same altitude on the two sides of the mountain. (See text for detailed explanation.)

CLIMATIC CLASSIFICATION BASED ON PRECIPITATION AND PO-TENTIAL EVAPOTRANSPIRATION. Climatic regions or zones can be distinguished qualitatively based on either P/E_p (precipitation divided by potential evapotranspiration) or $P - E_p$ (precipitation minus potential evapotranspiration). The classification can be based on a system like the one in the table below.

Climate Type	P/E_p	$P - E_p$ in cm
Humid	1.2 or greater	26.7 or greater
Sub-humid	1.2 to 0.8	26.7 to 0.0
Semi-arid	0.8 to 0.4	0.0 to −26.7
Arid	0.4 or lower	−26.7 or lower

VOCABULARY

water cycle	local water budget
infiltration	precipitation (P)
subsurface water	potential evapotranspiration (E_p)
runoff	change in soil storage (ΔSt)
zone of saturation	recharge $(+\Delta St)$
zone of aeration	usage $(-\Delta St)$
water table	soil storage (St)
ground water	actual evapotranspiration (E_a)
porosity	deficit (D)
sorted and unsorted particles	surplus (S)
permeability	climate
permeability rate	arid climate
capillarity	humid climate
capillary water	desert
capillary migration	latitudinal climate pattern
stream discharge	marine climate
aerobic bacteria	continental climate
anaerobic bacteria	orographic effect

QUESTIONS ON TOPIC VIII—WATER, ENERGY, AND CLIMATE

Questions in Recent Regents Exams (end of book)

June 1991:   5, 23, 25, 28, 76–80
June 1992:   2, 12, 21, 22, 24, 26, 27
June 1993:   18, 21–24, 52, 55
June 1994:   21, 25, 28, 29, 69, 77, 78, 79, 80

Questions from Earlier Regents Exams

1. For the earth as a whole, what happens to most of the precipitation?   (1) It recharges the soil moisture deficit.   (2) It becomes runoff and moves to the oceans.   (3) It is stored in the soil as capillary water.   (4) It is returned to the atmosphere through evapotranspiration.

2. The primary source of most of the moisture for the earth's atmosphere is   (1) soil-moisture storage   (2) rivers and lakes   (3) melting glaciers   (4) oceans

3. As the amount of precipitation on land increases, the depth from the surface of the earth to the water table will probably   (1) decrease   (2) increase   (3) remain the same

4. As the heat and pressure applied to buried sediments is increased, the porosity of the sediments will probably   (1) decrease   (2) increase   (3) remain the same

5. Which diagram best illustrates the condition of the soil below the water table?

KEY

▦ SOIL PARTICLES

■ WATER

□ PORE SPACE (AIR)

6. Which graph best represents the relationship between porosity and particle size for soil samples of uniform size, shape, and packing?

7. Which graph best represents the relationship between soil permeability rate and infiltration when all other conditions are the same?

8. Which earth material covering the surface of a landfill would permit the *least* amount of rainwater to infiltrate the surface?   (1) silt   (2) clay   (3) sand   (4) pebbles

9. As the temperature of the soil decreases from 10°C to −5°C, the infiltration rate of ground water through this soil will most likely (1) decrease   (2) increase   (3) remain the same

10. Surface runoff of precipitation occurs when   (1) porosity is exceeded by permeability   (2) the infiltration rate is greater than the precipitation rate   (3) the precipitation rate is greater than the infiltration rate   (4) there is no demand for evapotranspiration

11. Which graph best illustrates the relationship between the slope of the land and the amount of surface runoff?

12. Which graph best represents the typical relationship between population density near a lake and pollution of the lake?

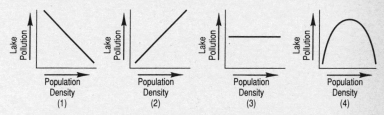

13. What is the main reason that a high concentration of aerobic bacteria is harmful to a lake?   (1) The bacteria release large amounts of oxygen.   (2) The bacteria use up large amounts of oxygen.   (3) The bacteria cause excessive cooling of the water.   (4) The bacteria provide food for predators.

14. During a given month in a certain locality, the potential evapotranspiration exceeded the actual evapotranspiration. Which probably occurred? (1) a water deficit   (2) a water surplus   (3) a higher potential evapotranspiration than usual   (4) low temperatures and high humidity

15. Which would cause the potential evapotranspiration to decrease in a given month?   (1) below-normal precipitation   (2) drilling of a large well   (3) a month-long cold spell   (4) a high actual evapotranspiration

16. The main source of moisture for the local water budget is (1) potential evapotranspiration   (2) actual evapotranspiration (3) ground water storage   (4) precipitation

17. The actual evapotranspiration (E_a) during the year is (1) always greater than potential evapotranspiration (E_p) (2) sometimes greater than potential evapotranspiration (E_p) (3) never greater than potential evapotranspiration (E_p)

Base your answers to questions 18 through 24 on the water budget diagram for Rockford, Illinois, below.

Water Budget Diagram for Rockford, Illinois

18. A water deficit occurred in Rockford, Illinois, during   (1) February   (2) June   (3) August   (4) December

19. During how many months of the year did Rockford have a water surplus?   (1) ten   (2) eight   (3) six   (4) four

20. During which of these months did the potential evapotranspiration equal the precipitation in Rockford?   (1) March   (2) January (3) September   (4) November

21. During which month was the soil moisture recharge the greatest?   (1) December   (2) November   (3) October   (4) August

22. If the storage capacity of Rockford were increased from 100 to 150 mm, which would not change?   (1) actual evapotranspiration (2) potential evapotranspiration   (3) deficit   (4) surplus

23. During which month are plants most likely in need of irrigation? (1) April   (2) June   (3) August   (4) October

24. Streams in this area probably carry the greatest volume of water during the month of   (1) April   (2) June   (3) August   (4) November

25. Dry soil will be recharged with moisture if potential evapotranspiration is   (1) less than precipitation   (2) greater than precipitation (3) equal to precipitation

26. During a 3-week period without rain in June, water continued to flow in a small New York State stream. The water in the stream most likely came from   (1) the roots of trees along the stream bank   (2) evapotranspiration in a region far away and unaffected by the dry period   (3) ground water flowing into the streambed   (4) condensation on the surface of rocks in the stream

27. A region with an arid climate has an annual precipitation that is   (1) less than the annual potential evapotranspiration   (2) greater than the annual potential evapotranspiration   (3) equal to the annual potential evapotranspiration

28. Which generally has the greatest effect in determining the climate of an area?   (1) degrees of longitude   (2) extent of vegetation cover   (3) distance from equator   (4) month of the year

29. As the number of degrees of latitude from the equator increases, the yearly average temperature generally   (1) decreases   (2) increases   (3) remains the same

Refer to the diagrams to answer question 30. Diagram I shows the planetary wind belts of the earth. Diagram II is a graph of the average yearly precipitation for locations between 90° north latitude and 90° south latitude.

DIAGRAM I
WIND BELTS OF THE EARTH

DIAGRAM II

30. Which statement about the earth's average amount of yearly precipitation is best supported by the diagrams?   (1) Precipitation is lowest at latitudes where planetary winds converge (meet).   (2) Precipitation is highest at latitudes where planetary winds converge (meet).   (3) Precipitation is highest at latitudes where planetary winds diverge (move apart).   (4) Precipitation is unrelated to planetary wind belts.

31. Although New York City is at approximately the same latitude as Omaha, Nebraska, its winter months are warmer and its summer months cooler. Which statement best explains why this is so?   (1) The sun's rays are more direct on New York City in the winter.   (2) Nebraska is nearer the Rocky Mountains.   (3) The water around New York City has a moderating effect on the temperature.   (4) The prevailing westerlies have a greater effect on Omaha than on New York City.

32. Which area of New York State would probably have the lowest annual temperature range?   (1) Long Island   (2) the Catskills   (3) the Adirondack peaks   (4) the Mohawk Valley

33. Bodies of water have a moderating effect on climate primarily because   (1) water gains heat more rapidly than land does   (2) water surfaces are flatter than land surfaces   (3) water temperatures are always lower than land temperatures   (4) water temperatures change more slowly than land temperatures do

34. Which locality has the greatest annual range of temperature? (1) Seattle, Washington   (2) Bismarck, North Dakota   (3) New York City   (4) Miami, Florida

35. A low-pressure storm center located over New York State will most likely move toward the   (1) southeast   (2) southwest   (3) northeast   (4) northwest

36. As a parcel of air rises, its temperature will   (1) decrease due to expansion   (2) decrease due to compression   (3) increase due to expansion   (4) increase due to compression

Base your answers to questions 37–42 on your knowledge of earth science and on the diagram. The diagram represents an imaginary continent on the earth surrounded by water. The arrows indicate the direction of the prevailing winds. Two large mountain regions are also indicated. Points A, B, E, and H are located at sea level; C, D, and F are in the foothills of the mountains; G is high in the mountains.

37. Which physical characteristic would cause location G to have a colder yearly climate than any other location?   (1) the nearness of location G to a large ocean   (2) the location of G with respect to the prevailing winds   (3) the elevation of location G above sea level   (4) the distance of location G from the equator

38. Which location probably has the greatest annual rainfall?   (1) A (2) F (3) C (4) D

39. Which location would be warmed by adiabatic changes?   (1) A (2) B (3) C (4) E

40. Which graph best represents the average monthly temperatures that would be recorded during one year at location E?

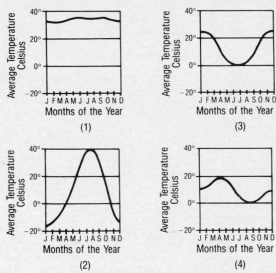

41. Which location probably has the greatest range in temperature during the year?   (1) A (2) B (3) H (4) D

42. Which location will probably record its highest potential evapotranspiration values for the year during January?   (1) A (2) F (3) C (4) D

The diagram below shows the positions of the cities of Seattle and Spokane, Washington. Both cities are located at approximately 48° north latitude, and they are separated by the Cascade Mountains.

43. How does the climate of Seattle compare with the climate of Spokane?   (1) Seattle—hot and dry; Spokane—cool and humid   (2) Seattle—hot and humid; Spokane—cool and dry   (3) Seattle—cool and humid; Spokane—warm and dry   (4) Seattle—cool and dry; Spokane—warm and humid

Additional Questions

Complete the water budget for Fairbanks, Alaska, given below to answer questions 1 through 4.

	J	F	M	A	M	J	J	A	S	O	N	D
P	27	13	10	6	18	36	48	60	28	22	15	13
E_p	0	0	0	0	71	114	115	86	48	0	0	0
$P-E_p$	27	13	10	6	-53	-78	-67			22	15	13
$\triangle St$	27	13	10							22	15	13
St	77	90	100							22	37	50
E_a	0	0	0							0	0	0
D	0	0	0							0	0	0
S	0	0	0							0	0	0

Values in millimeters of water   Maximum storage: 100 mm

1. Stream flow discharge would be the greatest in the month of
(1) February   (2) April   (3) October   (4) December

2. How would you classify the climate of Fairbanks from June to September?   (1) rain forest   (2) low-latitude   (3) arid   (4) moist

3. If streams are flowing in May in Fairbanks, the water in the streams would most likely come from   (1) precipitation   (2) surplus   (3) soil storage   (4) actual evapotranspiration

4. If the porosity of the soil in this area increases, which of the following would change the most?   (1) precipitation   (2) potential evapotranspiration   (3) soil storage   (4) precipitation minus potential evapotranspiration

Refer to the diagram below to answer questions 5 through 8.

5. Which location would have the coolest average temperature?
(1) A   (2) C   (3) D   (4) F

6. Which location would have the most condensation in the atmosphere above it during the year?   (1) B   (2) C   (3) E   (4) F

7. Which place would have the largest negative value for $P - E_p$ (precipitation minus potential evapotranspiration) during the year?
(1) A   (2) B   (3) D   (4) F

8. How is the potential evapotranspiration of area A-B affected by the ocean current?   (1) It is reduced.   (2) It is increased.   (3) It is unchanged.

WEATHERING

Weathering is the breakdown of rocks into particles called **sediment.** Rocks weather because they are adjusting to a new environment different from the one in which they were formed. Weathering occurs when rocks are exposed to the air, water, and living things at or near the earth's surface.

TYPES OF WEATHERING. There are two general types of weathering—*physical* and *chemical.*

Physical weathering is the breakdown of rock into smaller pieces (sediment) without chemical change. Physical weathering includes *frost action,* which breaks up rocks when water in the rocks freezes and expands.

Chemical weathering is the breakdown of rock by chemical action and results in a change in the mineral composition. Chemical weathering includes the uniting of minerals with oxygen *(oxidation)* or with water *(hydration),* and the dissolving of minerals by acids.

FACTORS AFFECTING THE RATE AND TYPE OF WEATHERING. Many variables determine the rate and type of weathering that will occur:

1. *Exposure.* The more exposed the rocks are to the air, water, and living things near the earth's surface, the faster the weathering.

2. *Particle size.* The smaller the particle size, the greater the total surface area per unit volume exposed to weathering and the greater the rate of weathering (see Figure 9-1).

Figure 9-1. Explaining why surface area increases as particle size decreases. A single division of the block at the left exposes two new surface areas. If the two blocks at the bottom are divided again and again into smaller and smaller pieces, the total surface area will increase rapidly, although the total mass of material will remain the same.

3. *Mineral composition.* A rock's mineral composition determines the rate of weathering because different minerals have different resistances to weathering.

4. *Climate.* Climate greatly influences the rate and type of weathering (see Figure 9-2). Chemical weathering is most pronounced in warm, moist climates. The higher the average temperatures and the more humid the climate, the more intense the chemical weathering becomes. In cold climates, frost action (a type of physical weathering) is the most common and most effective form of weathering. It is especially intense where the climate is moist and the temperature variations lead to much alternate freezing and thawing.

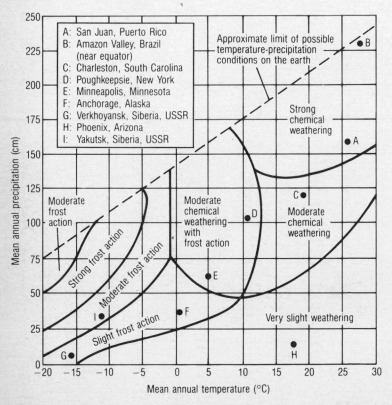

Figure 9-2. Dominant type of weathering for various climatic conditions. For example, if the mean annual temperature is 15°C and the mean annual precipitation is 100 cm, moderate chemical weathering is the main agent of weathering. The blank region of the chart in the upper left represents conditions that almost never occur on the earth.

PRODUCTS OF WEATHERING. Weathering results in the formation of three different types of sediment: (1) solid sediments such as sand and pebbles; (2) very small solid sediments called *colloids* (or clay-sized particles); and (3) dissolved ionic minerals, which are a major end product of much weathering. Dissolved minerals are what cause the "hardness" in all surface and ground water and what make the oceans "salty."

SOIL

One product of weathering is **soil,** which is the part of the regolith that will support rooted plants.

TYPES OF SOIL. Soil can be divided into two general types—*residual* and *transported*. A **residual soil** is a soil that formed from the rocks or regolith under the soil. A **transported soil** is one that has been moved into an area from another place by erosion.

SOIL FORMATION. The composition of soil varies with depth. This is indicated by horizontal layers or zones called **soil horizons,** which develop as a result of weathering processes. Soil and soil horizon development starts at the earth's surface and progresses downward with time, as illustrated in Figure 9-3.

Figure 9-3. Profile development of horizons in a residual soil. Originally, there is unweathered bedrock at the surface. Weathering gradually proceeds downward to deeper levels. Meanwhile, infiltration, capillary migration, the addition of plant material, and the movement of sediment by organisms in the developing soil produce horizons with characteristic features.

Living things play a significant part in soil formation. For example, plant roots break up rock by widening cracks; accumulation of organic matter is an important part of soil; decay of organic matter forms acids that dissolve rock; earthworms, ants, and burrowing animals expose fresh rock material to weathering.

EROSION

Weathering is a process that produces most sediments; **erosion** is the process by which sediments are obtained and transported. Erosion is also the process by which the earth's surface is worn away, sculpted, and lowered.

EROSION THROUGH TRANSPORTING SYSTEMS. Erosion of sediments is accomplished by means of *transporting systems.* A **transporting system** includes (1) the transporting agent (agent of erosion), such as running water (streams), glaciers, waves, density currents in water, wind, and people; (2) the "driving" force, which consists of gravity and the energy transfer from potential to kinetic energy; and (3) the material being transported, called sediment.

GRAVITY AND EROSION. Gravity plays a two-fold role in the erosional process:

1. Gravity is the primary driving force behind all transporting systems, causing sediment to move downslope. For example, glaciers and streams move and erode sediments downhill because of the pull of gravity.

2. Gravity may act alone (that is, without the transporting agents mentioned above) in transporting earth materials. Loose sediment on steep slopes may break away and move downhill under the direct influence of gravity, such as in a landslide.

EVIDENCE OF EROSION. Sediments displaced from their source are evidence of erosion. Such sediments can be seen in muddy streams, rock fields near glaciers, the assortment of rocks at shorelines, shifting sands, and earth moved by people in construction.

Weathered rock that is transported from its place of origin to its present location is called **transported sediment.** Weathered rock that remains in its place of origin is called **residual sediment.** Transported sediment is far more common than residual sediment.

STREAM, OR RUNNING WATER, EROSION. Running water is the dominant agent of erosion in terms of the amount of sediment moved, even in many arid climates. Streams obtain sediments by (1) the direct lifting of particles from the stream bottom, or **stream bed;** (2) by collisions between carried sediments and the stream bed (abrasion); and (3) by receiving dissolved minerals, produced by weathering, from ground water flow or by directly dissolving the stream bed.

Streams carry sediments in three major ways: (1) dissolved minerals are carried in solution; (2) solid sediments of small size, including colloids, are carried by suspension; and (3) larger solid sediments are carried by rolling and bouncing along the bed (see Figure 9-4).

Figure 9-4. Transport of sediments by a stream.

STREAM VELOCITY.   The two most important factors that determine the average velocity of a stream are the *slope,* or *gradient,* of the stream and the *discharge,* or volume of water. Generally, as either the slope or the discharge of a stream increases, the velocity will increase. When a stream changes direction, the region of maximum velocity shifts as shown in Figure 9-5.

Figure 9-5. Variations in stream velocity in the cross section of an idealized stream. Where the stream course is straight (as at A), the location of maximum velocity is at the center of the cross section. Where the stream course changes direction (as at B and C), the location of maximum velocity moves toward the outside of the curve, or meander. Low velocity at the inside of curves results in deposition of the larger and denser sediments. Velocity also varies with depth. It is greatest just below the surface and least near the stream bed. At the air-water interface and at the stream bed velocity is reduced by friction.

SEDIMENT SIZE AND STREAM VELOCITY. The sediments being transported by a stream generally flow much slower than the stream. The greater the velocity of a stream, the larger the sediment particles it can carry (see Figure 9-6). For any given stream, the greater its velocity the more total sediment it can carry.

Figure 9-6. **Relationship between stream velocity and maximum size of particle that can be moved.** (Also see *Relationship of Transported Particle Size to Water Velocity* in the *Earth Science Reference Tables.*)

EROSION BY WIND AND GLACIERS. Many of the factors that affect stream erosion are found also in glacial and wind erosion. The greater the slope of a glacier, the faster it generally moves. The positions of maximum velocity in a glacier are similar to those of a stream shown in Figure 9-5. The greater the velocity of the wind, the larger the size of sediment particles it can carry.

SEDIMENT FEATURES AND EROSIONAL AGENT. Each agent of erosion produces distinctive characteristics in the sediment it transports.

Figure 9-7. **Sediment features reflect the erosional or weathering agents that produced or transported them.**

A solid sediment in wind or stream erosion will become rounded and smooth. The longer the time the sediment is eroded, the more smooth and rounded it becomes. Wind-blown sediments are often more frosted (pitted) than stream sediments. Glacial sediments are only partly rounded and often have scratches of various sizes. Sediments produced by physical weathering or moved by gravity are often very angular in shape.

PEOPLE AND EROSION.   People greatly increase the erosion of land by their activities. The burning and cutting down of forests, poor farming methods, road and building construction, and mining expose loose soil and regolith to the agents of erosion and thereby increase erosion rates. The removal and lowering of the soil, regolith, and vegetation at the earth's surface is an aspect of erosion called **denudation.** Denudation has been greatly increased in the last few hundred years by the activities of people.

VOCABULARY

weathering	soil horizon
sediment	erosion
physical weathering	transporting system
chemical weathering	transported sediment
soil	residual sediment
residual soil	stream bed
transported soil	denudation

QUESTIONS ON TOPIC IX—WEATHERING AND EROSION

Questions in Recent Regents Exams (end of book)

Questions from Earlier Regents Exams

1. What is the main difference between chemical and physical weathering?   (1) Chemical weathering alters the composition of minerals, and physical weathering does not.   (2) Chemical weathering increases the surface area of minerals, and physical weathering does not. (3) Physical weathering alters the composition of minerals, and chemical weathering does not.   (4) Physical weathering increases the surface area of minerals, and chemical weathering does not.

2. Which property of water makes frost action a common and effective form of weathering?   (1) Water dissolves many earth materials.   (2) Water expands when it freezes.   (3) Water cools the surroundings when it evaporates.   (4) Water loses 80 calories of heat per gram when it freezes.

3. Chemical weathering will occur most rapidly when rocks are exposed to the   (1) hydrosphere and lithosphere   (2) mesosphere and thermosphere   (3) hydrosphere and atmosphere   (4) lithosphere and atmosphere

4. Which is the best example of physical weathering?   (1) the cracking of rock caused by the freezing and thawing of water   (2) the transportation of sediment in a stream   (3) the reaction of limestone with acid rainwater   (4) the formation of a sandbar along the side of a stream

5. The diagram below represents a geologic cross section with sedimentary rock layers *A*, *B*, *C*, and *D* exposed to the atmosphere. Which rock layer in the diagram is most resistant to weathering and erosion?
(1) *A*   (2) *B*   (3) *C*   (4) *D*

6. A rock normally weathers faster when broken up because of an increase in the rock's   (1) mass   (2) volume   (3) density   (4) total surface area

7. In which climate would the chemical weathering of limestone occur most rapidly?   (1) cold and dry   (2) cold and humid   (3) warm and dry   (4) warm and humid

8. In which climate does physical weathering by first action most easily occur?   (1) dry and hot   (2) dry and cold   (3) moist and hot   (4) moist and cold

9. Two different kinds of minerals, *A* and *B*, were placed in the same container and shaken for 15 minutes. The diagrams below represent the size and shape of the various pieces of mineral before and after shaking. What caused the resulting differences in shapes and sizes of the minerals?

KEY:
MINERAL A
MINERAL B

Container Before Shaking

Container After Shaking

(1) Mineral *B* was shaken harder.   (2) Mineral *B* had a glossy luster.
(3) Mineral *A* was more resistant to abrasion.   (4) Mineral *A* consisted of smaller pieces before shaking began.

10. Which is indicated by a deep residual soil?   (1) resistant bedrock   (2) a large amount of glaciation   (3) a long period of weathering   (4) a youthful stage of erosion

11. The chemical composition of a residual soil in a certain area is determined by the   (1) method by which the soil was transported to the area   (2) slope of the land and the particle size of the soil   (3) length of time since the last crustal movement in the area occurred   (4) minerals in the bedrock beneath the soil and the climate of the area

12. A variety of soil types are found in New York State primarily because areas of the state differ in their   (1) amounts of insolation (2) distances from the ocean   (3) underlying bedrock and sediments (4) amounts of human activities

13. Soil horizons develop as a result of   (1) capillary action and solution   (2) erosion and ionization   (3) leaching and color changes (4) weathering processes and biologic activity

14. Particles of soil often differ greatly from the underlying bedrock in color, mineral composition, and organic content. Which conclusion about these soil particles is best made from this evidence?   (1) They are residual sediments.   (2) They are transported sediments.   (3) They are uniformly large-grained.   (4) They are soluble in water.

15. Which change would cause the topsoil in New York State to increase in thickness?   (1) an increase in slope   (2) an increase in biologic activity   (3) a decrease in rainfall   (4) a decrease in air temperature

16. The primary force responsible for most of the transportation of rock material on the surface of the earth is   (1) gravity   (2) wind (3) running water   (4) glaciers

17. Which erosional force acts alone to produce avalanches and landslides?   (1) gravity   (2) winds   (3) running water   (4) sea waves

18. Transported rock materials are more common than residual rock materials in the soils of New York State. Which statement best explains this observation?   (1) Solid rock must be transported to break. (2) Weathering changes transported rock materials more easily than residual rock materials.   (3) Most rock materials are moved by some agent of erosion at some time in their history.   (4) Residual rock material forms only from bedrock that is difficult to change into soil.

19. The composition of sediments on the earth's surface usually is quite different from the composition of the underlying bedrock. This observation suggest that most   (1) bedrock is formed from sediments (2) bedrock is resistant to weathering   (3) sediments are residual (4) sediments are transported

20. Which is the best evidence that erosion has occurred?   (1) a soil rich in lime on top of a limestone bedrock   (2) a layer of basalt found on the floor of the ocean   (3) sediments found in a sandbar of a river (4) a large number of fossils embedded in limestone

21. Which agent probably contributes most to the general wearing down of the earth's surface?   (1) wind   (2) glaciers   (3) running water (4) ocean waves

22. The increase of dissolved materials in the ocean is primarily the result of the   (1) abrasion of the ocean floor   (2) transporting of material by rivers   (3) melting of continental glaciers   (4) deposition of materials by ground water

23. How are dissolved particles of sediment carried in a river? (1) by bouncing and rolling   (2) by precipitation   (3) in solution (4) in suspension

24. According to the *Earth Science Reference Tables*, which material would most easily be carried in suspension by a slow-moving stream? (1) clay   (2) silt   (3) sand   (4) gravel

25. In summer, a small stream has a depth of 3 meters and a velocity of 0.5 meter per second. In spring, the same stream has a depth of 5 meters. The velocity of the stream in spring is more likely closest to (1) 0.1 m/sec   (2) 0.2 m/sec   (3) 0.5 m/sec   (4) 0.8 m/sec

26. The velocity of a stream at a particular location is controlled mainly by the   (1) elevation of the stream at the location   (2) distance of the location from the source   (3) slope of the stream bed at the location   (4) amount of sediments carried at the location

27. As the kinetic energy of a stream increases, the size of the particle that can be moved   (1) decreases   (2) increases   (3) remains the same

28. A pebble is being transported in a stream by rolling. How does the velocity of the pebble compare to the velocity of the stream? (1) The pebble is moving slower than the stream.   (2) The pebble is moving faster than the stream.   (3) The pebble is moving at the same velocity as the stream.

29. Which graph best represents the relationship between the maximum particle size that can be carried by a stream and the velocity of the stream?

(1)   (2)   (3)   (4)

30. According to the *Earth Science Reference Tables*, which is the largest sediment that could be carried by a stream flowing at a velocity of 75 centimeters per second?   (1) silt   (2) sand   (3) pebbles   (4) cobbles

31. According to the *Earth Science Reference Tables*, which is the *slowest* stream velocity needed to maintain 1 cm particles moving downstream?   (1) 50 cm/sec   (2) 75 cm/sec   (3) 100 cm/sec   (4) 125 cm/sec

32. Which landscape characteristic best indicates the action of glaciers?   (1) few lakes   (2) deposits of well-sorted sediments   (3) residual soil covering large areas   (4) polished and scratched surface bedrock

33. While studying the movement of valley glaciers that are advancing from the north, geologists placed metal stakes extending in a straight line from one valley wall to the other. Which sketch would best illustrate the position of the stakes one year later?

1   2   3   4   N

34. Compared to its original shape, a rock that has been transported several kilometers by a stream will normally be more   (1) rounded (2) jagged   (3) flattened on one side   (4) rectangular

35. Based on the diagrams of rock fragments below, which shows the *least* evidence of erosion?

(1)   (2)   (3)   (4)

36. Sharp-edged, irregularly shaped sediment particles found at the base of a rock cliff were probably transported by   (1) gravity   (2) wind (3) ocean waves   (4) running water

37. As the amount of plant life in a region is decreased by the activities of humans, the amount of erosion will probably   (1) decrease (2) increase   (3) remain the same

38. The graph below compares erosion caused by changes in the discharge of a stream before and after a period of population growth.

The best interpretation of the graph is that the total amount of erosion (1) decreases with an increase in population   (2) increases with an increase in population   (3) is not affected by an increase in population

Deposition, also called *sedimentation,* is the process by which sediments are released, settled from, or dropped from an erosional system. Deposition includes the releasing of solid sediments and the process of *precipitation,* which is the releasing of dissolved ionic minerals from a water solution. Most final deposition occurs in large water bodies, because running water is the dominant erosional system.

FACTORS CAUSING DEPOSITION

Deposition usually occurs when the velocity of the stream, wind, or other erosional system decreases. Some of the factors that determine which sediments are deposited, and their rates of settling, are described below.

1. Size. All other factors being equal, when wind or running water slows down, the larger sediments settle out first. This occurs because the larger sediment particles are heavier and therefore sink faster. Very small particles (less than 0.0004 cm in diameter), called **colloids** (or clay), may remain suspended in water almost indefinitely.

2. Shape. The shape of a particle helps determine how fast it will be deposited from wind or running water. All other factors being equal, the more spherical a sediment, the faster it will settle out, and the more flattened it is, the greater its resistance to deposition.

Figure 10-1. Settling rates of sediments of various shapes. As sediments of equal volume and density become less spherical (or rounded) and more flattened it takes more time for them to settle, so settling rate decreases (gets slower).

3. Density. All other factors being the same, the higher the density of a sediment, the faster it will settle out of air or water. The reason for this is that if two particles have the same size and shape, the denser one will be heavier.

SORTING OF SEDIMENTS AND DEPOSITION

Sorting of sediments is the degree of similarity of sediment size in a given deposit. The greater the similarity of size, the more sorted the sediments are said to be.

GRADED BEDDING.   When a mixture of sediment sizes in water settles out rapidly, a horizontal layer *(bed)* develops with sediment size decreasing toward the top of the bed. Such an arrangement in a sediment layer is called **graded bedding** (see Figure 10-2). Graded bedding is most often associated with sediment-laden density currents, called *turbidity currents.* These turbidity currents are most common on the sloped ocean bottoms off the coasts of continents, and produce graded bedding on the flatter ocean bottom further offshore *(abyssal areas).* Graded bedding can also form in lakes fed by streams.

ONE BED
OR LAYER

Figure 10-2. Layers of sediment with graded bedding. In each bed or layer, sediment sizes decrease from bottom to top. Graded bedding results from rapid deposition in an erosional system, as by a turbidity current (see text). Each bed is the result of a single turbidity flow.

Figure 10-3. Horizontal sorting where a stream enters the ocean. The larger sediments settle first (nearer the shore). Sediments become smaller as distance from shore increases. Where solid sediments are rare, chemical precipitation is the dominant type of deposition. Precipitation nearer the shore may provide the cement for the formation of the types of sedimentary rocks indicated. Limestone and dolostone are common evaporite sedimentary rocks formed largely by precipitation.

HORIZONTAL SORTING. When the velocity of a wind or water erosional system gradually decreases (such as when a stream flows into the ocean at a delta), the larger, denser, and more spherical sediments settle out first. This results in layers with **horizontal sorting,** in which the sediment size, sphericalness, and density generally decrease in the direction the erosional system was moving (see Figure 10-3).

UNSORTED GLACIAL DEPOSITS. In a solid erosional system such as a glacier, sediments of all sizes, shapes, and densities are deposited together. This results in the unsorted deposits characteristic of direct glacial deposits (see Figure 10-4).

Figure 10-4. Unsorted glacial deposits. In glacial deposition there is no fluid medium in which sediments can become sorted. Thus, glacial deposits are characterized by a random distribution of sediment sizes and no bedding or layering. Note glacial scratches on sediments.

CHARACTERISTICS OF AN EROSIONAL-DEPOSITIONAL SYSTEM

MODEL OF AN EROSIONAL-DEPOSITIONAL SYSTEM. Figure 10-5 shows a side view and a top view of an imaginary stream used as a model of an erosional-depositional system. In this simple model it is assumed that the volume of flow (discharge) is the same throughout the length of the stream.

ENERGY TRANSFORMATIONS IN THE MODEL SYSTEM. At the beginning, or *source,* of the stream (A), the system has a maximum of potential energy. As the stream flows toward its end, or *mouth* (D), potential energy is continuously being transformed into kinetic energy. This kinetic energy is at the same time being lost to the environment in the form of heat produced by friction. Where the slope of the stream is steep, the transformation of energy occurs most rapidly, the stream has its greatest velocity, and the system has its greatest kinetic energy. Where the slope is small, the rate of energy transformation decreases, the stream slows down, and the kinetic energy of the system decreases. At the mouth of the stream, the velocity drops to zero, and the system has zero kinetic energy. Since the system has less potential energy because of its lower elevation, there has been a net loss of energy between the source and the mouth.

Figure 10-5. Model of a stream representing an erosional-depositional system. "O" indicates the outside of a curve and "I" indicates the inside. Some deposition may occur at **C**, where the slope and velocity decrease. Erosional-depositional interfaces will then exist between **B** and **C** and between **C** and **D**.

EROSION AND DEPOSITION IN RELATION TO ENERGY CHANGES. Wherever the kinetic energy of the system is large, erosion is the dominant process. Where the kinetic energy is small, deposition is the dominant process. Thus, erosion occurs in regions of steep slope, and deposition occurs in regions of gentle slope. Deposition is particularly rapid at the mouth of the stream, where the kinetic energy becomes zero. Stream velocity is also larger at the outside of curves and smaller at the inside. Therefore, erosion usually occurs at the outside of curves and deposition occurs at the inside.

EROSIONAL-DEPOSITIONAL INTERFACES. Since there are regions of erosion and regions of deposition along the length of the stream, an interface between an erosional and a depositional state can often be located in the system. Interfaces between erosion and deposition exist at the curves in the model stream, and near the mouth of the stream. They may also be found where changes in slope occur, as between B and C in Figure 10-5.

DYNAMIC EQUILIBRIUM OF THE SYSTEM. Since all sediments picked up by the stream during erosion must eventually be deposited, the system is in a state of *dynamic equilibrium*. Although erosion and deposition are occurring continuously, the rate of erosion equals the rate of deposition by the system as a whole. If a flood occurs, a stream will erode (pick up and transport) more sediment, but it will also deposit an equally increased volume of sediment, thus establishing a new balance of equilibrium.

VOCABULARY

deposition
colloid (clay)
sorting of sediments

graded bedding
horizontal sorting

QUESTIONS ON TOPIC X—DEPOSITION

Questions in Recent Regents Exams (end of book)

June 1991:   26, 33, 35, 81
June 1992:   32, 55, 97–100
June 1993:   26, 28, 46, 53, 84, 85
June 1994:   27, 34, 39, 82, 85

Questions from Earlier Regents Exams

1. The rate at which particles are deposited by a stream is *least* affected by the   (1) size and shape of the particles   (2) velocity of the steam   (3) stream's elevation above sea level   (4) density of the particles

2. The graph below shows the relationship between particle shape and settling rate.

Which statement best describes the relationship shown?   (1) Flatter particles settle more slowly than rounder particles.   (2) Flatter particles settle faster than rounder particles.   (3) All particles settle at the same speed.   (4) Particle shape does not affect settling rate.

3. A mixture of sand, pebbles, clay, and silt, of uniform shape and density, is dropped from a boat into a calm lake. Which material most likely would reach the bottom of the lake first?   (1) sand   (2) pebbles (3) clay (4) silt

4. A low hill is composed of unsorted sediments that have mixed grain sizes. This hill was probably deposited by   (1) a glacier   (2) the wind   (3) running water   (4) wave action

5. Small spheres that are identical in shape and size are composed of one of four different kinds of substances: *A, B, C,* or *D.* The spheres are mixed together and poured into a clear plastic tube filled with water. Which property of the spheres caused them to settle in the tube as shown in the diagram below?   (1) their size   (2) their shape   (3) their density   (4) their hardness

6. A stream is entering the calm waters of a large lake. Which diagram best illustrates the pattern of sediments being deposited in the lake from the stream flow?

7. The map below represents a winding stream. At which location is stream deposition most likely to be greater than stream erosion?   (1) *A*   (2) *B*   (3) *C*   (4) *D*

8. If the gradient of a stream increases at a certain location, the probability that sediment will be deposited at that location   (1) decreases   (2) increases   (3) remains the same

Base your answers to questions 9 through 12 on the *Earth Science Reference Tables* and the diagram below. The diagram represents a glacier moving out of a mountain valley. The water from the melting glacier is flowing into a lake. Letters *A* through *F* identify points within the erosional/depositional system.

9. Deposits of unsorted sediments would probably be found at location   (1) *E*   (2) *F*   (3) *C*   (4) *D*

10. An interface between erosion and deposition by the ice is most likely located between points   (1) *A* and *B*   (2) *B* and *C*   (3) *C* and *D*   (4) *D* and *E*

11. Colloidal-sized sediment particles carried by water are most probably being deposited at point   (1) *F*   (2) *B*   (3) *C*   (4) *D*

12. Which graph best represents the speed of a sediment particle as it moves from point *D* to point *F*?

13. More deposition than erosion will take place in a streambed when the   (1) density of the rock particles carried by the stream decreases   (2) slope of the stream increases   (3) discharge of the stream increases   (4) velocity of the stream decreases

14. Which is the most probable description of the energy of a particle in an erosional-depositional system?   (1) Particles gain kinetic energy during erosion and lose kinetic energy during deposition. (2) Particles lose kinetic energy during erosion and lose kinetic energy during deposition.   (3) Particles gain potential energy during erosion and gain potential energy during deposition.   (4) Particles lose potential energy during erosion and gain potential energy during deposition.

Additional Questions

To answer questions 1 through 8 refer to the diagram below, which shows the top and side views of a stream. Consider the volume of water in the stream to be everywhere the same.

1. At which place in the stream would there be the most clear interface between erosion and deposition?   (1) 1   (2) 2–3   (3) 3–4   (4) 7

2. What is true about the total amount of energy of this stream as it flows from 1 to 10?   (1) It steadily increases.   (2) It steadily decreases.   (3) It increases and decreases.   (4) It remains the same.

3. Between what two points would the most potential energy be converted to kinetic energy?   (1) 1–2   (2) 2–5   (3) 5–8   (4) 8–10

4. At which location would the most deposition occur because of loss of energy?   (1) 4   (2) 6   (3) 9   (4) 10

5. At which location would the stream be doing the most eroding of its side and banks?   (1) 1   (2) 3   (3) 5   (4) 8

6. If the stream is eroding as much as it is depositing between 8 and 10, the stream at this location can be said to   (1) be an interface   (2) have dynamic equilibrium   (3) be sorted   (4) have equal amounts of kinetic and potential energy

7. Which characteristic would usually decrease the most between locations 10 and 11?   (1) the amount of salt in solution   (2) the size of the sediments   (3) the density of the water   (4) the depth of the water

8. As the water of the stream flows from 1 to 10, the total potential energy of the stream will   (1) increase   (2) decrease   (3) remain the same

TOPIC XI | Rock Formation

Rocks are any naturally formed solid matter that makes up a part of the solid earth. Rocks are usually composed of a mixture of minerals. The **texture** of a rock is the size, shape, and arrangement of the grains (mineral crystals or sediments) of which it is composed.

ROCK TYPES.   Rocks are classified into three groups based on how they formed: *sedimentary, metamorphic,* and *igneous.* The igneous and metamorphic rocks may be grouped together as *nonsedimentary rocks*, so that rocks may also be classified as sedimentary and nonsedimentary.

SEDIMENTARY ROCKS

Sedimentary rocks are rocks that form from an accumulation of sediments derived from preexisting rocks and/or organic material.

FORMATION OF SEDIMENTARY ROCKS.   Most sedimentary rocks are made up of solid sediments, or **clasts,** weathered from other rocks. The sediments are then transported and deposited by running water, wind, or glaciers to new locations in water or on land. Most sedimentary rocks form under bodies of water such as lakes and oceans. Sedimentary rocks are formed in the following ways:

1. Cementation. Larger solid sediments, such as sand and pebbles, form rocks when the sediments are cemented together by minerals that are precipitated out of solution (see Figure 11-1, A and B).

Figure 11-1. Some characteristics of sedimentary rocks. (A) Conglomerate. Particles of unsorted sizes cemented together. **(B)** Sandstone. Particles of fairly uniform (sorted) size cemented together. **(C)** Shale. Rock formed by compression of very small (colloidal) sediments, possibly cemented as well. **(D)** Chemical sedimentary rock. Monomineralic crystalline rock (composed of intergrown mineral crystals) formed by evaporation and/or precipitation.

2. Compression/Compaction. When very small solid sediments (colloids) are compressed by the pressure of overlying water and sediments, they form rocks like the one in Figure 11-1C. Sedimentary rocks may also be formed by a combination of compression and cementation.

3. Chemical action. Ionic or dissolved minerals may **precipitate** out as the result of chemical processes or of evaporation of the water. A rock formed in this manner is **monomineralic** rock, that is, it consists of **crystals,** or grains, of a single mineral (see Figure 11-1D). Rocks formed by these chemical processes are called **chemical sedimentary rocks** or evaporites. Chemical limestone and rock salt are evaporites.

4. Biologic processes.   Some sedimentary rocks form as a result of biologic processes. Many forms of life that live in water, such as clams and corals, extract dissolved minerals from the water to form their hard parts. When the organisms die, these hard parts accumulate to form rocks such as fossil limestone. Bituminous coal is a rock formed when dead plant matter is deposited in water and compressed.

CHARACTERISTICS OF SEDIMENTARY ROCKS.

1. Most sedimentary rocks are clastic, composed of fragments or particles which strongly resemble sediments.

2. Some sedimentary rocks have a range of particle or sediment sizes (see Figure 11-1A).

3. Other sedimentary rocks consists mainly of one sediment size because of the sorting of sediments (see Figures 11-1B and 11-C).

4. Some sedimentary rocks are of **organic** origin; that is, they are composed of plant and animal products or remains.

5. Sedimentary rocks often have parallel layers, as shown in Figure 11-2. Such layers are also called **beds** or **strata.**

6. Sedimentary rocks often contain *fossils.*

Figure 11-2. Layers in a sedimentary rock. Layers may result from changes in the type of sediment during the period of deposition.

IDENTIFYING SEDIMENTARY ROCKS. Refer to the chart *Scheme for Sedimentary Rock Identification* in the *Earth Science Reference Tables.* As can be inferred from the chart, sedimentary rocks are classified and identified largely on the basis of size of solid sediments (particle diameter) and/or mineral composition of the rock. Monomineralic chemical sedimentary rocks, such as chemical limestone and dolostone, are identified primarily based on the one mineral they contain. For example, rock gypsum is composed of the mineral gypsum, and dolostone is composed of dolomite.

The vast majority of sedimentary rocks are composed of solid sediments (boulders to clay) that have been cemented and/or compacted together. These clastic sedimentary rocks are most commonly identified according to the size of the majority of the sediments they contain, regardless of their mineral composition. For example, if a rock is composed largely of solid sediments of 0.01 cm in diameter (sand size), the rock would be called a sandstone.

NONSEDIMENTARY ROCKS

Nonsedimentary rocks are those rocks that do not form from sediments. There are two groups of nonsedimentary rocks—the *igneous* and the *metamorphic* rocks.

IGNEOUS NONSEDIMENTARY ROCKS. Igneous rocks are those rocks that form from the cooling and **solidification** of liquid rock. (Liquid rock beneath the earth's surface is known as *magma*. When liquid rock reaches the earth's surface, it is called *lava*.) When liquid rock cools, it solidifies, usually by the growth of various mineral crystals in a type of solidification called **crystallization**. This results in a **crystalline** texture, consisting of intergrown mineral crystals of different sizes, shapes, and chemical composition, as shown in Figure 11-3. Such a rock is called **polymineralic,** because it contains two or more different minerals. Solidification includes the change from liquid rock to a noncrystalline glassy igneous rock (as shown in Figure 11-3C) and it includes the process of crystallization.

Figure 11-3. Cross sections showing three types of texture in igneous nonsedimentary rocks. (A) Slow cooling of the liquid rock results in large crystals visible to the unaided eye (coarse texture). **(B)** If cooling is more rapid, the crystals are too small to be seen without magnification (fine texture). A magnified section resembles the texture in **A. (C)** If cooling is very rapid, the solid rock has a glassy texture without mineral crystals.

1. Size of crystals. The size of the crystals in an igneous nonsedimentary rock depends on the conditions of the environment in which the rock formed. The immediate cause of the difference in the size of the crystals is the amount of time in which the cooling takes place. The longer the time of cooling, the larger the crystals become. However, the cooling time itself depends on the temperature and pressure of the environment. The pressure and temperature deep within the earth are very high, and therefore liquid rock cools slowly (possibly for thousands of years). The result is rocks with large crystals. (A body of rock formed by solidification below the earth's surface is called an **intrusion,** and the igneous rocks that form are called **intrusive.**)

The temperature and pressure at or near the earth's surface are much lower, and liquid rock cools there much more quickly than at great depths. This produces rocks with much smaller crystals. (A body of rock formed by solidification at the earth's surface is called an **extrusion,** and the igneous rocks that form are called **extrusive.**)

2. Texture of igneous rocks. The texture of igneous rocks depends on the size of the crystals, as well as on their shape and arrangement within the rock. Rocks with large crystals have a coarse texture (see Figure 11-3A). Those with crystals that are too small to be seen clearly with the unaided eye have a fine texture. Igneous rocks that cool very rapidly at the earth's surface have no crystals at all, and have a glassy texture. Some glassy igneous rocks have a porous texture resulting from solidification around gas bubbles.

IDENTIFYING IGNEOUS ROCKS.   Refer to the *Scheme for Igneous Rock Classification* in the *Earth Science Reference Tables*. The diagram shows a common method of classifying and identifying igneous rocks. Igneous rocks are identified largely on the basis of texture (coarse, fine, glassy, or porous) and percent mineral composition. The majority of the mineral crystals in a coarse-grained rock are easily visible to the unaided eye (1 mm or larger), while the majority of the mineral crystals in a fine-grained rock are *not* easily seen by the unaided eye.

Percent mineral composition divides igneous rocks on the diagram into vertical columns (igneous rock families). Within a rock family, rocks have similar mineral compositions.

Other information indicated by the *Scheme for Igneous Rock Identification* includes:

1. As rocks appear farther to the right on the diagram, they become more mafic (high in magnesium and iron) and less felsic or granitic (high in silicon and aluminum).

2. As rocks appear farther to the right on the diagram, their density increases.

3. As rocks appear farther to the right on the diagram, their overall color becomes darker.

METAMORPHIC NONSEDIMENTARY ROCKS.   Metamorphic rocks are those rocks that are formed from other rocks (igneous, sedimentary, or other metamorphic rocks) within the lithosphere. The formation of metamorphic rocks occurs in response to conditions of heat, pressure, and/or chemical change. Such conditions are often associated with the pressure, heat, and deep burial that result from mountain building processes; therefore, metamorphic rocks are often found in mountainous regions where weathering and erosion have exposed rock that was once deeply buried. **Regional metamorphism** occurs when metamorphic rocks occur in large areas due to mountain-building processes such as folding and faulting. Under conditions of high temperature and pressure, many metamorphic rocks form by the process of **recrystallization**, which is a growth of mineral crystals at the expense of surrounding sediments or other crystals of the original rock (see Figure 11-4). Recrystallization occurs without true melting.

Sedimentary Rock Rounded sediments

Cement

Metamorphic Rock

Crystals formed by recrystallization

Figure 11-4. Metamorphic rock formed by recrystallization. Under the influence of heat and pressure, minerals in the sediments or cement of a sedimentary rock combine to form mineral crystals, producing a crystalline texture. However, recrystallization occurs without melting of the rock.

Metamorphic nonsedimentary rocks often have certain textural and structural characteristics that result from the environment of formation:

1. Foliation is a layered arrangement (texture) in a metamorphic rock in which firmly joined crystals of like minerals are aligned in layers (see Figure 11-4). The layers are formed when the rock is subjected to extreme environmental pressure and high temperatures. Usually, the greater the pressure and temperature, the thicker the foliations (see Figure 11-5).

A

B

Mineral A
Mineral B

Thin foliations in the metamorphic rock slate

Thick foliations and coarse crystals in the metamorphic rock gneiss

Figure 11-5. Foliation in metamorphic nonsedimentary rocks.

2. Distorted structure is the curving and folding of the foliations in metamorphic rocks (see Figure 11-6). These distortions of the once-horizontal layers are caused by great environmental pressures exerted on the rocks from different directions.

ENVIRONMENT OF ROCK FORMATION

The type of environment in which a rock formed is inferred from its composition, structure, and texture. The following are examples of such inferences.

1. Composition. If a sedimentary rock is made of halite, the rock probably formed by means of evaporation and precipitation in a body of salt water. The presence of fossils indicates formation at or near the earth's surface.

2. Structure. The distorted structure of the metamorphic rock shown in Figure 11-6 was caused by an environment of great pressure.

Figure 11-6. Distorted structure in a metamorphic nonsedimentary rock.

3. Texture. The texture of a rock results from the size, shape, and arrangement of its mineral crystals or sediments. If the sediments found in a sedimentary rock are angular in shape, it may be inferred that the rock was formed near the source of the sediments.

DISTRIBUTION OF ROCK TYPES.   Sedimentary rocks are usually found as a *veneer* (relatively thin coating) over large areas of continents. The nonsedimentary rocks that occur at or near the surface are most often found in regions of volcanoes and mountains (see Figure 11-7). The nonsedimentary rocks in mountain regions are exposed on the surface after millions of years of weathering and erosion have removed the veneer of sedimentary rocks.

Figure 11-7. Veneer of sedimentary rocks in the Appalachian Plateau in the eastern United States. The solid black indicates nonsedimentary rock.

THE ROCK CYCLE.   The **rock cycle** is a model used to show how the rock types (sedimentary, igneous, and metamorphic) are interrelated, and the processes that produce each rock type. Figure 11-8 on page 152 is a diagram of the rock cycle.

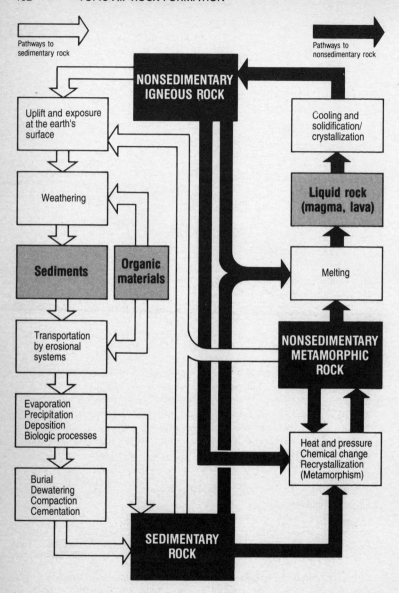

Figure 11-8. The rock cycle. Some of the processes by which one type of rock can be changed to another.

Some of the major concepts of the rock cycle are:

1. *Any one rock type can change into any other rock type.* Thus a specimen of any one type can have materials in it that were once part of any other type.

2. *There is no preferred direction of movement of materials in the rock cycle for any one mass of material.* Any one piece of material can stay in any one place for any length of time, or it can follow any of the arrows indicated on the diagram.

3. *There is no exact point of separation between the rock types.* For example, where local rock has been in contact with an intrusion of molten rock, or with a lava flow (extrusion), there is a **transition zone (contact metamorphic zone)** between the original local rock and the intrusion or the lava flow. In this transition zone there is a blending of the rock types and often no exact boundary (see Figure 11-9).

Figure 11-9. Formation of transition zones between rock types by a flow of molten rock. In **A,** molten rock has flowed up through a crack in sedimentary rock to the surface, forming an intrusion below the surface and an extrusion (lava flow) on the surface. In the contact zone between the original local rock and the intrusion or extrusion, there is a blending of rock types from sedimentary, through metamorphic nonsedimentary, to igneous nonsedimentary.

4. *Sedimentary rocks often contain sediments (clasts) that have varied origins.* This occurs because (a) sedimentary rocks form from the weathered products of any type of rock and/or organic materials, and (b) in any one depositional basin where sedimentary rocks form, the sediments can be brought from many different areas and by various methods of transport.

5. *The composition of some rocks suggests that the materials (sediments or minerals) in the rock have undergone multiple transformations (changes) within the rock cycle.* This is so because of the many possible paths within the rock cycle that can produce any one rock. For example, a sedimentary rock may contain fragments, or sediments, that were once part of a metamorphic rock that formed deep within the earth. However, that metamorphic rock itself may have been transformed from a sedimentary rock that formed near the earth's surface. A sedimentary rock may also contain sediments from previous sedimentary rocks and fragments which were once part of an intrusive igneous rock. The cement holding the rock together may once have been part of an igneous rock that was uplifted to the earth's surface and chemically weathered to form dissolved minerals; the minerals were then transported by water and later precipitated to become the cement.

MINERALS

A **mineral** is a naturally occurring, crystalline, inorganic substance with characteristic physical and chemical properties. That is, a mineral is a natural substance, a solid with a specific arrangement of constituent units, and either a chemical element or compound, which is not derived from parts of organisms (forms of life) or their products.

RELATION OF MINERALS TO ROCKS. Nearly all rocks are composed of minerals. (A few rocks, such as coal, are composed of organic substances not considered to be minerals.) Most rocks, such as those shown in Figure 11-5, are **polymineralic,** that is, they consist of more than one mineral. Some rocks are **monomineralic,** that is, they consist entirely of one mineral. Many sedimentary rocks and the metamorphic nonsedimentary rocks that form from those sedimentary rocks are monomineralic.

Only 20 to 30 minerals of the approximately 2,500 minerals are commonly found in most rocks. These are called the **rock-forming minerals.**

MINERAL COMPOSITION. Minerals are composed of *elements*. A few minerals, such as copper, sulfur, and graphite, are each composed of only one element. Most minerals are composed of two or more elements in chemical combination and are called *compounds*.

The circle graph and the table in Figure 11-10 illustrate the following points:

1. Most of the earth's crust and thus most minerals are made up of only a few elements.

2. Oxygen is the most abundant element by weight and volume.

3. Silicon is the second most abundant element by weight.

MINERAL PROPERTIES. Minerals have characteristic physical and chemical properties. Some of these properties are color, crystal shape, hardness, luster, streak, how the mineral breaks (cleavage and fracture), and density. Many of the physical properties of minerals are related to the structural arrangement of the mineral's constituent units (atoms or ions). A good example of this is the way the mineral halite (common salt) breaks into cubes because of a cubic arrangement of the constituent units (ions), as shown in Figure 11-11. Another example is the characteristic external crystal shape of minerals.

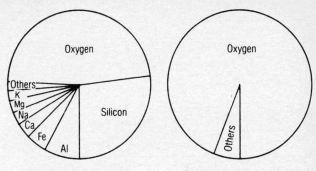

Relative amounts by mass   Relative amounts by volume

Composition of the Earth's Crust			
Element	Symbol	Percent by mass	Percent by volume
Oxygen	O	46.40	94.04
Silicon	Si	28.15	0.88
Aluminum	Al	8.23	0.48
Iron	Fe	5.63	0.49
Calcium	Ca	4.15	1.18
Sodium	Na	2.36	1.11
Magnesium	Mg	2.33	0.33
Potassium	K	2.09	1.42
All others	—	0.66	0.07

Figure 11-10. Percentages of the chief elements in the earth's crust by mass and by volume. "Volume" in this case means the amount of space occupied by the atoms of each element in the solid substances of the crust. Also see *Average Chemical Composition of Earth's Crust, Hydrosphere, and Troposphere* in the *Earth Science Reference Tables*

HALITE
(Sodium chloride)

Chlorine ion

Sodium ion

Figure 11-11. Cleavage of the mineral halite. When a piece of halite is broken, it tends to break into roughly cubic pieces. This is the result of a cubic arrangement of the constituent units (sodium and chlorine ions) in the halite crystal.

MINERAL STRUCTURE.   In the group of minerals called silicates, the constituent unit is in the form of a *tetrahedron* composed of silicon and oxygen (see Figure 11-12). This **silicon-oxygen tetrahedron** can combine with itself and with other elements to form different structures (such as chains and sheets). These different structural arrangements account for differences in the physical properties of silicate minerals.

Figure 11-12. The silicon-oxygen tetrahedron. A tetrahedron is a geometric figure having four faces, all of which are equilateral triangles of the same size. In silicates, there are oxygen atoms at the four corners of a tetrahedron, with a silicon atom at the center.

VOCABULARY

texture	intrusion
sedimentary rock	intrusive igneous rock
cementation	extrusion
compression/compaction	extrusive igneous rock
precipitation	metamorphic rock
monomineralic	regional metamorphism
crystal	recrystallization
chemical sedimentary rock	foliation
organic	distorted structure
beds/strata	rock cycle
nonsedimentary rock	transition zone
igneous rock	contact metamorphic zone
solidification	mineral
crystalline	rock-forming mineral
crystallization	silicon-oxygen tetrahedron
polymineralic	

QUESTIONS ON TOPIC XI—ROCK FORMATION

Questions in Recent Regents Exams (end of book)

Questions from Earlier Regents Exams

1. What do most igneous, sedimentary, and metamorphic rocks have in common?   (1) They are formed from molten material.   (2) They are produced by heat and pressure.   (3) They are composed of minerals.   (4) They exhibit crystals, banding, and distinct layers.

2. In which rock type are fossils usually found?   (1) igneous   (2) volcanic   (3) sedimentary   (4) metamorphic

3. Which rock was formed by the compaction and cementation of particles 0.07 centimeter in diameter?   (1) limestone   (2) sandstone   (3) shale   (4) basalt

4. Which sedimentary rocks are formed from organic matter?   (1) rock salt and shale   (2) bituminous coal and limestone   (3) chert and rock salt   (4) sandstone and conglomerate

5. According to the *Earth Science Reference Tables*, limestone, gypsum, and rock salt are rocks formed by the process of   (1) melting and solidification   (2) evaporation and precipitation   (3) erosion and deposition   (4) weathering and metamorphism

6. Which would most likely occur during the formation of igneous rock?   (1) compression and cementation of sediments   (2) recrystallization of unmelted material   (3) solidification of molten materials   (4) evaporation and precipitation of sediments

7. Which graph best shows the relationship between the size of the crystals in an igneous rock and the length of time it has taken the rock to solidify?

8. According to the *Earth Science Reference Tables*, generally, as the percentage of felsic minerals in a rock increases, the rock's color will become (1) darker and its density will decrease   (2) lighter and its density will increase   (3) darker and its density will increase   (4) lighter and its density will decrease

9. An igneous rock which has crystallized deep below the earth's surface has the following approximate composition: 70% pyroxene, 15% plagioclase, and 15% olivine. According to the *Earth Science Reference Tables*, what is the name of this igneous rock?   (1) granite   (2) rhyolite   (3) gabbro   (4) basalt

10. Which diagram below shows an area in which fine-grained igneous rock are most likely to be found?

(1)   (3)

(2)   (4)

11. According to the *Earth Science Reference Tables*, metamorphic rocks form as the direct result of   (1) precipitation from evaporating water   (2) melting and solidification in magma   (3) erosion and deposition of soil particles   (4) heat and pressure causing changes in existing rock.

12. The diagram below represents a cross section of a coarse-grained nonsedimentary rock. According to the *Earth Science Reference Tables*, this rock is most likely to be   (1) basalt   (2) rhyolite   (3) gabbro   (4) granite

PLAGIOCLASE FELDSPAR

MICA

AMPHIBOLE

ORTHOCLASI FELDSPAR

QUARTZ

13. Which rock is composed of materials that show the greatest variety of rock origins?   (1) a limestone composed of coral fragments cemented together by calcium carbonate   (2) a conglomerate composed of pebbles of granite, siltstone, and basalt   (3) a very fine-grained basalt with sharp edges   (4) a sandstone composed of rounded grains of quartz

14. What is the main difference between metamorphic rocks and most other rocks?   (1) Many metamorphic rocks contain only one mineral. (2) Many metamorphic rocks have an organic composition.   (3) Many metamorphic rocks exhibit banding and distortion of structure. (4) Many metamorphic rocks contain a high amount of oxygen-silicon tetrahedra.

15. The green sand found on some Hawaiian Island shorelines most probably consists primarily of   (1) quartz   (2) olivine   (3) plagioclase feldspar   (4) orthoclase feldspar

16. Large rock salt deposits in the Syracuse area indicate that the area once had   (1) large forests   (2) a range of volcanic mountains (3) many terrestrial animals   (4) a warm, shallow sea

17. According to the Rock Cycle diagram in the *Earth Science Reference Tables*, which type(s) of rock can be the source of deposited sediments?   (1) igneous and metamorphic rocks, only   (2) metamorphic and sedimentary rocks, only   (3) sedimentary rocks, only   (4) igneous, metamorphic, and sedimentary rocks

18. The data table shows the composition of six common rock-forming minerals.

Mineral	Composition
Mica	$KAl_3Si_3O_{10}$
Olivine	$(FeMg)_2SiO_4$
Orthoclase	$KAlSi_3O_8$
Plagioclase	$NaAlSi_3O_8$
Pyroxene	$CaMgSi_2O_6$
Quartz	SiO_2

The data table provides evidence that   (1) the same elements are found in all minerals   (2) a few elements are found in many minerals   (3) all elements are found in only a few minerals   (4) all elements are found in all minerals

19. The cubic shape of a crystal is most likely the result of that crystal's (1) hardness   (2) density distribution   (3) internal arrangement of atoms   (4) intensity of radioactive decay

20. Minerals are identified on the basis of   (1) the method by which they were formed   (2) the type of rock in which they are found   (3) the size of their crystals   (4) their physical and chemical properties

21. Which property is most useful in mineral identification? (1) hardness   (2) color   (3) size   (4) texture

22. The hardness of a mineral such as quartz is due to   (1) the internal arrangement of its atoms   (2) large amounts of impurities (3) its characteristic luster and color   (4) its formation in certain rock types

23. Which object is the best model of the shape of a silicon-oxygen structural unit?

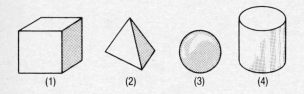

(1)   (2)   (3)   (4)

Additional Questions

To answer questions 1 through 7 refer to the diagrams below, which represent six rock samples. The shadings indicate different minerals, sediments, or fossils.

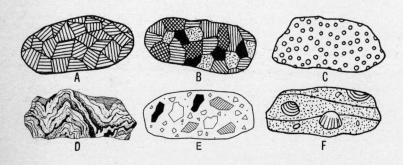

1. Which rock would be considered monomineralic?   (1) A (2) B   (3) D   (4) E

2. Which rock formed partly as the result of biologic processes?   (1) B (2) C   (3) D   (4) F

3. Which sample is nonsedimentary?   (1) B   (2) C   (3) E   (4) F

4. Which sample has distorted structure and foliation?   (1) A (2) B   (3) C   (4) D

5. Which sample is most likely breccia?   (1) B   (2) C   (3) E (4) F

6. If sample E were subjected to high heat and pressure, without melting, it would most likely form   (1) slate   (2) schist   (3) metaconglomerate   (4) marble

7. Rock D is most likely   (1) gneiss   (2) siltstone   (3) slate (4) pumice

TOPIC XII

The Dynamic Crust (Lithosphere) and the Earth's Interior

There is much evidence indicating that the crust is constantly undergoing change, and that all parts of it move to new locations, thereby changing the surface of the earth. In some cases we know the crust moves because its movement has been observed directly during earthquakes or the sudden birth of volcanoes. Evidence of past crustal movements must be indirect. Much of that indirect evidence is based on the concept of **original horizontality,** which assumes (on the basis of geologic evidence) that sedimentary rocks and some extrusive igneous rocks form in generally horizontal layers, or **strata.** Therefore, most strata found in other than horizontal positions are believed to have been deformed by crustal movement. Note: In this topic whatever is stated about the crust also applies to the lithosphere, except when the terms "granitic crust" or "basaltic crust" are used.

EVIDENCE OF MINOR CRUSTAL CHANGES

DEFORMED STRATA. Rock strata that no longer show their original horizontality are called *deformed strata.* Some of the types of deformed strata are **folded strata, tilted strata,** and **faulted strata** (see Figure 12-1). All such deformed strata are considered evidence of past crustal movements. A **fault** is a crack in a mass of rock along which there has been *displacement,* or movement, of the rock layers. Movement along a fault, or faulting, results in a shaking of the earth called an earthquake.

Figure 12-1. Three types of deformed horizontal strata. The numbers in Diagram D mark strata that were originally continuous.

161

MOVEMENTS DURING EARTHQUAKES. It is sometimes possible to observe the actual movement of the crust or immediate effects of that movement during an earthquake. This occurs when the movement along a fault results in obvious changes in the positions of surface features, sometimes forming cliffs (see Figure 12-2).

Figure 12-2. Displacement of surface features as the result of movement of strata along a fault. The portions of the power line, road, orchard, and fields in the foreground have moved down and to the right relative to their continuations at the top of the cliff. Displacements during a single fault movement seldom exceed a few meters. However, successive movements over millions of years may produce accumulated displacements of 1,000 meters or more.

DISPLACED FOSSILS. Marine (meaning ocean) fossils, such as corals and clams, found in sedimentary rock high (sometimes thousands of meters) above sea level indicate that the land has been uplifted to its present location. A lowering of the level of the sea could not have changed the location of the fossils so much because it is believed that sea level can vary only a few hundred feet. On the other hand, shallow water marine fossils found in deep ocean areas may indicate **subsidence,** or a sinking of part of the earth's crust.

VERTICAL MOVEMENTS. Along many shorelines there are raised beaches and other coastline features that normally occur at sea level (see Figure 12-3). These features are often associated with tilted rocks. Changes in elevation have also been observed directly in many locations by means of *bench marks.* A **bench mark** is a permanent marker set into the groundand labeled with its exact elevation at the time of placement. Later measurements often show changes in elevation. All these changes indicate that vertical movements of the earth's crust have taken place. Vertical movements often affect large portions of the earth's crust.

Figure 12-3. Evidence of vertical movement of the crust along a shoreline. The flat marine terrace can be recognized as having once been a beach. The beach was raised by crustal movement. When movement stopped, the ocean once again began to cut a level beach into the new shore.

EVIDENCE OF MAJOR CRUSTAL CHANGES

GEOSYNCLINES AND MOUNTAINS. Large thicknesses of sedimentary rock have been found in parts of various mountain systems. These rocks contain fossils and other evidence which indicate that they formed in shallow marine (ocean) water. For this reason, many geologists believe that the continental mountain systems formed from *geosynclines*. A **geosyncline** is a large shallow ocean basin, located near the margin of a continent, that subsides, or sinks, as sediments are added to it. This subsidence would explain how the great thicknesses of sediments needed to form mountains can be deposited in a relatively shallow geosyncline without filling it. In this way, the geosyncline can remain a shallow-water area for millions of years. Later, the sedimentary rock strata of the geosyncline are believed to be deformed and uplifted to form mountains and enlarge the continent. In terms of modern plate tectonics, an ocean-continent margin not at a plate boundary is a basin similar to a geosyncline called a **passive margin basin.** Figure 12-4 on page 164 indicates some possible geosynclines, that is, large shallow basins where sedimentation and possibly subsidence are presently occurring.

ISOSTASY AND GEOSYNCLINES. The principle of **isostasy** has been used to explain part, but not all, of the sinking of geosynclines. The principle states that the lithosphere of the earth is in a state of equilibrium, and that any change in mass of one part of the lithosphere will be offset by a change in mass of another part to maintain the equilibrium. Think of the lithosphere as floating on the denser rock of the mantle as an ice cube floats in water. If erosion causes the continental crust to lose sediments to a geosyncline, the continental crust will slowly rise and the geosyncline will slowly sink. This occurs because the continent has lost mass and therefore floats higher, while the geosyncline has gained mass and therefore floats lower (see Figure 12-5 on page 165). Isostasy is probably due partly to the partly liquid, plasticlike properties of the upper mantle layer called the **asthenosphere.**

Figure 12-4. Regions of the earth's major plates and zones of current crustal activity. Note that the borders of the plates are the locations of most current crustal activity, which includes volcanic eruptions and earthquakes. Most of the world's active volcanoes are located where mid-ocean ridges or young mountains are indicated on the map.

Figure 12-5. The theory of isostasy. As the geosyncline (passive margin basin) becomes heavier because of the accumulation of sediments, the oceanic crust sinks lower into the mantle. At the same time, the continental crust becomes lighter because of the erosion of material, and it rises higher. Note that where elevations are highest the crust is thickest.

ZONES OF CRUSTAL ACTIVITY AND OROGENY. Zones of frequent crustal activity can be located on the earth's surface. Earthquakes, volcanoes, ocean trenches, mid-ocean ridges (mountain ranges in the ocean), and young continental mountains occur in these zones, or belts, as shown in Figure 12-4. The fact that these features are found together indicates that they are closely related.

At some times large amounts of crustal activity result in mountain building. The process of mountain building is called **orogeny.**

CONTINENTAL DRIFT. In recent years much evidence has been presented to support the idea that the continents have been moving around on the earth's surface. This concept is called **continental drift.** Some of the evidence for continental drift is given below:

1. The outlines of the continents appear to fit together almost like a jigsaw puzzle. It is believed that at least twice in the geologic past all the continents were connected, and that for the last 230,000,000 years the continents have mainly moved apart. (See Figure 12-6 on page 166 and *Geologic History of New York State at a Glance* in the *Earth Science Reference Tables.*)

2. The present orientations of rock crystals with magnetic properties also give evidence of crustal shifts. When an igneous rock crystallizes from the molten state, any of its minerals that are magnetic will align themselves with the earth's magnetic field. By studying the alignment of these crystals, we can tell the relative direction of the earth's magnetic poles at the time the rock formed. When rocks of different geological times are studied in this way, it is found that the earth's magnetic poles *seem* to have wandered around the earth. However, it is more likely that the magnetic poles have remained approximately where they are, and that it was the gradual shifting of the crust during geologic time that caused crystals to change direction, the change being greater the greater the age of the rock. (See Figure 12-6.)

3. At places where the continents may have fitted together, the similarity of the minerals, fossils, and rock types indicates that these rocks of the different continents are similar in age and origin. The northern Appalachian Highlands (see Figure 14-2, page 205) contain many rock types, structures, and fossils similar to those in parts of western Europe. This suggests that the continents were together when the rocks were formed.

4. Today the continents are separated and their respective life forms are greatly different. However, fossil evidence shows that at times in the past many land (terrestrial) plants and animals were the same throughout the world. Similar dinosaurs lived on most land areas during the Triassic Period, but not during the Cretaceous Period (see the *Geologic History of New York State at a Glance* in the *Earth Science Reference Tables*). Such a wide distribution of the same plants and animals probably could not have occurred unless the continents were connected.

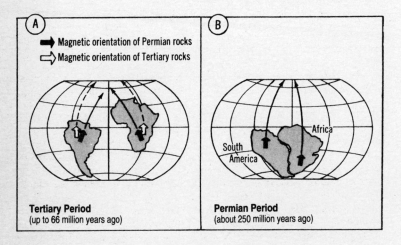

Figure 12-6. Evidence of continental drift. The present continents have shapes that suggest that they once were parts of larger landmasses, which have drifted apart by crustal movement. Magnetic orientation of rock crystals supports this hypothesis. Diagram A shows the magnetic orientation of rocks of different ages in South America and Africa. Crystals in rocks of relatively recent formations are magnetically oriented toward the earth's magnetic poles. Older rocks are oriented in different directions. If, however, it is assumed that South America and Africa were parts of a single landmass when these older rocks were forming, as shown in Diagram B, then the magnetic orientation of these older formations is found to agree reasonably well.

OCEAN-FLOOR SPREADING. Much evidence indicates that the sea floor has spread out, or **rifted**, from the **mid-ocean ridge** systems (mountain ranges in the ocean). This concept is called **ocean-floor spreading** or sea-floor spreading. The location of mid-ocean ridges is shown in Figure 12-4. Here is some of the evidence for ocean-floor spreading:

1. Molten rock rises and crystallizes into basaltic igneous rock in the mid-ocean ridges, as shown by high heat flows and observed volcanic activity. Samples of this basaltic rock taken from the ocean floor show that the age of the rock increases with distance from the center of the mid-ocean ridge. Heat flow also decreases with distance from the mid-ocean ridges in oceanic crust. This indicates that the basaltic rock formed at the ridges and spread outward (see Figure 12-7A, page 168).

2. The spreading of the oceanic crust is also shown by the magnetism in the basaltic rocks. The earth's magnetic poles flip-flop in polarity (north changes to south or south to north) in periods of thousands of years in a process called **reversal of earth's magnetic polarity.** The earth's magnetic fields have reversed polarity thousands of times since its origin. When the basaltic rock crystallizes at the mid-ocean ridges, its magnetic minerals are aligned so that they record the particular polarity of the earth at the time of crystallization. It has been found that there are corresponding parallel strips of basaltic rock on either side of the mid-ocean ridges. Some strips show normal polarity (poles as they are today) and others show reverse polarity. This evidence suggests that the corresponding strips were formed at similar times and that ocean-floor spreading has separated them.

PLATE TECTONICS AND CRUSTAL CHANGE. Since the total mass and volume of the earth are fixed, the creation of new areas of oceanic crust by ocean-floor spreading requires that the crust be destroyed elsewhere at the same rate. As part of a major revolution in scientific thought about the earth's structure, geologists are attempting to explain crustal changes in terms of the creation, motion, and destruction of large sections of the lithosphere called **plates.** This revolutionary idea is called the **plate tectonic theory.** It includes the concepts of continental drift and ocean-floor spreading. (*Tectonics* is a term that applies to changes in the earth's crust and the forces that cause them.)

According to the plate tectonic theory, the earth's lithosphere is divided into an irregular pattern of solid, moving plates that are created at one edge and destroyed at the other edge (see Figures 12-4 and 12-7). The tectonic plates and their associated continents are thought to be moving at rates of approximately a few centimeters a year. The plates move on the plasticlike layer of the upper mantle called the asthenosphere.

Earthquakes, volcanoes, ocean trenches, and young continental mountains occur together, as shown in Figure 12-4. It is believed that these zones of frequent crustal activity mark the boundaries of plates. The features and events of these zones are assumed to be the result of plate movements.

Figure 12-7 shows the three major types of plate boundaries. One of these boundary types is where two plates are spreading apart at a mid-ocean ridge. This is called a **divergent plate boundary.** The spreading is due to plate growth from volcanic activity. Another type of plate boundary is where plates collide. This is called a **convergent plate boundary.** The colliding edges of the plates become distorted, and young continental mountains may form between them. An existing passive margin basin along a continental margin near the boundary of colliding plates would then be uplifted and changed into folded mountains. Often in plate collisions the edge of one plate is pushed down under the other. The subsiding plate plunges or subducts down into the hot mantle, where it is destroyed. The **subduction** and resultant melting of the plate forms liquid rock, which rises and produces the many volcanic and intrusive features associated with plate collisions. *Oceanic trenches* and *volcanic island arcs* often occur in areas of subduction. The third type of plate boundary occurs where the plates slide by each other in a sideways motion. This is called a **lateral (or transform) fault plate boundary.** The San Andreas fault in California is an example of a lateral fault plate boundary.

PLATE TECTONICS AND MANTLE CONVECTION. In order for tectonic plates to move, it is assumed that the mantle under the lithosphere and asthenosphere must behave like a fluid. Some geologists believe that there are convection currents within the mantle that cause plate movement. A proposed source of energy for these currents is the decay of radioactive materials within the earth. One form of evidence for these mantle convection currents is that there are variations in heat flow from the earth. The heat flow at the mid-ocean ridge, where it is believed the convection currents are rising, is higher than average, and heat flow decreases as distance from the mid-ocean ridges increases.

EARTHQUAKES

An **earthquake** is natural, rapid shaking of the lithosphere caused by displacement of rock, such as along faults. The energy of an earthquake is transferred away from its point of origin, which is called the **focus** (plural: *foci*). The energy is transmitted as **seismic** or earthquake **waves,** which are studied by scientists using an instrument called a **seismograph**.

Figure 12-7. Types of plate boundaries. (A) Diverging (rifting) plate boundary with a mid-ocean ridge, shallow-depth earthquakes, igneous intrusions, extrusions of lava flows, and volcanoes. Plate 1 is moving west and Plate 2 is moving east. **(B)** Converging plate boundary with an oceanic trench, volcanic island arcs, igneous intrusions, young mountains, and subduction of oceanic plate. Earthquake foci exist at various depths, indicating subduction. Plate 1 is moving east and Plate 2 is moving west. **(C)** Lateral (transform) fault plate boundary where there is sideways movement of the two plates. This boundary is associated with many shallow-focus earthquakes, and no igneous activity.

A

B

C

KEY

░	Asthenosphere
⣿	Oceanic crust
⩗	Continental crust
⧖	Lithosphere
××=	Earthquake foci

TYPES OF EARTHQUAKE (SEISMIC) WAVES. Earthquakes create **compressional**, or **primary**, waves (**P-waves**), and **shear**, or **secondary**, waves (**S-waves**). Compressional waves cause the particles of the material through which they travel to vibrate in the direction the waves are moving. Shear waves cause the particles to vibrate at right angles to the direction in which the waves are moving.

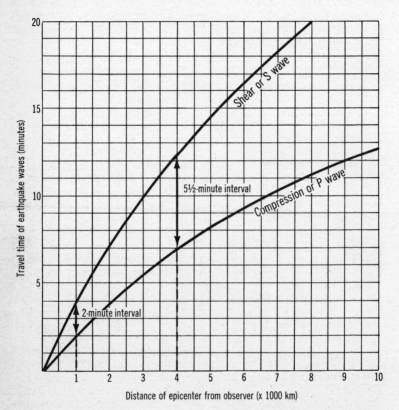

Figure 12-8. Travel times of P and S waves. The two curves in this graph show the time required for P waves and S waves to travel a given distance from the epicenter of an earthquake. Since the S waves travel slower than the P waves, the S waves take longer to reach an observer, and they arrive later than the P waves. For example, if the observer is 1,000 km from the epicenter, the P waves arrive 2 minutes after the earthquake occurs and the S waves arrive 4 minutes after the occurrence. There is thus a 2-minute interval between observation of the P waves and observation of the S waves. At 4,000 km from the epicenter, it takes 7 minutes for the P waves to arrive and 12½ minutes for the S waves; the time interval between them is thus 5½ minutes. The graph can be used to find the distance from the epicenter if the time interval between the arrival of the two waves is known. A similar diagram can be found in the *Earth Science Reference Tables*.

PROPERTIES OF EARTHQUAKE WAVES

1. In any one medium, *compressional waves travel faster than shear waves*. Thus when an earthquake occurs, compressional waves will reach a seismograph before shear waves (see Figure 12-8).

2. The velocity of seismic waves in the earth depends upon the physical properties of the material they are passing through. Generally, the more dense the material, the greater the velocity of the waves. As they pass from a material of one density to a material of another density, seismic waves are bent or refracted.

3. Within the same material, an increase in pressure increases the velocity of seismic waves.

4. Compressional waves will pass through solids, liquids, and gases, while shear waves will pass through solids only.

LOCATION OF AN EPICENTER. The **epicenter** of an earthquake is the place on the earth's surface directly above or closest to the point of origin, or focus, of the earthquake. Epicenters are located by using the velocity differences between compressional (P-waves) and shear (S-waves). P-waves move faster than S-waves; therefore, the farther an observer is from an epicenter, the larger the *time interval* between the arrival of the P-waves and S-waves. The distance to the epicenter is determined by comparing the interval with the graph data.

To find the position of the epicenter, at least three seismograph locations must be used, and epicenter distances must be calculated for each. For each of the three locations, the epicenter distance is then used as a radius and circles are drawn on a globe or map, as shown for locations A, B, and C in Figure 12-9. The place where all three circles intersect is the epicenter of the earthquake.

FINDING THE ORIGIN TIME OF EARTHQUAKES. The time at which an earthquake originates can be determined from the epicenter distance and seismic-wave travel time. The farther an observer is from the epicenter, the longer it takes the seismic waves to travel to the observation point. For example, suppose the observer is 4,000 kilometers from the epicenter. Figure 12-8 shows that it took the P-wave seven minutes to arrive; thus the earthquake occurred seven minutes earlier than the time at which the P-waves were observed on the seismograph. As another example, if the S-wave first arrived at a station at 10 hr:12 min:30 sec G.M.T. (Greenwich Mean Time) and the seismograph station is 5,500 kilometers away from the epicenter, when did the earthquake occur?

A MODEL OF THE EARTH'S INTERIOR

ZONES OF THE EARTH. Analysis of seismic waves indicates that the earth is composed of a number of zones. The **crust** and the upper part of the **mantle** (the rigid mantle) make up the lithosphere. The boundary between the crust and the rigid mantle is called the Moho. The rocks of the lithosphere become more dense below this boundary. The asthenosphere is the

Figure 12-9. Locating the epicenter of an earthquake. Seismograph observations at three widely spaced locations are needed. For the time interval between the P and S waves, the distance to the epicenter can be determined for each station. A circle with this radius is then drawn around the station on a map or globe. The epicenter must lie somewhere on this circle. The same is done for all three stations. The one point that lies on all three circles must be the epicenter.

partly molten, plasticlike part of the mantle. Below it are the stiffer part of the mantle, the **outer core,** and the **inner core.**

Figure 12-10 shows the approximate dimensions and locations of these zones and how they relate to the velocity and type of earthquake waves. *The outer core is believed to be liquid because the S-waves do not penetrate it and because of the sharp decrease in P-wave velocity.* Because S-waves do not pass through the outer core, there is an area on the side of the earth away from the focus of an earthquake where S-waves are not recorded. This area is known as the earthquake's shadow zone.

As depth into the earth increases, temperature, pressure, and density generally increase. Be sure to study the diagram *Inferred Properties of the Earth's Interior* in the *Earth Science Reference Tables.*

EARTH'S CRUST.   The earth's crust, or upper lithosphere, is divided into two major divisions: the **continental crust** and the **oceanic crust.** The continental crust is usually much thicker than the oceanic crust (see Figure 12-5). The crust is thickest where it is highest—in mountain regions.

The two crusts are also distinguished by differences in composition and density. The continental crust is made mostly of granitic rocks, rocks with a composition similar to granite. The oceanic crust is composed mostly of basaltic rocks, rocks similar in composition to basalt. The granitic continental crust is less dense than the basaltic oceanic crust, as shown on the *Scheme for Igneous Rock Identification* in the *Earth Science Reference Tables.*

COMPOSITION OF THE EARTH'S INTERIOR. The iron and nickel composition of metallic meteorites suggests that the composition of the earth's interior is mostly iron and nickel. A combination of iron and nickel at the temperature and pressure believed to be in the earth's core can account for some of the observed properties of seismic waves in the core. The high-density iron-nickel composition of the core and the low-density oxygen-silicon composition of the crust indicate that the mantle must have a composition different from the crust and the core.

Figure 12-10. Zones of the earth's structure as deduced from characteristics of P and S waves. (Also see *Inferred Properties of the Earth's Interior* in the *Earth Science Reference Tables.*)

VOCABULARY

original horizontality	divergent plate boundary
strata	convergent plate boundary
folded strata	subduction
tilted strata	lateral (or transform) fault
faulted strata	plate boundary
fault	earthquake
subsidence	focus (of earthquake)
bench mark	seismic waves
geosyncline	seismograph
passive margin basin	compressional wave
isostasy	(primary or P-wave)
asthenosphere	shear wave (secondary
continental drift	or S-wave)
orogeny	epicenter
mid-ocean ridge	crust
ocean-floor spreading	mantle
reversal of earth's	outer core
magnetic polarity	inner core
plates	continental crust
plate tectonic theory	oceanic crust

QUESTIONS ON TOPIC XII—THE EARTH'S CRUST AND INTERIOR

Questions in Recent Regents Exams (end of book)

June 1991:   36, 38–41, 91–95
June 1992:   39–41, 43, 44, 86–90
June 1993:   36–40, 49, 86–90
June 1994:   37, 38, 40, 41, 42, 96, 100, 103

Questions from Earlier Regents Exams

1. Which statement about the earth's crust in New York State is best supported by the many faults found in the crust?   (1) The crust has moved in the geologic past.   (2) The crust has been inactive throughout the geologic past.   (3) New faults will probably not develop in the crust. (4) An earthquake epicenter has not been located in the crust.

2. Folded sedimentary rock layers are usually caused by   (1) deposition of sediments in folded layers.   (2) differences in sediment density during deposition   (3) a rise in sea level after deposition (4) crustal movement occurring after deposition

3. The diagram below represents a cross section of a portion of the earth's crust. What do these tilted rock layers suggest?

(1) This area remained fairly stable since the sediments were deposited. (2) The sediments were deposited at steep angles and then became rock.   (3) Metamorphism followed the deposition of the sediments. (4) Crustal movement occurred some time after the sediments were deposited.

4. The diagram below represents a vertical cross section of sedimentary rock layers which have not been overturned. Which principle best supports the conclusion that these layers have undergone extensive movement since deposition?
(1) Sediments are deposited with the youngest layers on top.   (2) Sediments are deposited in horizontal layers.   (3) Rock layers are older than igneous intrusions.   (4) Sediments containing the remains of marine fossils are deposited above sea level.

5. The landscape shown in the diagram below is an area of frequent earthquakes.

This landscape provides evidence for   (1) converging convection cells within the rocks of the mantle   (2) density differences in the rocks of the mantle   (3) movement and displacement of the rocks of the crust (4) differential erosion of hard and soft rocks of the crust

6. Which is the most logical conclusion to be drawn from marine fossils found on a mountaintop?   (1) marine animals once lived on land (2) sediments once under water were uplifted   (3) the fossils were transported there   (4) the mountain is composed of igneous rock

7. A line of former beaches along a coast, all 50 meters above sea level, is evidence of   (1) present erosion   (2) the present melting of polar ice caps   (3) land uplift   (4) a decrease in the deposition of marine fossils

8. The thick sedimentary rocks of central and western New York State, which were formed from shallow water deposits, were most probably produced by   (1) glaciation   (2) the uplift of this region   (3) deposition in a geosyncline   (4) volcanic eruption

9. In which region is a geosyncline in the process of formation? (1) Adirondack Mountains   (2) Great Lakes   (3) Colorado Plateau (4) Mississippi River delta

10. The term isostasy refers to a   (1) line of equal air pressure (2) series of anticlines   (3) deflection of winds on the earth caused by rotation   (4) condition of balance between segments of the earth's crust

11. Where do most earthquakes originate?   (1) within the earth's outer core   (2) along specific belts within the crust   (3) randomly across the entire earth's surface   (4) evenly spaced along the Moho interface

Base your answers to questions 12 through 16 on the diagram below. The diagram is a model which represents one possible interpretation of the movements of the earth's rock surfaces according to the theory of plate tectonics (continental drift and sea floor spreading). According to this interpretation, the earth's lithosphere consists of several large "plates" which are moving in relationship to one another. The arrows in the diagram show some of this relative motion of the "plates." The diagram also shows the age of formation of the igneous rocks that make up the oceanic crust of the northern section of the Pacific Plate.

KEY

➤|◄ Movement of plates toward each other

◄|► Movement of plates away from each other

AGE OF ROCKS OF PACIFIC PLATE

A Jurassic   B Early Cretaceous   C Middle Cretaceous   D Late Cretaceous   E Eocene

12. Which statement is best supported by the relative movement shown by the arrows in the diagram?   (1) North America and South America are moving toward each other.   (2) The India Plate is moving away from the Eurasia Plate.   (3) The Africa Plate and Eurasia Plate are moving away from the America Plate.   (4) The Antarctica Plate is moving away from the America Plate.

13. The boundaries between all of these "plates" are best described as the sites of   (1) frequent crustal activity   (2) deep ocean depths   (3) continental boundaries   (4) magnetic field reversals

14. Which geologic structure is represented by the double line separating the America Plate from the Africa and Eurasia Plates?   (1) thick continental crust   (2) thick layers of sediment   (3) mid-ocean ridge   (4) granitic igneous rock

15. Which provides the best explanation of the mechanism that causes these "plates" to move across the earth's surface?   (1) convection currents in the mantle   (2) faulting of the lithosphere   (3) the spin of the earth on its axis   (4) prevailing wind belts of the troposphere

16. The age of formation of the igneous rocks A, B, C, D, and E which make up the oceanic crust of the northern half of the Pacific Plate suggests that this section of the Pacific Plate is generally moving in which direction?   (1) from north to south   (2) from south to north   (3) from west to east   (4) from east to west

17. Recent volcanic activity in different parts of the world supports the inference that volcanoes are located mainly in   (1) the centers of landscape regions   (2) the central regions of the continents   (3) zones of crustal activity   (4) zones in late stages of erosion

18. Which evidence does *not* support the theory that Africa and South America were once part of the same large continent?   (1) correlation of rocks on opposite sides of the Atlantic Ocean   (2) correlation of fossils on opposite sides of the Atlantic Ocean   (3) correlation of coastlines on opposite sides of the Atlantic Ocean   (4) correlation of living animals on opposite sides of the Atlantic Ocean

19. Which statement best supports the theory of continental drift? (1) Basaltic rock is found to be progressively younger at increasing distances from a mid-ocean ridge.   (2) Marine fossils are often found in deep-well drill cores.   (3) The present continents appear to fit together as pieces of a larger landmass.   (4) Areas of shallow-water seas tend to accumulate sediment, which gradually sinks

20. According to the *Earth Science Reference Tables*, during which geologic time period were the continents of North America, South America, and Africa closest together?   (1) Tertiary   (2) Cretaceous   (3) Triassic   (4) Ordovician

21. According to the concept of continental drift, the distance between two continents on opposite sides of a mid-oceanic ridge will generally (1) decrease   (2) increase   (3) remain the same

22. Two samples of ocean floor basaltic bedrock are found at equal distances from, and on opposite sides of, a mid-ocean ridge. The best evidence that both were formed at the ridge during the same time period would be that both samples also   (1) have the same density   (2) contain different crystal sizes   (3) are located at different depths below sea level   (4) have the same magnetic field orientation

23. Which of the cross-sectional diagrams below best represents a model for the movement of rock material below the crust along the mid-Atlantic ridge?

24. The drawing below represents the ocean floor between North America and Africa.

Which graph best represents the age of the bedrock in the ocean floor along line *AB*?

25. Which observation provides the strongest evidence for the inference that convection cells exist within the earth's mantle?   (1) Sea level has varied in the past.   (2) Marine fossils are found at elevations high above sea

level.   (3) Displaced rock strata are usually accompanied by earthquakes and volcanoes.   (4) Heat-flow readings vary at different locations in the earth's crust.

26. Placing a seismograph on the moon enables us to determine if the moon has   (1) water   (2) an atmosphere   (3) radioactive rock   (4) crustal movements

27. The place on the earth's surface directly above the point at which an earthquake originates is the   (1) epicenter   (2) focus   (3) Moho   (4) zenith

28. The immediate result of a sudden slippage of rocks within the earth's crust will be   (1) isostasy   (2) an earthquake   (3) erosion   (4) the formation of convection currents

29. The action of particles as compression waves (P-waves) pass is most nearly like   (1) a line of parked cars being hit from behind by a moving car   (2) the bobbing of corks on the surface of water   (3) the twisting of a rubber hose   (4) the spinning of a top

30. A characteristic of compressional waves and shear waves (S-waves) is that they both   (1) travel at the same speed   (2) travel faster through more dense solid materials   (3) travel through liquid and solid materials   (4) cause rock particles to vibrate in the same direction

The diagram illustrates how the epicenter of an earthquake is located by observatories in Pasadena, California; Chicago, Illinois; and Washington, D.C. Base your answers to questions 31 through 33 on the diagram.

31. The epicenter of the earthquake is located nearest letter   (1) A   (2) B   (3) C   (4) F

32. The separation in time between the arrival of primary and secondary waves is   (1) greatest at Pasadena (G)   (2) greatest at Chicago (D)   (3) greatest at Washington, D.C. (E)   (4) the same at all stations

33. If the method illustrated by the diagram is used to locate the epicenter of an earthquake, it appears unlikely for an individual observatory, operating independently, to determine the   (1) direction to the epicenter   (2) distance to the epicenter   (3) distance to an epicenter located under the ocean   (4) interval between the initial and subsequent seismic waves

34. The time lapse between the arrival of the P-waves and S-waves on *one* seismograph recording can be used to determine the   (1) magnitude of the earthquake   (2) exact location of the focus   (3) exact location of the epicenter   (4) distance to the epicenter

Base your answers to questions 35 through 39 on the *Earth Science Reference Tables* and the diagram below. The diagram represents a cross section of the earth showing the paths of earthquake waves from a single earthquake source. Seismograph stations are located on the earth's surface at points *A* through *F*, and they are all located in the same time zone.

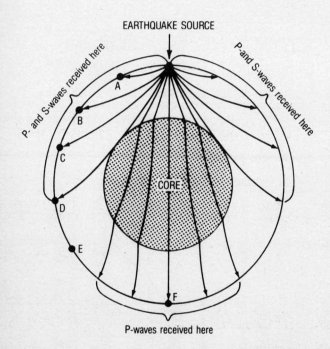

EARTHQUAKE SOURCE

P- and S-waves received here

P- and S-waves received here

CORE

P-waves received here

35. At which station is the distance in time between the arrival of P- and S-waves the greatest?   (1) *A*   (2) *B*   (3) *C*   (4) *D*

36. Station *E* did *not* receive any P-waves or S-waves from this earthquake because the P-waves and S-waves   (1) cancel each other out   (2) are bent, causing shadow zones   (3) are changed to sound energy   (4) are converted to heat energy

37. What explanation do scientists give for the reason that station *F* did *not* receive S-waves?   (1) The earth's inner core is so dense that S-waves cannot pass through.   (2) The earth's outer core is liquid, which does not allow S-waves to pass.   (3) S-waves do not have enough energy to pass completely through the earth.   (4) S-waves become absorbed by the earth's crust.

38. Seismograph station *D* is 7700 kilometers from the epicenter. If the P-wave arrived at this station at 2:15 P.M., at approximately what time did the earthquake occur?   (1) 1:56 P.M.   (2) 2:00 P.M.   (3) 2:04 P.M. (4) 2:08 P.M.

39. Seismograph station *B* recorded the arrival of P-waves at 2:10 P.M. and the arrival of S-waves at 2:15 P.M. Approximately how far is station *B* from the earthquake epicenter?   (1) 1400 km   (2) 2400 km (3) 3400 km (4) 4400 km

40. The diagrams below represent seismographic traces of three different disturbances A, B, and C recorded by the same seismograph.

The traces indicate that the distance from the station to the epicenters of the three disturbances is   (1) least for disturbance A   (2) least for disturbance B   (3) least for disturbance C   (4) the same for all three disturbances

41. What total distance does an earthquake compression wave (P-wave) travel in its first 8 minutes?   (1) 2200 km   (2) 4850 km (3) 6500 km   (4) 11,200 km

42. A seismic station is 2000 kilometers from an earthquake epicenter. According to the *Earth Science Reference Tables*, how long does it take an S-wave to travel from the epicenter to the station?   (1) 7 minutes 20 seconds   (2) 5 minutes 10 seconds   (3) 3 minutes 20 seconds   (4) 4 minutes 10 seconds

43. In developing a model of the earth's deep interior, most of the evidence was derived from   (1) deep wells   (2) mining operations (3) observing other planets   (4) seismic data

44. Through which zones of the earth do compressional waves (P-waves) travel?   (1) crust and mantle, only   (2) mantle and outer core, only   (3) outer and inner core, only   (4) crust, mantle, outer core, and inner core

45. According to the *Earth Science Reference Tables*, in which group are the zones of the Earth's interior correctly arranged in order of increasing average density?   (1) crust, mantle, outer core, inner core   (2) crust, mantle, inner core, outer core   (3) inner core, outer core, mantle, crust   (4) outer crust, inner core, mantle, crust

46. According to the *Earth Science Reference Tables*, what is the relationship between density, temperature, and pressure inside the earth?   (1) As depth increases, density, temperature, and pressure decrease.   (2) As depth increases, density and temperature increase, but pressure decreases.   (3) As depth increases, density increases, but temperature and pressure decrease.   (4) As depth increases, density, temperature, and pressure increase.

47. The temperature of rock located 1000 kilometers below the Earth's surface is about   (1) 1000°C   (2) 2600°C   (3) 3300°C   (4) 4300°C

48. Which evidence best supports the inference that the earth's outer core possesses liquid characteristics?   (1) The velocities of both primary and shear waves increase through the outer core.   (2) The primary wave velocity decreases, while the shear wave velocity increases in the outer core.   (3) Primary waves pass through the outer core but shear waves do not.   (4) Both primary waves and shear waves pass through the outer core.

49. How does the composition of the oceanic crust compare with the composition of the continental crust?   (1) The oceanic crust is mainly limestone, while the continental crust is mainly sandstone.   (2) The oceanic crust is mainly limestone, while the continental crust is mainly granite.   (3) The oceanic crust is mainly basalt, while the continental crust is mainly sandstone.   (4) The oceanic crust is mainly basalt, while the continental crust is mainly granite.

50. As one travels from an ocean shore to the interior of a continent, the thickness of the earth's crust generally   (1) decreases   (2) increases   (3) remains the same

51. Which statement best describes the continental and oceanic crusts?   (1) The continental crust is thicker and less dense than the oceanic crust.   (2) The continental crust is thicker and more dense than the oceanic crust.   (3) The continental crust is thinner and less dense than the oceanic crust.   (4) The continental crust is thinner and more dense than the oceanic crust.

52. Which part of the earth is probably most responsible for its high average density?   (1) core   (2) crust   (3) mantle   (4) mountains

53. The composition of some meteorites supports the inference that the earth's core is composed of   (1) aluminum and calcium   (2) iron and nickel   (3) silicon and oxygen   (4) magnesium and potassium

Geologic history is recorded in the rocks. Observations of the composition, structure, position, and fossil content of the rock record leads to interpretations of the geologic history of the earth. Carefully study the *Geologic History of New York State at a Glance* and the *Generalized Bedrock Geology of New York State* in the *Earth Science Reference Tables* before reading further in this topic.

RELATIVE DATING OF ROCKS AND EVENTS

Relative dating is the process of obtaining the chronological sequence of rocks or geologic events in an area. The **relative age** of a rock or event is its age as compared to other rocks or events. It should not be confused with the actual age, called the **absolute age,** which refers to the date when the event actually occurred or the rock was formed. Some of the methods of relative dating are described below.

PRINCIPLE OF SUPERPOSITION. In layers of sedimentary rock and some extrusive igneous rocks, the bottom layer is inferred to be the oldest, with each overlying layer being progressively younger, so that the top layer is the youngest. This inference is called the **principle of superposition,** and it may be used as the basis for relative dating. Superposition is due to the original horizontality of deposited sediments. Exceptions to the principle occur in certain types of rock deformation resulting from crustal change. When there are overturns in folds, or when movement along faults has thrust older rock layers over younger layers, the principle of superposition does not hold true (see Figure 13-1 on page 184).

INTRUSIONS AND EXTRUSIONS. When molten rock (magma) invades pre-existing rocks and crystallizes, it forms a body called an **intrusion.** The intrusion is younger than any rock it cuts through (see Figure 13-2 on page 184). When molten rock (lava) flows on the earth's surface and solidifies, it forms a feature called an **extrusion.** The extrusion or lava flow is younger than any rocks beneath it but will be older than any rocks that may later form on top of it.

ROCK STRUCTURAL FEATURES. A rock is older than any fault, *joint,* or fold that appears in the rock. Like a fault, a **joint** is a crack in rocks. However, a joint differs from a fault because there has been no movement of rocks along the crack. If movement (displacement) of the rocks should occur, the joint would become a fault (see Figure 13-3 on page 185).

Figure 13-1. The principle of superposition and possible exceptions. (A) Normally, a rock layer is younger than any layers below it. **(B)** Overturned folds can result in an exception to the principle. Layer 1 at lower right is actually a continuation of Layer 1 at upper left. **(C)** and **(D)** Movement of layers along an overthrust fault can result in an exception to the principle. Layers numbered alike are the same age.

Figure 13-2. Relative ages of intrusions and extrusions. Intrusion A is younger than the layers it intrudes. Intrusion B is younger than A because B cuts A. The layers above the extrusion must be younger than the extrusion because of the absence of contact metamorphism along their common boundary. The rocks are numbered in order of increasing age.

INTERNAL ROCK CHARACTERISTICS. In sedimentary rocks, the sediments are older than the rock itself because they are required to form the rock. In nonsedimentary rocks, individual crystals or fragments are also older than the rock itself.

A **vein** is a mineral deposit, formed from a solution that has filled some crack or permeable zone in rocks. A vein is thus younger than the rock it is in. Mineral cements in sedimentary rocks are also younger than the original sediments in the rock.

Figure 13-3. Relative ages of structural features of rocks. Folds, faults, joints, and veins are younger than the rocks in which they occur.

CORRELATION

Correlation is the process of showing that rocks or geologic events that occurred in different places are the same age. Correlation is useful in finding mineral deposits, because certain minerals are often found in rocks of a specific age. Correlation is also important in unraveling the sequence of geologic events in an area. Some of the methods of correlation are described below.

CORRELATION BY "WALKING THE OUTCROP." An **outcrop** is local rock, or **bedrock,** that is exposed at the earth's surface. In areas of outcrops, correlation can be accomplished by directly following the continuity of the individual layers or rock formations at the earth's surface; this procedure is called **walking the outcrop** (see Figure 13-4 on page 186). A **formation** is a layer or group of layers of rock and is the basic unit of geologic mapping. The rocks of one formation have similar features, such as rock type, mineral composition, and environment of formation.

CORRELATION BY SIMILARITY IN ROCKS. Where rock formations are separated from one another, they may be tentatively correlated on the basis of similar overall appearance, color, and mineral composition, as indicated in Figure 13-4.

LIMITATIONS OF CORRELATION BY SIMILARITY. Correlation of rock formations by similarity of the rocks they contain is usually valid over small areas only, and even then may be incorrect. Two rock formations, and even separate parts of the same formation, may be similar and yet be of different ages. For example, Figure 13-5 shows a sedimentary rock formation in which the environment of deposition gradually shifted over a long period of time. Therefore, the rock that formed from the original sediments is much older than the rock that formed in the later stages of deposition, although both parts of the formation are similar in appearance.

Figure 13-4. Correlation by direct observation. A geologist can follow the strata in an exposed hillside by "walking the outcrop," for example, by walking along the road on the left side of this river valley. The geologist may also be able to correlate strata on opposite sides of the valley by observing similarities in color, texture, and sequence of the rock strata.

Figure 13-5. Variations in the age of a formation. A sedimentary formation composed of the same type of sediment (for example, sand) may be of different ages in different locations because of movement of the environment of deposition. In this diagram, the sandstone at the left is 10,000,000 years older than the sandstone at the right, even though the formation is continuous and similar in composition.

CORRELATION BY USE OF INDEX FOSSILS. The use of certain *fossils* or groups of fossils is one of the best methods of correlation. A **fossil** is any evidence of former life. With minor exceptions, fossils are found exclusively in sedimentary rocks. Fossils are rarely found in igneous and metamorphic rocks because fossils are usually destroyed by melting and pressure associated with the formation of these nonsedimentary rocks. The fossils used in correlation are called **index fossils.** To be useful as an index fossil, the particular life form must have lived over a large geographic area; that is, it must have a large horizontal distribution throughout rocks formed at the same time. Also, the life form must have lived only a short period of time, thus having a small vertical distribution in the strata in which the fossils occur (see Figure 13-6).

Figure 13-6. Correlation of rocks by means of index fossils. In **A,** a fossil of an organism known to have lived only during the Devonian Period is found in rock layer 4. This layer was therefore deposited during Devonian times. The layers above it are younger and those below it are older. In **B,** a similar fossil is found in one of the layers. This is therefore also a Devonian layer. A second index fossil of the Silurian Period is found in layer 7. This tells us that layers 5 and 6 are not younger than the Devonian and not older than the Silurian. Relative ages of the layers in both formations are indicated by the numbers in order of youngest to oldest.

CORRELATION BY VOLCANIC ASH DEPOSITS. **Volcanic ash** consists of small pieces of extrusive igneous rock that are shot into the air during volcanic eruptions. In large eruptions, volcanic ash is scattered over wide areas of the earth. The ash may then settle among other sediments being deposited in many different regions. If these ash deposits can be detected and identified in rock formations, they are very useful in correlation, because they represent a very small interval of time and because they are widely distributed. They can therefore serve as correlating age markers in rock formations that may be hundreds or thousands of kilometers apart.

GEOLOGIC HISTORY FROM THE ROCK RECORD

FOSSILS AND RELATIVE AGE.   Just as the fossils found in rocks can be used to correlate rock strata, they can also be used to place the events in an area in order according to their relative ages. This is possible because the life forms on earth have constantly evolved and some forms existed or were dominant only during specific intervals of geologic time. For example, the rock record shows that the dinosaurs as a group existed in a large interval of geologic time (called the Mesozoic Era), but certain types of dinosaurs existed only during smaller intervals. When these life forms appear as fossils in a given rock formation, they serve to establish the relative age of the formation and to give it a specific place in geologic history.

GEOLOGIC TIME SCALE.   Mainly on the basis of such fossil evidence, geologists have been able to divide geologic time into units, called *eons, eras, periods,* and *epochs.* This division of geologic time is called the **geologic time scale** and is often represented as a chart, such as the *Geologic History of New York State at a Glance* in the *Earth Science Reference Tables*. Note that an era, period, or epoch is not an exact unit of measurement such as an hour. A glance at the geologic time scale will show, for example, that no two eras represent the same amount of time.

The Precambrian Eon is the earliest division of geologic time and represents about 88% of the total. Fossils are difficult to detect and identify in the Precambrian, because the earliest living things were very small and did not have the hard parts needed to form fossils easily. Fossils are also uncommon in the Precambrian because many of these ancient rocks have been metamorphosed, melted, or weathered and eroded. Fossils in the rock record indicate that human or humanlike mammals have existed on earth for a relatively extremely short time—only about 0.04% (the Quaternary Period) of the earth's existence.

UNCONFORMITIES.   In attempting to read the rock record, geologists often find evidence of buried erosional surfaces called **unconformities** (see Figure 13-7). An unconformity in the rock record of an area indicates that at some time in the geologic history of the area, crustal movement had produced uplift. This uplift had exposed the rocks to weathering and erosion, and part of the rock record was removed. A later subsidence lowered the area, it was covered by water, and new sediments were deposited on the eroded surface, thus producing the unconformity. In most unconformities, there is a lack of parallelism between the older layers below the erosional surface and the younger ones above it as the result of folding or tilting during the uplift or subsidence. However, this is not always the case.

The presence of an unconformity means that some of the layers of the rock record of an area are missing. Although there is a gap in geologic time, an unconformity is useful in relative dating. The rocks above an unconformity are younger than the unconformity, and the rocks below it are considerably older.

Events producing an unconformity with lack of parallelism.

(A) Deposition forms sedimentary rock layers.

(B) Crustal deformation and uplift occur.

(C) Weathering and erosion remove part of the rock record.

(D) Submergence and new deposition result in an unconformity along the now buried erosional surface.

An unconformity in parallel strata.

(E) Uplift, erosion, and submergence have also occurred here, but without deformation. Evidence of a gap in the rock record may be given by widely different ages of the fossils in the layers above and below the unconformity.

Figure 13-7. Development of an unconformity.

UNIFORMITARIANISM.   One of the basic principles geologists use to interpret geologic history is **uniformitarianism,** or uniformity of process, which implies that "the present is the key to the past"; that is, it is assumed that the geologic processes happening today also happened in the past, and that much of the rock record can be interpreted by observing present geologic processes. Uniformitarianism does not mean that different processes could not have happened in the past or that the geologic processes always occurred at the same rates as they do today.

As an example of uniformitarianism, suppose a geologist finds a sedimentary rock formation that is unsorted, has a wide range of sediment sizes, and has sediments with partly rounded shapes with scratches of various sizes. On the basis of knowledge of glacial processes today, the geologist will infer that this formation was the result of past glaciation.

ABSOLUTE DATING OF ROCKS USING RADIOACTIVE DECAY

The use of fossil evidence, superposition, and similar methods gives geologists only relative dates. *Radioactive dating* is their major way of knowing the actual, or absolute, dates for the events of geologic history.

ISOTOPES.   An *element* is a substance consisting of atoms that are chemically alike. Most elements exist in several varieties called **isotopes.** The difference between one isotope of an element and another is in the mass of its atoms. For example, the mass of an atom of the most common isotope of carbon is 12 units. This isotope is called carbon-12, to distinguish it from other isotopes of carbon, such as carbon-14, in which the atoms have a mass of 14 units.

RADIOACTIVE DECAY.   Almost all the mass of an atom is concentrated in a central region called the *nucleus* (plural, *nuclei*). The nuclei of the atoms of many isotopes are *unstable.* This means that they tend to emit particles and electromagnetic energy, and change to atoms of other elements. This process is called **radioactive decay.** The nucleus that remains after a radioactive decay may also be unstable, and it will decay in its turn. Eventually, a stable isotope (one that does not undergo radioactive decay) is formed.

URANIUM-238.   One of the most important radioactive isotopes for the dating of rocks is **uranium-238,** the isotope of uranium whose atoms have a mass of 238 units. The nuclei of its atoms pass through a series of radioactive decays, eventually producing atoms of *lead-206,* a stable isotope of the element lead.

HALF-LIFE.   The decay of any individual nucleus is a random event. That is, it may occur at any time. However, among the billions of atoms in any sample of an isotope, a certain definite fraction will decay in a given time. In the next time interval of the same length, the same fraction of the remaining atoms will decay. The time required for half the atoms in a given mass of an isotope to decay is called the **half-life** of the isotope. For any isotope, at the end of one half-life period, half the original atoms will have decayed to other elements, and half will remain unchanged. At the end of the next half-life period, half of these remaining atoms will have decayed, leaving one-fourth of the original atoms unchanged. After a third half-life period, half of these will have decayed, leaving one-eighth of the original atoms unchanged. This halving of the number of unchanged atoms during each successive half-life period continues indefinitely.

The half-life is different for each radioactive isotope, but it is always the same for a given isotope. The half-life of an isotope is not affected by any known environmental factors, such as temperature, pressure, or involvement in chemical reaction. The half-life of an isotope also is not affected by the amount or size of the sample. Each half-life is assumed to have been the same throughout the earth's history. Half-lives vary over a wide range, from fractions of a second to billions of years. (See *Radioactive Decay Data* in the *Earth Science Reference Tables*.)

RADIOACTIVE DATING. The known half-life period of radioactive isotopes can be used to estimate the age of a rock by determining the ratio between the amount of a radioactive isotope and the amount of its decay products in a rock sample. The method is called **radioactive dating.** For example, suppose a rock formed with minerals containing uranium-238 and no lead-206. As time passed, the uranium would slowly change to lead-206 (its stable decay product) at its fixed half-life rate. At the end of one half-life period (4.5 billion years for uranium-238), half the uranium-238 atoms would have changed to atoms of lead-206. In terms of number of atoms, there would be equal amounts of uranium-238 and lead-206, where originally the rock contained no lead-206. If a rock is found today with this 1:1 ratio of uranium-238 atoms to lead-206 atoms, it can be concluded that the rock of formed 4.5 billion years ago. If there is relatively more uranium and less lead, the rock is less than 4.5 billion years old.

The age corresponding to any particular ratio of uranium to lead can be calculated mathematically. The curves in Figure 13-8 on page 192 show how the percentage of uranium-238 decreases and the percentage of lead-206 increases with time in a given rock.

CARBON-14 DATING. Radioactive elements with *long* half-lives (such as uranium-238) are used to date rocks because most rocks have ages measured in hundreds of millions, or even billions, of years. In such long periods, any element with a short half-life would have decayed to such an extent that any remaining amounts would be too small to measure. Some radioactive elements with *short* half-lives, such as *carbon-14* (half-life 5,700 years), are useful for dating remains of *organic materials and rocks of relatively recent origin*. For example, **carbon-14 dating** (also called **radiocarbon dating**) can be used for organic remains up to about 50,000 years in age, which is only the last part of the Pleistocene Epoch ice age.

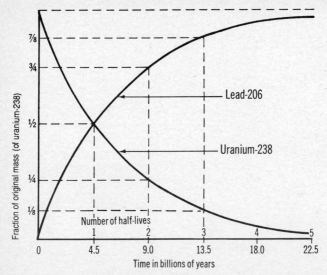

Figure 13-8. Curves showing radioactive decay of uranium-238 and formation of the stable decay product lead-206. After one half-life (4.5 billion years), half the original atoms of uranium have become atoms of lead.

ANCIENT LIFE AND EVOLUTION

VARIATIONS IN FOSSILS AND ENVIRONMENTS.   The fossil record, of mostly sedimentary rocks, shows that a great variety of plants and animals have lived in the past in a great variety of environments. Most of these life forms are now extinct. Comparison of fossils with similar life forms alive today allows geologists to interpret past environments, as shown in Figure 13-9.

The chances of fossilization are very small, so there are probably more types of life forms that have left no evidence of their existence than types of life forms found as fossils.

FOSSILS AND EVOLUTION.   A **species** includes all the life forms that are similar enough to be able to interbreed and produce fertile young. Just by looking around at people, house cats, and dogs, which are three species of life, it can be observed that many *variations* in a species can exist. When graphed, the variations in a species often form bell-shaped curves, as shown in Figure 13-10.

The theory of **organic evolution** assumes that some of the variations within a species give the individuals with those variations a higher chance of surviving and reproducing. If these variations are inheritable, they will be passed on to the offspring, and the favorable variations will be preserved, while unfavorable variations will gradually die out. If this process continues for long periods of time, the accumulated variations may eventually result in a new species—one that can no longer interbreed with the earlier varieties of the species.

The fossil record provides evidence for the theory of evolution. Fossils from adjacent intervals of geologic time show a *gradual transition,* or change, from one species to the next. Recently some scientists have inferred from evidence in the rock record that there are times of rapid organic evolution (punctuated evolution), possibly due to extinctions resulting from collisions between celestial bodies and the earth.

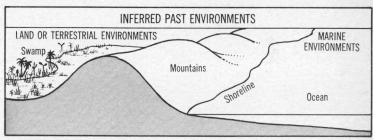

Figure 13-9. Reconstruction of past environments from fossil evidence and rock formations. From the dinosaur and marine fossils and the gradual change in sedimentary rock type as we go further to the right, we infer the former shoreline and ocean. From the types of plant fossils and the occurrence of coal, we infer the former swamp on the left.

Figure 13-10. Variation in a species trait. In any population of a species, each trait usually has an average value. In most individuals, the trait will be close to the average. In a few, it will be much below average; in a similar number, it will be much above average. If the departure from average in either direction has an advantage for survival and can be inherited, the average will shift in this favorable direction in later generations.

VOCABULARY

relative age	volcanic ash
absolute age	geologic time scale
principle of superposition	unconformity
intrusion	uniformitarianism
extrusion	isotope
joint	radioactive decay
vein	uranium-238
correlation	half-life
outcrop	radioactive dating
bedrock	carbon-14 (radiocarbon)
walking the outcrop	dating
rock formation	species
fossil	organic evolution
index fossil	

QUESTIONS ON TOPIC XIII
INTERPRETING GEOLOGIC HISTORY

Questions in Recent Regents Exams (end of book)

June 1991:   42–47, 50, 55, 86–89
June 1992:   42, 45–48, 51, 52, 82, 91–95, 102
June 1993:   41–45, 50, 53, 91–95, 98, 100
June 1994:   43–46, 48–50, 89, 92, 94, 99, 101

Questions from Earlier Regents Exams

1. According to the *Generalized Geologic Map of New York State,* what is the geologic age of the bedrock found at the surface at 43°30′ N. latitude by 75°00′ longitude?   (1) Devonian   (2) Cambrian   (3) Early Ordovician   (4) Middle Proterozoic

2. Which area in New York State is located on rock formations that contain large amounts of salt deposits?   (1) Syracuse   (2) Long Island (3) New York City   (4) Old Forge

3. What is the age of the surface bedrock at Niagara Falls, New York? (1) Devonian   (2) Silurian   (3) Ordovician   (4) Cambrian

4. In a certain section of sedimentary rock, fossil dating shows that younger rock layers are on top of older rock layers. This relationship indicates that   (1) the rock layers were formed according to the principle of superposition   (2) the rock layers have been overturned (3) fossil dating is often inaccurate   (4) the sediments that formed the rock layers were composed of many different minerals

5. The diagram below represents a cross-sectional view of a portion of the earth's crust showing sedimentary rock layers that have not been overturned. The letters identify the specific layers. Which rock layer probably is the oldest?   (1) *A*   (2) *B*   (3) *C*   (4) *D*

6. The diagram below shows a portion of the earth's crust. What is the relative age of the igneous rock?   (1) It is older than the limestone but younger than the shale.   (2) It is younger than the limestone but older than the shale.   (3) It is older than both the limestone and the shale.   (4) It is younger than both the limestone and the shale.

KEY:

Limestone

Shale

Igneous rock formation

Contact metamorphism

7. The diagram below represents an exposed rock outcrop. Which geologic event occurred *last*?   (1) the intrusion of *A*   (2) the fault along line *B*   (3) the fold at *C*   (4) the deposition of gravel at *D*

8. The simplest way to correlate exposed rock layers in the same general vicinity when they contain no fossils is by   (1) following vertical veins   (2) radioactive dating   (3) walking the outcrop   (4) tracing a fault

9. The fossil remains of organisms which were once common and widespread but which survived only a short period of geologic time might be especially useful for   (1) correlating sedimentary deposits in places distant from each other   (2) establishing the absolute age of a deposit   (3) tracing the evolution of organisms related to that species   (4) determining some of the factors that led to extinction

10. The diagram below shows a sample of conglomerate rock. The oldest part of this sample is the   (1) conglomerate rock sample   (2) calcite cement   (3) limestone particles   (4) mineral vein

Base your answers to questions 11 through 13 on the diagram below.

	Alluvium		Limestone
	Sandstone		Conglomerate
	Shale		Igneous

11. The disturbed rock structure shown is probably the result of (1) warping   (2) folding   (3) volcanism   (4) faulting

12. Which is the oldest sedimentary rock in this diagram?   (1) conglomerate   (2) sandstone   (3) shale   (4) limestone

13. Rock layer B is the same age as layer   (1) C   (2) D   (3) E   (4) F

14. Below are diagrams of three profile sections showing fossil deposits W, X, Y, and Z, found at widely separated locations. Which would be the best index fossil?   (1) W   (2) X   (3) Y   (4) Z

Rock Layer 1	W			W		W Z
Rock Layer 2	W Z			Y		Z
Rock Layer 3	W X			X		X Z
	LOCALITY A			LOCALITY B		LOCALITY C

15. The diagram below represents cross sections of three rock outcrops approximately 100 kilometers apart. What would be the best method of correlating the rock layers of each outcrop?   (1) comparing rock types   (2) comparing mineral composition   (3) comparing index fossils   (4) comparing thickness of rock layers

16. Which rock type most likely would contain fossils?   (1) sedimentary rock   (2) metamorphic rock   (3) intrusive igneous rock   (4) extrusive igneous rock

17. Why can layers of volcanic ash found between other rock layers often serve as good geologic time markers?   (1) Volcanic ash usually occurs in narrow bands around volcanoes.   (2) Volcanic ash usually contains index fossils.   (3) Volcanic ash usually contains the radioactive isotope carbon-14.   (4) Volcanic ash usually is rapidly deposited over a large area.

18. According to the *Earth Science Reference Tables*, which rock is most likely the oldest?   (1) conglomerate containing the tusk of a mastodon   (2) shale containing trilobite fossils   (3) sandstone containing fossils of flowering plants   (4) siltstone containing dinosaur footprints

19. The best basis for concluding that a certain layer of shale rock in New York State was deposited at the same time as one in California is that both   (1) are the same distance below the surface   (2) contain similar fossil remains   (3) are sedimentary rocks   (4) have the same chemical composition

20. Which rock layer is *not* found in the rock record of New York State? (1) Devonian   (2) Silurian   (3) Ordovician   (4) Permian

21. During which time was the majority of the exposed bedrock in New York State deposited?   (1) Precambrian   (2) Mesozoic (3) Cenozoic   (4) Paleozoic

22. Rocks containing fossils of the earliest land plants could most likely be found in New York State bedrock near   (1) Syracuse (2) Oswego   (3) Ithaca   (4) Old Forge

23. Approximately how long ago were the Taconic Mountains uplifted?   (1) 540 million years ago   (2) 440 million years ago   (3) 310 million years ago   (4) 120 million years ago

24. According to the Geologic Time Scale in the *Earth Science Reference Tables*, what is the estimated age of the earth as a planet in millions of years?   (1) 540   (2) 4000   (3) 4600   (4) 5000

25. The Geologic Time Scale has been subdivided into a number of time units called periods on the basis of   (1) fossil evidence   (2) rock thicknesses   (3) rock types   (4) radioactive dating

26. Which line is the best representation of the relative duration of each of the geologic time intervals?

Base your answers to questions 27 through 31 on the diagram below.

27. Which is the most recently formed rock?   (1) A   (2) B   (3) C (4) D

28. An unconformity is located between   (1) A and B   (2) B and C (3) C and D   (4) F and G

29. The conclusion that the limestone layer (D) is younger than the basalt layer (E) is supported by evidence of   (1) faulting   (2) contact metamorphism   (3) igneous intrusion   (4) fossils

30. The last event before faulting occurred was formation of   (1) C   (2) D   (3) E   (4) J

31. Which must have preceded the formation of layer D?   (1) faulting   (2) submergence   (3) intrusion   (4) uplift

32. An unconformity between two sedimentary layers is most likely produced by   (1) the deposition of gravel followed by the deposition of sand and silt   (2) continuous sedimentation in a deep basin over a long period   (3) uplift followed by extensive erosion, submergence, and deposition   (4) a period of extrusive vulcanism followed by another period of extrusive vulcanism

33. The diagram below shows a cross-sectional view of part of the earth's crust. What does the unconformity (buried erosional surface) at line *XY* represent?   (1) an area of contact metamorphism   (2) a time gap in the rock record of the area   (3) proof that no deposition occurred between the Cambrian and Carboniferous periods   (4) overturning of the Cambrian and Carboniferous rock layers

34. The physical and chemical conditions which long ago produced changes on the earth's surface are still producing changes. This statement is one way of stating the principle of   (1) catastrophism   (2) diastrophism   (3) uniformitarianism   (4) isostasy

35. The age of the earth is most accurately estimated from   (1) the salinity of the oceans   (2) the thickness of sedimentary rock   (3) studies of fossils   (4) radioactive dating of rock masses

36. "The present is the key to the past." This statement is best interpreted as meaning that   (1) rocks now exposed were formed in the past   (2) the processes by which rocks are formed today have been going on throughout the earth's history   (3) activity occurring now will cease in the near future   (4) animals living now are unlike any that lived in the geologic past

Base your answers to questions 37 through 41 on the graph below, which shows the radioactive decay curve for uranium to lead.

37. The half-life of uranium-238 as shown on this graph is closest to (1) 2.5 billion years   (2) 3.5 billion years   (3) 4.5 billion years   (4) 5.5 billion years

38. Because of the half-life nature of the decay process, uranium-238 will theoretically   (1) decay completely before 4.5 billion years (2) decay completely in 18 billion years   (3) decay completely in 200 billion years   (4) continue to decay indefinitely

39. A uranium mineral is obtained from an intrusive granite formation. It is then analyzed and found to contain about 1 gram of lead-206 to every 3 grams of uranium-238. Approximately how many billions of years old is the granite?   (1) one   (2) two   (3) three   (4) four

40. Which curve represents the expected decay rate of uranium-238 if its temperature were raised almost to the melting point?

41. If the decay curve for the element carbon-14 were plotted, the general shape of the curve would be

42. The half-life of a particular radioactive substance   (1) decreases as pressure on it increases   (2) decreases as its mass decreases   (3) increases as the temperature increases   (4) is independent of mass, temperature, and pressure

43. If a specimen of a given radioactive substance is reduced in size, its half-life   (1) decreases   (2) increases   (3) remains the same

44. Which radioactive substance shown on the graph below has the longest half-life?   (1) A   (2) B   (3) C   (4) D

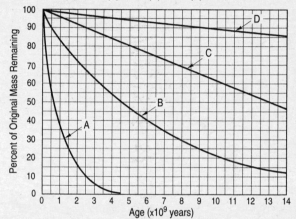

45. Why is carbon-14 *not* usually used to accurately date objects more than 50,000 years old?   (1) Carbon-14 has a relatively short half-life and too little carbon-14 is left after 50,000 years.   (2) Carbon-14 has a relatively long half-life and not enough carbon-14 has decayed after 50,000 years.   (3) Carbon-14 has been introduced as an impurity in most materials older than 50,000 years.   (4) Carbon-14 has only existed on earth during the last 50,000 years.

46. The element K^{40} radioactively decays to Ar^{40}. The diagram at the right shows a model of the relative amounts of K^{40} and Ar^{40} remaining after one half-life. Which diagram below best illustrates the relative amounts of K^{40} and Ar^{40} remaining after two half-lives?

(1)   (2)   (3)   (4)

47. Uranium-238 is used to date the age of the earth rather than carbon-14 because uranium-238   (1) was more abundant when the earth formed   (2) has a longer half-life   (3) decays at a constant rate   (4) is easier to collect and test

48. The diagram below represents a section of the earth's crust. The symbols in the diagram indicate the location on a horizontal surface of certain fossils that formed during the Carboniferous Period. For what purpose would the fossil information on the map be most useful?

(1) to find the location of the shoreline during the Carboniferous Period
(2) to measure the age of the bedrock by carbon-14 radioactive dating
(3) to provide evidence of the evolution of humans   (4) to indicate the extent of folding that occurred during the Devonian Period

49. Shark and coral fossils are found in the rock record of certain land areas. What does the presence of these fossils indicate about those areas?   (1) They have undergone glacial deposition.   (2) They were once covered by thick vegetation.   (3) They have undergone intense metamorphism.   (4) They were once covered by shallow seas.

50. Earth scientists studied fossils of a certain type of plant. They noted slight differences in the plant throughout geologic time. What inference is best made from this evidence?   (1) When the environment changed, this type of plant also changed, allowing it to survive.   (2) When uplifting occurred, the fossils of this type of plant were deformed.   (3) The processes which form fossils today differ from those of the past.   (4) The fossils have changed as a result of weathering and erosion.

51. The changes observed in the fossil record from the Precambrian era to the Cenozoic Era best provide evidence of   (1) sublimation   (2) radioactive decay   (3) evolution   (4) planetary motion

52. Which statement is false?   (1) Two members of one species must be exactly alike.   (2) The members of a species can vary in physical features.   (3) The members of a species can interbreed and produce fertile young.   (4) A species may exist on earth for millions of years.

TOPIC XIV | Landscape Development and Environmental Change

Landscapes (topography) are the features of the earth's surface at the interface between the atmosphere, hydrosphere, and lithosphere (crust). Some of the characteristics of landscapes are the slope of the land, shape of the surface features, stream drainage patterns, stream slope, and soil characteristics. A **stream drainage pattern** is the shape of the aerial view of the stream courses in an area (see Figure 14-6 on pages 210–211).

MEASURING LANDSCAPE CHARACTERISTICS

The shape and slope of the land, stream drainage patterns, and some soil features can be measured using actual observations or models such as contour maps, aerial photographs, satellite images, and the types of maps and diagrams used in this topic. The use of these tools has shown that landscape features such as hills, slopes, and stream drainage patterns have distinctive shapes by which they can be identified.

GRADIENT AND PROFILES. *Slope,* or *gradient,* a measurable characteristic of the land and streams, is described in Topic III. *Profiles,* also described in Topic III, are useful to show the shape and slope of the earth's surface and streams, and the thickness and development of soil horizons.

MOUNTAINS, PLATEAUS, AND PLAINS. On the basis of gradient, elevation, and rock structure, landscapes are divided into three major types—*mountains, plateaus,* and *plains* (see Figure 14-1).

Figure 14-1. Profiles and structures of the major types of landscapes.

A **mountain** is an area of high elevation compared to the surrounding area or sea level, which usually has many changes in slope as well as regions of steep gradient. Internally, mountains are characterized by distorted rock structures such as faults, folds, and tilted rocks, and are often composed of much nonsedimentary rock.

A **plateau** is also an area of high elevation, but it has undistorted horizontal rock structure and often a more level slope or gradient than mountains. A plateau may have steep slopes where streams have cut valleys, such as at the Grand Canyon in the Colorado Plateau.

A **plain** has a generally level surface with little change in slope and has a low elevation. Plains usually have horizontal rock structure unless they are remnants of old mountain areas that have been leveled by erosion and weathering.

SOIL ASSOCIATIONS.   Soils differ in composition, particle size, structure, permeability, porosity, fertility, and degree of horizon development. Soils of similar characteristics are grouped together as a **soil association,** which is similar to a formation in rocks. The boundaries of different associations in an area are often indicated on maps.

LANDSCAPE REGIONS

Landscape characteristics (amount of slope, elevation, bedrock structure, stream drainage patterns, and soil characteristics) appear to occur in combinations that form identifiable areas called **landscape regions** or physiographic provinces. For example, the combination of high elevation, steep slopes, thin soils, and trellis, annular, and radial stream patterns is common in mountain landscape regions (see Figure 14-6).

CONTINENTAL LANDSCAPE REGIONS.   Any continental land mass has several landscape regions that can be identified. The general landscape regions of the continental United States are shown in Figure 14-2. These types of landscape regions, as well as others, are found in many parts of the earth. You should carefully study the New York State landscape regions on the inside back cover of this book and in the *Earth Science Reference Tables.*

LANDSCAPE BOUNDARIES.   The boundaries between landscape regions are usually well defined, or distinct, as illustrated on the maps of New York State listed above. Landscape boundaries usually consist of features or characteristics of the landscape that have been brought about by changes in the structure of rocks. Such features and characteristics include the edges of mountains, cliffs, changes in type or amount of slope, or river courses that follow the direction of structural changes.

FACTORS OF LANDSCAPE DEVELOPMENT

The process of landscape development is very complex and involves many factors that may or may not be operating at a particular time and

Figure 14-2. Major landscape regions of the continental United States.

place. Therefore, generalizations about landscape development may not apply in any one specific area.

UPLIFTING AND LEVELING FORCES.   There are two groups of forces that operate to form and change landscapes—the *uplifting* (or constructional) forces and the *leveling* (or destructional) forces.

Uplifting forces originate beneath or within the earth's crust and displace rock material to raise the land, build mountains, and cause continental growth. The uplifting forces include volcanic action, isostasy, earthquakes, and many plate tectonic events.

Most **leveling forces** operate on the earth's surface. They break down the rocks of land masses and transport material along the earth's surface from higher to lower elevations under the force of gravity, thus tending to level out the land. The leveling forces include weathering, erosion, deposition, and subsidence.

Leveling forces (such as erosion or weathering) are always at work in all areas of the earth's solid surface, but uplifting may or may not be present at the same time. When both groups or forces are present, the landscape will be uplifted or leveled, depending on which forces are dominant (operating at a faster rate).

If uplifting is dominant, level land of low elevation may be changed into mountains with steep hillslopes and high elevations, stream drainage patterns may be altered as the streams begin to erode new landscapes, and wind patterns may change as the mountains act as barriers to the wind. Uplifting forces are usually dominant in plate boundary regions of earthquakes and volcanic action, where mountain building is going on. The landscape reflects the effects of those forces.

In areas where the leveling forces are acting alone or are dominant, elevation is decreasing and the land is becoming flatter or smoother in slope. Weathering and erosion are destroying the rocks faster than uplift (if any) is occurring. Deposition by running water, wind, and glaciers contributes to the leveling and also forms depositional features on the landscape.

TIME AND LANDSCAPE STAGES. The condition of a landscape at any one time is partly the result of the length of time the uplifting and leveling processes have acted on the rocks. Often an area experiences a time when uplifting is dominant, followed by a long time when leveling forces are dominant. When this happens, an area's landscape goes through **stages of development,** with each stage having characteristic conditions.

Figure 14-3 is a model of the stages of landscape development in a mountainous region in a humid climate. In stage A (youth), the uplifting forces are dominant. Uplifting gives the leveling forces such as streams and possibly glaciers a large amount of potential energy, and the rate of

Youth. Uplifting forces are dominant, causing folding and faulting, and forming mountains with high elevations and steep slopes.

Maturity. Leveling forces are dominant, creating a rugged landscape with lower elevations.

Old age. Leveling forces are still dominant, but less effective because low elevations and gentle slopes provide little potential energy.

Rejuvenation. Uplifting forces are again dominant. As elevations increase, streams acquire more potential energy and form new valleys and steeper slopes.

Figure 14-3. Stages of landscape development.

leveling is great. As the uplifting forces decrease in effect, the destructional forces carve away the land, creating a rugged landscape of lower elevation characteristic of stage B (maturity). If the leveling forces continue to be dominant for millions of years, the landscape will become progressively smoother in slope and lower in elevation. When the former mountain region is smooth enough to resemble a plain, it is considered to be in stage C (old age). In stage C the leveling forces are usually less active than in earlier stages because of flat slopes and low elevation, so that streams have small potential energy and small gradient.

DYNAMIC EQUILIBRIUM IN LANDSCAPES. Although landscape development is a continuous process leading to gradual change in the landscape, at any one time the landscape condition reflects a state of balance among many environmental factors. This is a condition of **dynamic equilibrium.** If a change occurs in any of the factors, a change in the landscape features will occur until a new equilibrium is established (Stage D in Figure 14-3).

FACTORS OF
LANDSCAPE DEVELOPMENT—CLIMATE

The rate of development and the characteristics of the landscape of an area are greatly influenced by the temperature and moisture conditions of the area. Any change in an area's climate will alter the rate of development and characteristics of the landscape. On the other hand, changes in landscape sometimes cause changes in climate. For example, the growth of a new mountain range will block air mass movement and change moisture and temperature patterns, thereby changing the climate of affected areas. In turn, more landscape changes will occur in response to the climatic change. The effect of mountain ranges on climate, called the *orographic effect*, is described in Topic VIII, pages 117-118.

HILLSLOPES IN ARID AND HUMID CLIMATES. The steepness of hillslopes is partly affected by the balance between production of sediments by weathering and the removal of these sediments by erosion. In

Figure 14-4. Landscape development of a plateau as affected by climate. The rock formations are assumed to be similar in both diagrams. **A** illustrates the steep slopes characteristic of an arid climate. **B** illustrates the smoother, more rounded landscape features of a humid climate, such as the Catskills of New York State.

arid climates there is little vegetation to hold sediments in place on slopes, or as deposits at the base of slopes, so wind and running water can rapidly carry the sediments away. This rapid removal of sediments causes many arid regions to be characterized by the steep slopes and sharp landscape features common in the southwestern United States. Arid regions are also characterized by sand dunes and by bedrock sculptured by wind-blown sand.

In humid climates, sediments on and at the bottom of hillslopes are better held in place by vegetation; therefore, areas with humid climates are characterized by the smoother and more rounded landscape features common in the eastern United States. The greater rate of chemical weathering of bedrock in humid climates contributes to their more rounded landscapes.

GLACIATION AND LANDSCAPES.   In climates where glaciers exist or existed in recent times (such as during the Pleistocene—see the *Geologic History of New York State at a Glance* in the *Earth Science Reference Tables*), the landscape will show much evidence of glacial erosion and deposition. Some of the landscape features of glaciation are (1) mountaintops and steep slopes without much soil, (2) transported soil covering large areas, (3) soil with a wide range of particle sizes even at the surface, (4) wide valleys with U-shaped profiles (as compared with a stream's V-shaped profile), (5) many lakes, (6) disrupted stream drainage patterns, (7) many small hills composed of sediment, (8) polished and scratched bedrock, and (9) the features of the glaciers themselves where the glaciers still exist.

STREAMS AND CLIMATE.   Some of the characteristics of streams are controlled by climate. In arid regions, most streams, being temporary, are without water for much of the time; streams in humid regions are permanent, having discharge most or all of the time.

Internal drainage is common in arid regions. Internal drainage occurs when water is channeled into basins that are not connected by streams to the oceans. Examples of such basins include the Great Salt Lake and others in Death Valley, California. Internal drainage is characteristic of arid regions because the streams have not had the time to carve interconnecting valleys for drainage to the oceans.

SOILS AND CLIMATE.   One of the most important factors in determining soil characteristics is climate. Soils in arid regions are often thin or nonexistent, because there is little or no vegetation to make and hold the soil. The soil that does exist is often very sandy, because smaller sediments have been blown away. Arid soils often contain many mineral salts that are not found in the soil of humid regions, where infiltration and runoff dissolve and carry the salts away. In humid regions, the soils tend to be thicker and more acidic; they are also higher in organic content and thus darker in color. If the climate is very hot and humid, the soil will be infertile because chemical weathering and infiltration rapidly remove organic and mineral nutrients, leaving the soil deficient in these components.

FACTORS OF
LANDSCAPE DEVELOPMENT—BEDROCK

The composition and structural features of the bedrock are major factors in the rate of development and the characteristics of landscapes.

Homogeneous nonsedimentary bedrock. The landscape consists of a random distribution of rounded hills.

Horizontal sedimentary bedrock (plateau). The landscape has generally uniform elevation, with steep-sided valleys cut by streams.

Folded strata of varying resistance. The landscape consists of roughly parallel ridges, with steep-sided escarpments of resistant rock.

Domed structure. Landscape features resemble **C**, but ridges and escarpments have a generally circular arrangement.

Fault block mountains. The landscape features consist of ridges of varying elevation, with steep slopes along the fault plantes.

Complex bedrock structure. The landscape consists of a great variety of elevations and slopes.

Figure 14-5. Effect of bedrock structure on landscape features.

ROCK RESISTANCE AND HILLSLOPES.   In any one climate, different rock types and formations have varying degrees of **rock resistance,** or resistance to weathering and erosion. If all the rocks in an area exposed to the surface have about the same resistance, the landscape features will be controlled by structural features, such as faults and joints, and the agents of leveling and uplift (E and F in Figure 14-5 on page 209). If there are no special structural features, the landscape features will be random in location and without rapid changes in hillslopes (A in Figure 14-5).

If rocks exposed at the surface have different degrees of resistance, the different rocks will weather and erode at different rates. For example, in sedimentary strata, sandstone layers will generally be more resistant than shale and will weather and erode more slowly. The result will be marked differences in slope between the layers of different resistance, often with a steep slope called an **escarpment** along the eroded edge of the more resistant layer (B, C, and D in Figure 14-5).

Figure 14-6. Effect of bedrock structure on stream drainage patterns. Under each sketch of the landscape there is a corresponding contour map showing the stream drainage.

Random or dendritic drainage. This pattern is characteristic of horizontal sedimentary rocks with little difference in rock resistance.

Trellis or block drainage. This is observed in folded rocks with much difference in resistance, and also in faulted or jointed rock.

STRUCTURAL FEATURES AND HILLSLOPES. Often the types of **rock structure,** such as horizontality, folds, faults, and joints, have a major effect on hillslopes. A study of the diagrams in Figure 14-5 will show the influence of horizontal rocks, folded rocks, and faulted rocks. Generally, the greater the variety of structural features found in an area, the more varied the changes in hillslope and types of landscape features (F in Figure 14-5).

STREAMS AND BEDROCK CHARACTERISTICS. The direction, pattern, and gradient of streams are often directly related to the resistance and structure of underlying bedrock. In horizontal rocks with little difference in resistance, the streams will develop a random pattern and have few rapid changes in gradient, as shown in A of Figure 14-6. When the rocks in an area have varying degrees of resistance, or there are tilted, folded, faulted, or jointed rocks, the patterns and directions of the streams will be at least partly if not totally controlled by these rock features, as shown in B, C, and D. In such cases there is often sharp change in gradient, as indicated by falls and rapids.

Radial drainage. This pattern occurs in an area of domed structure with little difference in rock resistance.

Annular drainage. This pattern of concentric circles is found in areas of domed structure with much difference in rock resistance.

SOILS AND ROCK COMPOSITION.   The different compositions of the soil associations are due in part to differences in the underlying bedrock or in transported material from which the soil formed. A soil formed from a sedimentary rock such as sandstone will be much different in composition from a soil formed from an igneous rock such as basalt, because of major differences in the mineral and chemical composition of the rocks. A soil association map and a geologic map (see *Generalized Bedrock Geology of New York State* in the *Earth Science Reference Tables*) will often show a close correlation between soil and rock type.

PEOPLE AND ENVIRONMENTAL CHANGE

People have greatly affected their environment, including the landscape. They have cut down forests and plowed up the land, allowing soil to be carried away or *denuded;* they have carved up or smoothed out the land for mining and construction of roads, buildings, and airports; they have polluted the land with their discards; they have added chemicals to the land, air, and water which aid weathering, and they have even made new land by filling in lakes and parts of the ocean with their garbage. Thus people are a major factor in landscape development.

LANDSCAPE POLLUTION AND POPULATION.   Figure 14-7 is a graph showing that the human population has been increasing at a rapid or exponential rate in recent times. Landscape pollution is generally greatest in areas of high population density. This is so because it is there that people erode and deposit material in concentrations large enough to adversely affect their lives and the life forms and landscape.

Modern people can cause rapid changes in their environment because of **technology**—the application of scientific discoveries to the methods of producing goods and services. Catastrophic events may occur as the environment reacts to the changes caused by technology. The effects of atomic bombs, deforestation of thousands of acres a year, the plowing-up of thousands of acres of grassland a year, the use of millions of tons of pesticides a year, and similar changes cause rapid responses in wildlife, soil and stream characteristics, and rates of landscape evolution. Many of these changes have resulted in the extinction of wildlife and the loss of useful landscapes.

ATMOSPHERIC POLLUTION AND LANDSCAPE CHANGE.   The addition of liquid and solid aerosols to the atmosphere by people can increase reflection and scattering of insolation. This may result in less energy at the surface of the earth for natural landscape-producing processes such as weathering. On the other hand, the addition of carbon dioxide and water vapor to the atmosphere can increase the greenhouse effect and thus cause an increase of energy at the earth's surface for landscape change. Many industrial and community activities add substances to the atmosphere that cause areas to have greater amounts of cloud coverage than would naturally occur. Increased cloud coverage affects precipitation and temperatures and thereby can alter the type and rate of landscape development. The addition of sulfur compounds to the atmosphere, largely by burning fossil fuels and mineral refining,

Figure 14-7. Estimated human population of the world in recent centuries (projected to the year 2000).

has significantly increased the acid content of precipitation. This acid precipitation (acid rain) has increased the chemical weathering of rocks, regolith, and vegetation, resulting in changed landscapes.

ENVIRONMENTAL CONSERVATION.   Resources, such as soil for agriculture, land for homesites, pure water for consumption and recreation, and clean air for biologic activity, can be conserved by careful planning and by the control of environmental pollutants.

Some of the goals of environmental planning are elimination of landscape pollution and a net elimination of *denudation*. **Denudation** is the loss or removal of regolith (soil and sediments) and life forms, such as trees, due to leveling forces. Often denudation is due to or accelerated by human activities. Another goal is the reclaiming of landscapes that have been made unusable by misuse.

For successful programs in conservation of the environment, there must be education to make people aware of the problems and to change attitudes that lead to misuse of the environment. Finally, people must *act* to stop further misuse and to repair former destruction.

VOCABULARY	
landscape	leveling forces
stream drainage pattern	stages of landscape development
mountain	dynamic equilibrium in landscape
plateau	rock resistance
plain	escarpment
soil association	rock structure
landscape region	technology
uplifting forces	denudation

QUESTIONS ON TOPIC XIV—LANDSCAPE DEVELOPMENT AND ENVIRONMENTAL CHANGE

Questions in Recent Regents Exams (end of book)

June 1991:   8, 48, 49, 51, 81, 96–100
June 1992:   38, 49, 50, 53, 54, 81, 83, 84, 105
June 1993:   1, 30, 39, 46–48, 51, 99
June 1994:   47, 51–54, 91, 93

Questions from Earlier Regents Exams

1. Which New York State landscape region is best represented by the block diagram below?   (1) Allegheny Plateau   (2) Adirondack Mountains   (3) Atlantic Coastal Plain   (4) Erie-Ontario Lowlands

2. Although the Adirondacks are classified as a mountain landscape, the Catskills are classified as a plateau landscape because of a major difference in their   (1) amounts of rainfall   (2) bedrock structure   (3) index fossils   (4) glacial deposits

3. Characteristics such as composition, porosity, permeability, and particle size are used to describe different types of   (1) hillslopes   (2) stream drainage patterns   (3) soils   (4) landscapes

4. The major landscape regions of the United States are identified chiefly on the basis of   (1) similar surface characteristics   (2) similar climatic conditions   (3) nearness to major mountain regions   (4) nearness to continental boundaries

5. According to the *Earth Science Reference Tables*, the location 44° N latitude and 74°30′ W longitude is found in which New York State landscape region?   (1) Hudson-Mohawk Lowlands   (2) St. Lawrence Lowlands   (3) Adirondack Mountains   (4) the Catskills

6. The primary reason that several landscape regions have formed in New York State is that the various regions of the State have different   (1) climates   (2) latitudes   (3) soil characteristics   (4) bedrock characteristics

7. According to the *Earth Science Reference Tables*, which New York State landscape region has the lowest elevation, the most nearly level land surface, and is composed primarily of Cretaceous through Pleistocene unconsolidated sediments?   (1) the Hudson-Mohawk Lowlands

(2) the Atlantic Coastal Plain   (3) the Champlain Lowlands   (4) the Erie-Ontario Lowlands

8. Boundaries between landscape regions in New York State are best described as being   (1) straight lines running north and south   (2) invisible on the surface   (3) usually well defined   (4) generally unchanging

9. The boundaries between landscape regions are usually indicated by sharp changes in   (1) bedrock structure and elevation   (2) weathering rate and method of deposition   (3) soil associations and geologic age   (4) stream discharge rate and direction of flow

10. Landscape regions in which leveling forces are dominant over uplifting forces are often characterized by   (1) volcanoes   (2) mountain building   (3) low elevations and gentle slopes   (4) high elevations and steep slopes

11. When most landscape regions are uplifted, the amount of weathering and erosion that occurs will generally   (1) decrease   (2) increase   (3) remain the same

12. Which change would be occurring in a landscape region where uplifting forces are dominant over leveling forces?   (1) topographic features that are becoming smoother with time   (2) a state of dynamic equilibrium existing with time   (3) streams that are decreasing in velocity with time   (4) hillslopes that are increasing in steepness with time

13. Which cross-sectional diagram below best represents a landscape region that resulted from faulting?

(1)   (3)

(2)   (4)

14. Which characteristics of a landscape region would provide the best information about the stage of development of the landscape?   (1) the age and fossil content of the bedrock   (2) the type of hillslopes and the stream patterns   (3) the amount of precipitation and the potential evapotranspiration   (4) the type of vegetation and the vegetation's growth rate

15. The three diagrams below represent the same location at different times. What is the best explanation for the differences in appearance of this location?

(1) This region was exposed to leveling forces for different lengths of time.   (2) This region has different underlying bedrock structures. (3) This region developed in different climate regions.   (4) This region has the same type of underlying rock layers.

16. Which factor is most important in determining the evolution of a landscape?   (1) surface topography   (2) plant cover   (3) climate (4) development of drainage

17. A landscape is characterized by much transported soil, scratched rock surfaces, and wide U-shaped valleys. The development of this landscape is probably the result of   (1) stream action   (2) wind erosion   (3) uplifting   (4) glaciation

18. Which diagram best represents a cross section of a valley which was glaciated and then eroded by a stream?

(1)   (2)   (3)   (4)

19. In the cross section of the hill shown below, which rock units are probably most resistant to weathering?

(1) I and II   (2) II and III   (3) I and III   (4) II and IV

20. How was the valley shown in the diagram below most likely formed?

(1) by the deposition of sediments   (2) by the extrusion of igneous material   (3) by the faulting of rock layers   (4) by the folding of rock layers

21. Which of the following stream patterns is most characteristic of horizontal rock structure?

Base your answers to questions 22 and 23 on the diagram below of a section of the earth's crust.

22. Which kind of stream pattern would most likely be found on the type of landscape shown in the diagram?

(1)   (2)   (3)   (4)

23. According to the surface landscape development indicated in the diagram, which rock type or types are most resistant to weathering and erosion in this environment?   (1) rock *E*   (2) rock *H*   (3) rocks *C* and *F*   (4) rocks *D* and *G*

24. The diagram below shows a New York State highway road cut.

The water well has probably gone dry because   (1) crustal uplift has altered the landscape   (2) human activities have altered the landscape   (3) the climate has become more humid   (4) the bedrock porosity has changed

25. Humans can cause rapid changes in the environment, which may produce catastrophic events. Which statement below is the best example of this concept?   (1) Mountainside highway construction causes a landslide.   (2) Lightning causes a forest fire.   (3) Shifting crustal plates cause an earthquake.   (4) Changing seasonal winds cause flooding in an area.

26. Which graph best represents human population growth?

27. As population increases, the amount of alteration of the landscape by human activity will most likely   (1) decrease   (2) increase   (3) remain the same

28. The addition of pollutants to the atmosphere may change the rate of energy absorption and radiation. This could result in   (1) a renewal of volcanic activity   (2) the formation of a new fault zone   (3) a landscape-modifying climate change   (4) a change in the times of high and low tides

Additional Questions

1. Models of hillslopes and landform shapes can be made with the use of   (1) isobars   (2) contour lines   (3) isotherms   (4) parallels

2. The different types of soil found at the earth's surface are classified as   (1) soil profiles   (2) soil horizons   (3) soil associations   (4) soil formations

3. If a landscape is in dynamic equilibrium and uplift occurs, (1) there can never again be dynamic equilibrium in the area   (2) the dynamic equilibrium will remain the same   (3) a new dynamic equilibrium will be established   (4) a new landscape will form without dynamic equilibrium

4. If a new mountain range were to form where the Mississippi River is today, the landscape east of this new mountain range would become more angular and less rounded because the climate would become   (1) drier and warmer   (2) drier and cooler   (3) moister and warmer   (4) moister and cooler

5. Which of the following would *not* explain why soils are different in separate locations?   (1) different climates   (2) different compositions of the rocks the soils formed from   (3) different amounts of time for soil formation   (4) different ages of the rocks the soil formed from

Refer to the diagram below to answer questions 6 through 11.

6. The climate of this area is most likely   (1) arid   (2) humid (3) hot   (4) cold

7. The cliffs around location *A* are most directly the result of (1) igneous intrusion   (2) resistant rock layers   (3) the different ages of the rock   (4) movement along faults

8. What can be said about rock layer *B* compared to rock layer *F*? (1) *B* is younger   (2) *B* is more resistant   (3) *B* is less resistant   (4) *B* is lower because of its environment of deposition

9. How would you classify the geologic forces producing the landscapes at locations *C* and *G*? (1) At both places uplifting forces are dominant.   (2) At both places leveling forces are dominant.   (3) At *C* uplifting is dominant, and at *G* leveling is dominant.   (4) At *C* leveling is dominant, and at *G* uplifting is dominant.

10. What immediate effects would increased rainfall have on the rate of leveling of this landscape?   (1) increase   (2) decrease (3) remain the same

11. The primary reason for the cliff at *D* is   (1) volcanic action (2) resistant rock layers   (3) movement along a fault   (4) joints in the rock layers

12. What is the most practical way to control pollution?   (1) slowing down the rate of technological growth   (2) decreasing the population   (3) careful planning of environmental usage   (4) more government control of industry

13. The most practical way individuals can help fight pollution is by (1) becoming aware of the problems and thus changing their attitudes and actions   (2) recycling paper   (3) using fewer products produced by technology   (4) changing their life-styles to conform to that of nineteenth-century rural America

Glossary

absolute age: The actual age of an object (rock) or geologic event in years. Often determined by radioactive dating methods. See **relative age.**

absolute humidity: The actual amount (weight) of water vapor in a given volume of air. Directly related to vapor pressure.

absolute zero: Theoretically, the lowest possible temperature. No heat energy can be extracted from matter at this temperature.

absorption: The interception or taking in of electromagnetic energy by a material. When electromagnetic energy is absorbed by a material it is usually changed into other forms of energy, often heat, which causes a temperature rise.

actual evapotranspiration *(E$_a$):* In reference to the water budget, the total amount of water lost through evaporation and transpiration from an area in a given period of time. Usually expressed as a depth (mm of water).

adiabatic temperature change: A change in temperature that occurs without heat being added or removed. The cooling of air as it rises and expands and the warming of air as it descends are adiabatic temperature changes.

aerobic bacteria: Bacteria that require the presence of free oxygen to carry on their life functions.

aerosol: Small solid or liquid particles suspended in a gas. Suspended solid or liquid water particles are the aerosols in fog and clouds.

air mass: A large body of air in the lower atmosphere (troposphere) with approximately uniform air temperature, pressure, and moisture at any given level.

air pressure: See **atmospheric pressure.**

altitude: (1) The vertical distance (elevation) between a point and sea level. (2) The angle of a celestial object above the horizon. Usually expressed in degrees; often measured with a sextant.

anaerobic bacteria: Bacteria that do not require the presence of free oxygen to carry on their life functions. They are associated with polluted water.

angle of insolation: The angle at which the sun's rays hit the earth's surface. The higher the sun is in the sky, the higher the angle of insolation.

anticyclone: A high-pressure mass of air within the troposphere in which air moves out from the center. They rotate clockwise in the Northern Hemisphere and counterclockwise in the Southern Hemisphere. Anticyclone Also called *HIGHS.*

aphelion: The point in a planet's orbit when it is farthest from the sun. For the earth, aphelion occurs about July 4th, when it is about 152,000,000 kilometers from the sun.

apparent diameter: The diameter a celestial object (such as the sun or a planet) appears to have, depending on its distance from an observer; not the actual diameter. It is usually expressed in angular units. The closer a celestial object is to the earth, the larger its apparent diameter.

apparent solar day: A day of varying length determined by the time it takes for the sun to arrive at its highest point in the sky on two consecutive days at the same location. It is always slightly longer than the time it takes for one complete rotation of the earth. Can be measured by a sundial. See also **mean solar day.**

apparent solar time: Time based on the apparent solar day. Also called *local* or *sundial time.*

arc: A curved line that is part of a circle. An arc is the shape of the path of most celestial objects, such as the sun, in their daily paths through the earth's sky.

arid climate: A dry climate where the precipitation (P) is less than the potential evapotranspiration (E_p) for a large part of the year. Thus there is a deficit (D) of moisture and a drought much of the time.

astronomical unit: The mean distance of the earth from the sun—about 150,000,000 kilometers. Commonly used as a unit of distance in astronomy.

atmosphere: The shell of gases surrounding the earth. It is divided into layers according to differences in chemical and physical properties.

atmospheric pressure: The weight of the overlying atmosphere pushing down on a given unit of area. It is affected by changes in temperature, moisture, and altitude. Also called *air pressure* or *barometric pressure.*

atmospheric variables: The changeable conditions in the atmosphere that cause weather. The variables include temperature, air pressure, wind, and moisture.

axis: An imaginary line through the earth from the north to the south geographic poles, about which the earth rotates.

banding: The layered arrangement of mineral crystals in some metamorphic rocks due to the alignment and separation of like minerals.

barometric pressure: See **atmospheric pressure.**

bedrock: The solid and largely unweathered portion of the crust and lithosphere in an area that is underneath the soil and other loose material. Also called the *local rock.*

benchmark: A permanent marker, usually metal, at a specific location, that indicates an exact elevation or altitude at the time of installation.

calorie: A unit of heat energy defined as the quantity of heat needed to raise the temperature of 1 gram of water 1°C.

capillarity: The process by which water is drawn into pores due to molecular attraction.

capillary migration: The upward movement of water, against gravity, in part of the soil, regolith, or bedrock due to capillarity. Also called *capillary action.*

capillary water: The water held in pores in the soil and rocks in the zone of aeration as a result of the process of capillarity.

carbon-14: A radioactive isotope of carbon with a short half-life (5700 years). Used only to date recent (up to 50,000-year-old) remains of organic material.

celestial object: Any object outside the earth's atmosphere, including moons, comets, planets, stars, and galaxies.

cementation: The process by which solid sediments are "glued" together by precipitated minerals, forming a sedimentary rock.

change: The observation or inference that the characteristics of a portion of the environment have altered.

change in soil storage (ΔSt): In reference to the water budget, the amount of water added to or taken from an area's soil storage. A positive change in soil storage is called *recharge,* and a negative change is called *usage.*

chemical weathering: The process whereby chemicals, such as oxygen and water, alter rocks and other earth materials, resulting in new minerals (chemicals). Rusting is a common example.

classification: The grouping together of objects and/or events with similar observed properties to make them more meaningful for study.

clay: See **colloids.**

climate: The total view or concept of an area's weather over a long period of time. It includes not only averages but also extremes.

cloud: A mass of suspended liquid water droplets and/or ice crystals in the atmosphere.

cold front: A weather front in which the colder air mass is pushing the warmer air mass. Cold fronts are characterized by a steep slope, rapid changes in weather, and often thunderstorms.

colloids: Very small solid particles (less than 0.0004 cm in diameter) that remain suspended in water for long periods of time. They make muddy water muddy. Also called **clay.**

compression: The process by which deposited sediment is pressed down by overlying sediments, water, and/or earth movements, resulting in the formation of sedimentary or metamorphic rocks. Also called *compaction.*

compression waves: In earthquakes, the waves that cause particles through which the waves travel to vibrate in the direction the waves are moving. Compression waves are the fastest-moving of earthquake waves. Also called *primary,* or *P, waves.*

condensation: The change in phase from a gas to a liquid, such as when water vapor changes to liquid water droplets as clouds form.

condensation surface: A solid surface required for the condensation of water. Aerosols, such as dust, salt crystals, and ice, act as condensation surfaces in the formation of clouds. In dew and frost formation, the condensation surfaces are the earth's surface features.

conduction: The transfer of heat energy from atom to atom, in any state of matter, through contact when atoms collide. Conduction of energy occurs most readily in solids, especially metals.

conservation of energy: The concept that energy is neither created nor destroyed, but remains the same in total amount in a closed system.

constituent unit: Those parts that make up a material, such as the minerals or sediments in a rock or the crystal structure of a mineral.

contact metamorphic zone: A special type of *transition zone* between rock types caused by the baking or altering of older bedrock by contact with molten rock (lava or magma). Changes older rock into nonsedimentary metamorphic rock.

continental climate: The climate of inland areas not moderated by a large body of water; characterized by hot summers and cold winters, and thus having a wide annual temperature range.

continental crust: The part of the earth's crust (upper lithosphere) that makes up the continental blocks. Compared to oceanic crust, it is thicker, lower in density, and granitic rather than basaltic in composition.

continental drift: The concept that the continents have been and are presently shifting their position on the earth's surface; really due to plate tectonics.

continental polar air mass (cP): Very common cold and dry air masses that invade the contiguous United States from Canada.

continental tropical air mass (cT): Relatively rare hot and dry air masses that form in the southwestern United States or Mexico, that may affect weather of the contiguous United States in the summer.

contour line: An isoline on contour, or topographic, maps that represents points of equal elevation on the earth's surface.

contour map: A model of the elevation field of the earth's surface using contour lines and other symbols. Also called a *topographic map.*

convection: The transfer of heat energy by circulatory movements in a fluid (liquid or gas) that results from differences in density within the fluid.

convection current: A circulatory motion in a fluid due to convection. Also called *convection cell.*

convergence: (1) the coming together of air currents at the earth's surface and at the top of the troposphere. (2) The direct collision of tectonic plates in the **plate tectonic theory.**

coordinate system: A grid or system of lines for determining the location of a point on a surface.

core: The innermost region of the earth, thought to be composed of iron and nickel. The outer part of the core is thought to be liquid and the inner part solid.

Coriolis effect: The deflection of all moving particles of matter at the earth's surface, which provides evidence for the earth's rotation; the deflection is to the right in the Northern Hemisphere and to the left in the Southern Hemisphere.

correlation: In geology, the process of showing that rocks or geologic events in different places are the same in relative or absolute age.

crust: The outermost portion of the earth's solid lithosphere. It is separated from the uppermost mantle by the Moho interface.

crystal: (1) The individual mineral constituent units of rocks. (2) A solid with a definite internal structure because its constituent atoms are arranged in a characteristic, regular, repeating pattern.

crystalline: A term used to describe a rock that is composed of intergrown mineral crystals.

crystallization: A type of solidification in which molten rock (magma or lava) cools to form nonsedimentary igneous rocks composed of minerals that have a definite arrangement of their atoms. Also see **solidification.**

cyclic change: Orderly changes in the environment in which the events constantly repeat themselves with reference to time and space.

cyclone: A low-pressure portion of the troposphere that has air moving toward its center. Cyclones in the Northern Hemisphere rotate counterclockwise and in the Southern Hemisphere they rotate clockwise. Types of cyclones include hurricanes, tornadoes, and mid-latitude cyclones. Also called a *LOW.*

daily motion: The apparent east-to-west movement of celestial objects in the sky at 15 degrees per hour actually caused by the earth's west-to-east rotation. Daily motion causes the sun, stars, etc. to appear to move in circular or arc-shaped paths in the sky.

deficit (D): The condition in the local water budget when actual evapotranspiration (E_a) does not equal potential evapotranspiration (E_p) because there is not enough water from precipitation (P) and soil storage (St). A long period of deficit is a drought.

density: The ratio of the mass of an object to its volume. $\text{density} = \dfrac{\text{mass}}{\text{volume}}$

denudation: The stripping off and removal (erosion) of the plants, soil, and regolith at the earth's surface. Denudation is often caused or increased by the careless activities of human beings.

deposition: The process by which sediments are released, dropped, or settled from erosional systems; it includes the precipitation of dissolved minerals from water in the formation of chemical sedimentary rocks. Also called *sedimentation.*

desert: A region with an arid climate where the average yearly precipitation (P) is much smaller than potential evapotranspiration (E_p).

dew point: The temperature at which the air is saturated with moisture and the relative humidity is 100%. At temperatures below the dew point, condensation of water vapor occurs.

direct rays: Rays of sunlight that strike the earth at an angle of 90°. Also called *vertical rays* or *perpendicular insolation.*

distorted structure: The curving and folding of the banded layers in nonsedimentary metamorphic rocks due to heat and compression.

divergence: (1) The spreading out of air from rising or falling currents of air in the troposphere. (2) The type of plate movement in which lithospheric plates move away or spread from each other, according to the **plate tectonic theory.**

duration of insolation: The length of time insolation is received at a location in a day, or how long the sun is in the sky in a day.

dynamic equilibrium: A condition of changing balance between opposing processes, such as evaporation and condensation or erosion and deposition.

earthquake: A natural, rapid shaking of the crust or lithosphere of the earth caused by the displacement of rocks; most often associated with fault movement, but also associated with other causes, such as volcanic eruptions.

eccentricity: The degree of ovalness of an ellipse, or how far an ellipse is from being a circle. Eccentricity is computed using the formula

$$\text{eccentricity} = \frac{\text{distance between foci}}{\text{length of the major axis}}$$

electromagnetic energy: Energy that is emitted (radiated) in the form of transverse waves, into any part of the universe. Electromagnetic energy radiates from all objects not at a temperature of absolute zero. Examples include visible light, radio waves, and infrared energy.

electromagnetic spectrum: A model, such as a chart, that shows the full range of the types of electromagnetic energy, usually in order of wavelength.

ellipse: A closed curve around two fixed points, called foci, in which the sum of the distances between any point on the curve and the foci is a constant. All planetary orbits, including the earth's, are elliptical in shape.

energy: The ability to do work.

environmental equilibrium: The balance that exists among the natural parts of the environment even though all parts of the environment are constantly changing.

epicenter: The place on the earth's surface lying directly above the point at which an earthquake originates (the focus).

equator: The parallel on earth midway between the geographic north and south poles with a latitude of 0 degrees.

equinox: A time when the sun is directly overhead at noon at the equator, and there are 12 hours of daylight and 12 hours of darkness over the whole earth. The spring (vernal) equinox is about March 21st, and the fall (autumnal) equinox is about September 23rd.

erosion: The carrying away of soil and pieces of rock by wind, water, ice, etc. Erosion is the process by which sediments are obtained and transported. Erosion also refers to the wearing away and lowering of the earth's surface.

error: The amount of deviation or incorrectness in a measurement. See also **percent error.**

escarpment: A steep slope or cliff in layered (stratified) rocks. Formed from certain rock layers that are resistant to weathering and erosion.

evaporation: The change in phase from liquid to a gas, such as liquid water into water vapor (steam). Also called *vaporization.*

evaporite: A type of sedimentary rock formed directly by precipitation of dissolved minerals from water. Evaporites, which include rock salt and gypsum, are composed of intergrown mineral crystals.

evapotranspiration: The combination of the processes of evaporation and transpiration.

event: The name used to describe the occurrence of a change in the environment.

extrusion: A body of nonsedimentary igneous rock formed by the cooling and solidification of liquid rock (lava) at the earth's surface.

extrusive igneous rock: Igneous rocks, such as basalt and rhyolite, that form through the cooling and solidification of liquid rock (lava) at the earth's surface.

fault: A crack in a mass of rock with displacement, or movement, of rock along the crack.

field: Any region of space that has some measurable value of a given quantity at every point, such as the earth's magnetic field.

focus (plural **foci**): (1) In an ellipse, either of two fixed points located so that the sum of their distances to any point on the ellipse is a constant. The sun is at one of the two foci of the orbit of each of the planets. (2) The place where an earthquake actually originates.

folded strata: The bends in layered rock due to movement in the lithosphere; a type of deformed strata.

formation: See **rock formation.**

fossil: Any evidence of former life, either direct or indirect.

Foucault pendulum: A freely swinging pendulum whose path appears to change in a predictable way, thus providing evidence for the earth's rotation.

frames of reference: Properties or characteristics by which something can be described, studied, or compared. Time and space are frames of reference for studying change.

frictional drag: Friction at the interface of the atmosphere and the earth's surface caused by wind, air-mass movement, the Coriolis effect, etc. Heat produced by frictional drag minimally heats the atmosphere.

front: The interface between two air masses of different characteristics.

geocentric model: An early concept of celestial objects and their motions in which all celestial objects revolved around the earth, which was stationary and was the center of the universe.

geographic poles: The North and South poles of the earth, with a latitude of 90 degrees. The geographic poles are located at opposite ends of the earth's axis of rotation.

geologic time scale: A chronological model of the geologic history of the earth using divisions called eons, eras, periods, and epochs. See the *Earth Science Reference Tables* for details.

geosyncline: A large, shallow ocean basin near continental margins that slowly subsides under large quantities of sediment. It is thought that geosynclines are eventually uplifted, forming mountains and continental areas.

graded bedding: A layering of sediment or sedimentary rock that shows a gradual change in particle size, with the largest particles on the bottom and the smallest ones on top.

gradient: The rate of change from place to place within a field. Also called *slope*.

$$\text{gradient} = \frac{\textbf{amount of change in the field}}{\textbf{distance through which change occurs}}$$

gravitation: The attractive force that exists between any two objects in the universe. It is proportional to the product of the masses of the objects and inversely proportional to the square of the distance between their centers.

$$\text{force} \propto \frac{\textbf{mass}_1 \times \textbf{mass}_2}{\textbf{(distance between their centers)}^2}$$

gravity: The force that pulls objects toward the center of the earth.

greenhouse effect: A process that warms the atmosphere and reduces heat loss by terrestrial radiation from the earth's surface. It results from the fact that the atmosphere transmits the short-wave radiation received from the sun, but absorbs and is heated by the long-wave radiation from the earth's surface.

ground water: The portion of the subsurface water found beneath the water table; the water in the zone of saturation. Also see **subsurface water.**

half-life: The time required for one half of the atoms in a given mass of a radioactive isotope to decay, or change, to a different isotope.

heat energy: Energy that is transferred from one body to another as a result of a difference in temperature between the two bodies; also called *thermal energy.*

heliocentric model: The modern concept of celestial objects and their motions, in which the rotating earth and other planets revolve around the sun.

HIGH: See **anticyclone.**

horizontal sorting: The sorting of particles of sediments into layers in which particle size and density decrease in one horizontal direction—the direction toward which the erosional system was moving.

humid climate: A moist or wet climate where precipitation (P) equals or is greater than potential evapotranspiration (E_p) on a yearly average.

hydrosphere: The liquid water that rests on much of the earth's surface. The oceans constitute most of the hydrosphere.

igneous rock: A nonsedimentary rock formed by the cooling and solidification of molten material (lava or magma) above or below the earth's surface.

index fossil: A fossil used in correlation and relative dating of rocks. A species used as an index fossil generally lived for only a short time and was distributed over a large geographic area.

inference: An interpretation (conclusion, theory, or explanation) of observation(s).

infiltration: The seeping and entering of liquid water from the earth's surface into the ground (bedrock and soil), where the water becomes subsurface water.

inner core: The innermost zone of the earth's core, which is thought to be composed of iron and nickel in a solid state.

insolation (INcoming SOLar radiATION): The part of the sun's radiation that is received by the earth.

instrument: A device made by people, that aids or extends the human senses beyond their normal limits in order to obtain more accurate observations.

intensity of insolation: The relative strength energy of the sun's radiations intersecting a specific area of the earth in a specific amount of time, such as calories per square meter per minute. The higher the angle of insolation the greater the intensity of insolation and the sun's heating effect.

interface: The boundary zone between regions with different properties. Energy is usually exchanged across an interface.

intrusion: A mass of nonsedimentary igneous rock formed by the cooling and solidification of liquid rock (magma) below the earth's surface.

intrusive igneous rock: An igneous rock, such as granite or gabbro, that forms by the cooling and solidification of liquid rock beneath the earth's surface.

isobar: An isoline used on weather and climatic maps to connect points of equal air pressure.

isoline: A line used on a model of a field, such as a map, which connects points of equal value of a field quantity. Examples of isolines are isotherms, isobars, and contour lines.

isostasy: A principle that states that the earth's crust is in a state of equilibrium and that any change in the mass of one part of the crust will be offset by a change in mass of another part to maintain the equilibrium. Isostasy is often used to explain why the continental crust floats higher than the denser oceanic crust and why mountains and other continental areas rise as they are eroded.

iso-surface: A surface in a model of a three-dimensional field in which all points on the surface have the same field value.

isotherm: An isoline used on weather and climatic maps to connect points of equal air temperature.

isotope: One of the varieties of an element. The various isotopes of an element all have the same atomic number and chemical properties. However, they differ in their atomic masses and physical properties. For example, carbon-12 and carbon-14 are isotopes of carbon.

joint: A crack in rocks along which there has been no relative movement or displacement, such as there is in a fault.

kinetic energy: The energy of movement of a mass or object. The greater the velocity or speed of an object, the greater the kinetic energy.

landscape: The characteristics of the earth's surface at the interface between the atmosphere and the hydrosphere and lithosphere. Also called *topography*.

landscape region: A portion of the earth's surface with landscape characteristics that distinguish it from other areas. Some of the distinguishing characteristics are rock structure, elevation, degree of slope, and stream patterns. Also called a *physiographic region*.

latent heat: Energy absorbed or released by a substance during a change of phase. This transfer of energy occurs without a change in temperature.

latitude: Angular distance north or south of the equator; usually expressed in degrees. Minimum latitude is at the equator (0°), and maximum is at the geographic poles (90°N or 90°S).

latitudinal climatic patterns: East-west belts, or zones, of climate types on the earth caused by latitudinal changes in climatic factors, such as temperature, moisture, winds, and ocean currents.

leveling forces: Forces that operate constantly at or near the earth's surface and that break down rocks, transport material from higher to lower elevations, and tend to level off and lower the land. Leveling forces include weathering, erosion, denudation, deposition, and subsidence. Also called *destructional forces*.

lithosphere: The outer, solid, rocky part of the earth as distinguished from the hydrosphere and atmosphere. The crust is the part of the lithosphere above the mantle.

local noon: Noon, determined by when the sun is at its highest position on a given day at a specific location; it is also called *sundial noon* or *apparent solar noon*.

local water budget: See **water budget.**

longitude: Angular distance east or west of the prime meridian; usually expressed in degrees. Minimum longitude (0°) is at the prime meridian, which runs through Greenwich, England, and maximum longitude is 180°E or W. The International Date Line, which runs through the Pacific Ocean, follows the 180° meridian along most of its length.

LOW: See **anticyclone.**

mantle: Solid intermediate zone between the earth's crust and the outer part of the core.

marine climate: A coastal climate moderated by the effects of a large body of water (ocean, lake, etc.). Such areas have warmer winters and colder summers than areas of similar latitude not near a large body of water, thus they have a small annual temperature range.

maritime polar air mass (mP): Cool and humid air masses that invade the contiguous United States from the oceans to the northeast and the northwest.

maritime tropical air mass (mT): A very common warm and humid air mass that invades the contiguous United States from the oceans to the south, east, and west.

mass: The quantity of matter in an object. Unlike weight, mass is not affected by location.

mean solar day: The 24-hour day established for convenience in time-keeping; it was derived by averaging the apparent solar days in a year.

measurement: An observational process of obtaining more precise or accurate dimensions of properties of objects and events by making comparison with some standard of reference, often using instruments. An example would be using a ruler.

meridian: North-south trending lines on maps or globes of the earth that have constant longitude.

metamorphic rock: A nonsedimentary rock formed without melting from other rocks (igneous, sedimentary, or other metamorphic rocks) within the lithosphere in response to heat, pressure, or chemical action. Metamorphic rocks are often associated with mountain-building processes.

mid-ocean ridge: Huge chain of largely underwater mountain ranges in the oceans; associated with lithospheric plate divergence, ocean-floor spreading, earthquakes, and volcanoes.

mineral: A naturally occurring, crystalline, inorganic solid with physical and chemical properties that vary within certain specified limits.

model: Any way of representing (illustrating) the properties of an object, event, or system. Models include graphs, drawings, charts, mental pictures, numerical data, or scaled physical objects.

Moho: Short for *Mohorovicic discontinuity*. The interface, or boundary zone, between the crust and the mantle.

moisture: Water vapor in the atmosphere or subsurface water.

moisture capacity: See **absolute humidity.**

monomineralic: A rock composed of just one mineral, such as gypsum or halite.

mountain: A landscape characterized by relatively high elevations, many changes in slope, and steep slopes. Internally, mountains are characterized by distorted rock structures, such as faults, folds, and tilted rocks. Often composed of much nonsedimentary rock. Old mountains may be low in elevation and have little slope.

nonsedimentary rock: Rocks that do not form directly from sediments. Igneous and metamorphic rocks are nonsedimentary rocks.

North Star: See **Polaris.**

oblate spheroid: A sphere that is slightly flattened at the top and bottom (the polar regions) and slightly bulging at the middle (the equatorial region); the shape of the earth.

observation: An interaction of one of the human senses, with or without the aid of instruments, to an aspect of the environment; a reaction that is not an inference.

occluded front: Formed when an advancing cold weather front pushes into a warm front, causing the warm air mass to be lifted off the earth's surface, forming mid-latitude cyclones (LOWs).

ocean-floor spreading: The principle that the oceanic crust spreads outward (plate divergence) at mid-ocean ridges. Also called *sea-floor spreading*.

oceanic crust: The portion of the earth's crust that is usually below the oceans and not associated with the continental blocks. Oceanic crust is thinner and higher in density than continental crust and is basaltic rather than granitic in composition.

orbit: The path of an object revolving around another object, such as the path of the earth around the sun.

orbital speed: The speed of an orbiting body along its orbit at a given time. Also called *orbital velocity*.

organic: Refers to an earth material that is composed of and/or was formed by life forms. *Inorganic* means "not organic."

organic evolution: The theory that new species of organisms arise by gradual transitional changes from existing species.

original horizontality: A principle that states that sedimentary rocks and some extrusive igneous rocks are originally formed in horizontal layers. There are exceptions to this principle, but most sedimentary rock not found in horizontal layers is thought to have been deformed after formation by crustal change.

orographic effects: The effects that mountains have on climate.

outcrop: Exposed bedrock without a cover of soil or regolith.

outer core: The zone of the earth between the mantle and the inner core. It is thought to be a liquid because shear waves from an earthquake do not go through it. It is believed to be composed of iron and nickel.

parallel: East-west trending lines on maps and globes that have constant latitude.

percent error or **percent deviation:** The numerical amount, expressed as a percent, that a measurement differs from a given, standard, or accepted value.

perihelion: The point in a planet's orbit when it is closest to the sun. Perihelion for the earth occurs about January 3, when it is about 147,000,000 kilometers from the sun.

period: (1) The amount of time it takes a planet to make one orbit, or revolution, around the sun. This amount of time is called the *year* for that planet. (2) In geology, a part of the geologic time scale smaller than an era.

permeability: The degree to which a porous material (such as rock or soil) will allow fluids, such as water, to pass through it.

permeability rate: The speed at which fluids, like water, can pass through a porous material. The speed at which water moves from above to below the earth's surface, becoming subsurface water, is a special type called *infiltration rate*.

perpendicular insolation: See **direct rays.**

phase: (1) One of the three main forms of matter—liquid, solid, or gas. Also called *state*. (2) The varying amount of the lighted portion of the moon, Venus, or Mercury visible from the earth.

phase change: The change of a substance from one phase, or state, to another.

physical weathering: The mechanical or physical alteration of rock and other earth materials at or near the earth's surface into smaller fragments (sediments) without a change in the mineral or chemical composition of the materials. Frost action is the most common type.

plain: A landscape of low elevation and gentle slopes; usually characterized by horizontal rock structure, unless it is a remnant of an old mountain region.

planetary wind belts: East-west zones on the earth where the wind blows from one direction much of the time. An example is the prevailing southwest winds that blow over much of the United States.

plateau: A landscape of relatively high elevation with generally undistorted horizontal sedimentary rocks or extrusive igneous lava flows.

plate tectonic theory: A theory stating that the earth's lithosphere is divided into about 20 sections called plates. The plates can move up and down or sideways on a plastic part of the upper mantle called the asthenosphere. Plates diverging, converging, and sliding by each other result in many of the earth's physical features and events, including continent and mountain formation, volcanoes, and earthquakes; includes the concepts of continental drift and ocean-floor spreading.

Polaris: The star that is almost directly over the geographic North Pole of the earth. Also called the *North Star*.

pollutants: Substances or forms of energy that pollute the environment; they include solids, liquids, gases, life forms, heat, sound, and nuclear radiation.

pollution: The occurrence in the environment of a substance or form of energy in concentrations large enough to have an adverse effect on people, their property, or plant and animal life.

polymineralic: Refers to rocks that contain more than one mineral.

porosity: Amount of open space (pores) in rocks or soils compared to total volume.

potential energy: The energy possessed by an object as a result of its position or location, chemical conditions, or phase of matter.

potential evapotranspiration (E_p): The amount of water that would be lost from an area through evaporation and transpiration over a given time if the water were available. Potential evapotranspiration is determined by the amount of heat energy available and the amount of surface area for evapotranspiration.

precipitation: (1) The falling of liquid or solid water from clouds toward the earth's surface. (2) A type of deposition in which dissolved substances come out of solution to form solids, as in formation of chemical sedimentary rocks.

present weather: The conditions or state of atmosphere for a short period of time at a location determined by comparison with a standard list produced by the U.S. Weather Service. A partial abbreviated list is found on the sample station model on page 95.

pressure gradient: The amount of difference in air pressure over a specific distance; the greater the pressure gradient, the greater the speed of the wind.

primary waves: See **compression waves.**

probability: The odds of some environmental change, such as rain or an earthquake, taking place.

P-waves: See **compression waves.**

radiation: (1) The emission or giving off of energy in the form of electromagnetic energy. (2) The method by which electromagnetic energy moves from place to place by way of transverse waves.

radiative balance: A condition in which an object gives off as much energy as it receives. Under such conditions its average temperature remains the same.

radioactive dating: The use of radioactive isotopes to determine the absolute age of rocks of geologic events.

radioactive decay: The natural spontaneous breakdown of the nucleus of unstable atoms into more stable atoms of the same or other elements. The process releases energy, continues at a constant rate for any particular radioactive isotope, and is not affected by changes in temperature, pressure, or other environmental conditions. Also called **radioactivity.**

recharge ($+ \Delta St$): In reference to the water budget, the addition of water to the soil storage by infiltration. Recharge can occur only if the soil is not saturated and if precipitation (P) is greater than potential evapotranspiration (E_p).

recrystallization: A process in the formation of many metamorphic rocks by which some mineral crystals grow in size at the expense of other crystals or sediments without true melting.

reflection: A change in direction of waves when the waves strike the surface of a material, in which the waves leave the surface at the same angle at which they arrived.

refraction: A change in direction and velocity of waves when they pass from one medium into another with a different density.

regolith: All the unconsolidated material at the earth's surface, including the soil.

relative age: The age of rocks or geologic events as compared to other rocks or events with no reference to a specific year or absolute date.

relative humidity: The ratio of the actual amount of water vapor in the air to the maximum amount of water vapor the air can hold. It is often expressed as a percent. Relative humidity can be calculated by the following formula:

relative humidity (%) =

$$\frac{\textbf{specific humidity}}{\textbf{maximum specific humidity (capacity)}} \times \textbf{100}$$

residual sediment: Weathered material that has remained in its place of origin.

residual soil: Soil formed from rocks and/or regolith under the soil; soil that has not been transported from its place of origin.

reversal of earth's magnetic polarity: The fact that the earth's magnetic field and poles switch polarity (north for south and south for north) in intervals of thousands of years but in no known cycle.

revolution: Movement of one body about another in a path called an *orbit*.

rock: Any naturally formed solid that is part of the earth's lithosphere. Most rocks are composed of one or more minerals; a few rocks, such as coal, volcanic glass, and coral, are not composed of minerals at all.

rock cycle: A model of the interrelationships of the different rock types, the materials they form from, and the processes that produce them.

rock formation: The basic unit of geologic mapping, consisting of a body of rocks with similar features.

rock-forming mineral: Any one of a small number of minerals (20–30) that are commonly found in rocks; most of them are silicates.

rock resistance: The ability of a body of rock to withstand erosion and weathering.

rock structure: The features of rock that can be observed in an outcrop. Structural features include folds, faults, joints, and tilting and thickness of strata.

rotation: The spinning of an object on its own axis, like a top.

runoff: All natural flowing of water at the earth's surface, including stream flow.

saturation: The condition of being filled to capacity. When the atmosphere contains all the water vapor it can hold, it is filled to saturation and the relative humidity is 100%.

saturation vapor pressure: The vapor pressure of a parcel of air when it is filled or saturated with water vapor; the vapor pressure when relative humidity is 100%.

scalar field: A field that can be totally described in terms of magnitude (amount) alone. Temperature and relative humidity are scalar fields.

scattering: The refraction and/or reflection of waves in various directions.

seasons: The divisions of the year with characteristic weather conditions.

secondary wave: The type of earthquake wave that causes particles through which it travels to vibrate at right angles to the direction of the wave motion. Secondary waves will travel only through solids, not through liquids or gases. Also called *shear waves* or *S-waves*.

sediment: Particles or materials formed by the weathering or erosion of rocks or organic materials; particles or materials transported by erosional systems.

sedimentary rock: The rocks that form directly from sediments by processes of cementation, precipitation of minerals, dewatering, and compression.

seismic waves: The energy waves generated by an earthquake, including primary and secondary waves. Also called *earthquake waves*.

seismograph: An instrument used to record seismic waves.

senses: The five abilities or faculties—sight, touch, hearing, taste, and smell—by which one observes.

shear waves: See **secondary waves.**

silicon-oxygen tetrahedron: The most common constituent unit of minerals. This four-sided pyramid unit contains four atoms of oxygen and one atom of silicon.

sink: In an energy system, a region that has a lower energy concentration than its surroundings. Energy flows toward a sink.

soil: The part of the regolith that will support rooted plants. Soil is produced by weathering and the action of bacteria, plants, and animals.

soil association: A basic mapping unit or unit of soil classification composed of soils with similar characteristics, such as composition, structure, porosity, permeability, and fertility.

soil horizon: A vertical layer of soil with certain characteristics such as the high organic content of the top soil horizon. The combination of all the horizons in an area is called the area's *soil profile*.

soil storage (St): In terms of the water budget, the amount of liquid water stored in the soil.

solar noon: See **local noon.**

solar system: Our star, the sun, and the portion of the universe occupied by the objects that revolve around the sun, including planets, comets, and asteroids.

solidification: The processes by which a liquid changes phase to a solid, such as when molten rock (lava and magma) changes into igneous rocks. In the case of the igneous rock volcanic glass, there are no minerals, thus no orderly arrangement of atoms, because the lava solidified so rapidly. Most igneous rocks are produced by a type of solidification called crystallization. Also see **crystallization.**

solstices: The two times of the year when the vertical rays of the sun fall the farthest from the equator. At the summer solstice (about June 21st) the vertical rays fall on 23½° north latitude and the duration and angle of insolation are greatest for most of the Northern Hemisphere and least in the Southern Hemisphere. At the winter solstice (about December 21st) the vertical rays fall on 23½° south latitude and the duration and angle of insolation are greatest for most of the Southern Hemisphere and least in the Northern Hemisphere.

sorted particles: See **sorting of sediments.**

sorting of sediments: The degree of similarity of size in the particles in a mass of sediments or sedimentary rocks. The greater the degree of similarity of particles the more **sorted** the sediments; the greater the difference in the size of particles the more **unsorted** the material.

source: In an energy system, a region that has a higher energy concentration than its surroundings. Energy flows from the source.

source region: The area of the earth's surface over which an air mass forms and acquires its characteristics.

species: The basic unit in the classification of life forms. All members of the same species are similar in body features, environment, and life habits. Our species is *sapien.*

specific heat: The amount of heat, in calories, needed to raise the temperature of 1 gram of a substance 1 degree C; or the degree of difficulty a material offers to heating up or cooling off. Liquid water has the highest specific heat (1 cal/g/degree C) of all common substances.

stages of landscape development: The stages (including Youth, Maturity, Old Age, and Rejuvenation) in the evolution of a landscape feature or region. The stage is characterized by certain features, including the types of dominant forces, the amount of slope, elevation, and the amount of change in slope.

stationary front: A weather condition in which the boundary between two air masses remains in the same position without moving.

strata: The layers, or beds, of sedimentary rock; *stratum* is the singular form.

stream bed: The bottom, or floor, of a stream.

stream discharge: The volume of water passing a certain spot in a stream in a given amount of time.

stream drainage pattern: An aerial view of the stream courses in an area. The patterns are determined by the shape of the landscape, rock structure, and rock resistance.

structure: See **rock structure.**

sublimation: The phase change from a gas directly to a solid or from gas to a solid with no intermediate liquid phase. Frost forms by sublimation.

subsidence: The sinking or depression of a part of the earth's surface.

subsurface water: All water found in the soil, regolith, and bedrock beneath the earth's surface. Also see **ground water.**

sundial: An ancient time-keeping device that uses the position of the sun to determine apparent solar, local, or sundial time.

superposition: A principle applied in the relative dating of layered sedimentary and some extrusive igneous rocks. It states that the youngest rock layer is found on top and that rock age increases with depth. There are many instances where this theory does not apply, such as in deformed rocks, and where there are igneous intrusions.

surplus (S): In terms of the water budget, liquid water that is not removed from the surface by infiltration or evapotranspiration and thus becomes runoff. There is always a surplus when the soil is saturated (maximum St) and when precipitation (P) is greater than potential evapotranspiration (E_p).

S-waves: See **secondary waves.**

technology: The application of scientific discoveries to the methods of producing goods and services; the means by which a society provides objects required for human subsistence and comfort.

temperature: A measure of the average kinetic energy of the particles of a body of matter. Heat energy always flows from a higher temperature to a lower temperature.

terrestrial: (1) Relating to the earth as compared to any other part of the universe. (2) Relating to land or continental environments as compared to air or water environments.

terrestrial motions: The motions of the whole earth, including rotation and revolution about the sun.

terrestrial radiation: The electromagnetic energy given off by the earth's surface; it is mostly long wavelength infrared energy.

texture: Size, shape, and arrangement of mineral crystals or sediments in a rock.

thermal energy: See **heat energy.**

tilted strata: A type of deformed rock in which the strata, or layers, have been forced out of a horizontal position, usually by crustal movement.

topographic maps: See **contour maps.**

topography: See **landscape.**

track: The path of movement of an air mass and/or front. Tracks are often predictable, which helps in weather forecasting.

transformation of energy: The changing of energy from one form to another.

transition zone: An area where a mass of rock changes from one class (sedimentary, metamorphic, or igneous) to another. In many cases in a transition zone it is impossible to determine which class a particular segment belongs to. Also see **contact metamorphic zone.**

transpiration: A process by which plants release water vapor into the atmosphere as part of their life functions.

transported sediment: Weathered or eroded rock and organic materials that have been moved by an erosional system from their place of origin.

transported soil: Soil that has been moved from its place of original formation. Examples would be glacial soils common in the northern United States and the alluvial soils found around rivers and deltas.

transporting system: A system that accomplishes erosion. It includes an agent of erosion, a driving force, and the material that is transported.

transverse wave: A wave that vibrates at right angles to its direction of motion. Examples are electromagnetic radiations and secondary earthquake waves.

ultraviolet radiation: A form of electromagnetic energy of shorter wavelength than visible light. Most of the ultraviolet energy insolation is absorbed by gases of the atmosphere, such as ozone, before reaching the earth's surface.

unconformity: A break, or gap, in the rock record caused by the burial of an erosion surface by newer rocks or sediments. The rocks below an unconformity are older than those above it, unless there has been overturning of strata.

uniformitarianism: A principle stating that the geologic processes taking place today also took place in the past, and that we can interpret past events by studying present geologic processes. Uniformitarianism does not mean that geologic processes always occur at the same rate. Also, it does allow for the possibility that there were processes that occurred in the past (such as the earth's formation) that are not happening today.

unsorted particles: See **sorting of sediments.**

uplifting forces: Forces that originate beneath or within the earth's crust that raise the land, build mountains, and cause continental growth. The uplifting forces include volcanic action, isostasy, earthquakes, continental drift, ocean-floor spreading, and plate tectonics. Also called *constructional forces.*

uranium-238: A radioactive isotope of uranium that decays to lead-206 with a half-life of 4.5 million years. Because of its long half-life, U-238 is useful for dating very old rocks.

usage ($-\Delta St$): In terms of the water budget, the loss of water from soil storage by evapotranspiration. Usage occurs when potential evapotranspiration (E_p) is greater than precipitation (P) and soil storage (St) is greater than zero.

vaporization: See **evaporation.**

vapor pressure: The pressure exerted by water vapor in a given volume of air. It is a measure of the amount of water vapor in the atmosphere and is directly related to the absolute humidity of the atmosphere.

vector field: A field that must be described in terms of both magnitude and direction. Gravitational, magnetic, and wind fields are examples of vector fields.

vein: A sheetlike mineral deposit formed from a solution that has filled a crack or permeable zone in previously formed rocks; thus a vein is younger than the rocks into which it intrudes.

vertical rays: See **direct rays.**

visibility: The farthest distance that one can see a prominent object at the horizon with the naked eye. Fog, air pollution, and precipitation are common causes of low visibility.

volcanic ash: Small pieces of extrusive igneous rock shot into the air during a volcanic eruption. Volcanic ash is very important in geologic dating because all the ash from one eruption will be about the same age, no matter what type of rock it is found associated with; thus it is a time marker useful in correlation.

volume: The amount of space an object occupies.

walking the outcrop: A method of correlation done by actually following the continuity of the individual layers of formations in outcrops of bedrock. Generally, this is useful only for short distances, except in arid regions where a large expanse of bedrock may be uncovered.

warm front: A weather front in which a warmer air mass is pushing a colder air mass. Warm fronts are characterized by a gentle slope and long periods of precipitation.

water budget: A numerical model of an area's water supply. Often shown on a monthly basis using the average figures from date gathered over many years.

water cycle: A model, often in diagram form, used to illustrate the movement and phase changes of water at and near the earth's surface.

water table: The interface between the zone of saturation and the zone of aeration; the top of the zone below which the regolith and/or bedrock is saturated with liquid water.

water vapor: Water in the form of a gas.

wavelength: The distance between a point on a wave and the corresponding point on the next wave, such as the distance between two successive peaks in an electromagnetic wave.

weather: The condition of the atmospheric variables, such as temperature, pressure, wind, and moisture, at a location for a relatively short period of time.

weathering: The chemical and physical alterations of rock and other earth materials at or near the earth's surface. Weathering occurs through the action of water, chemical agents, and living things.

wind: The horizontal movement of air over the earth's surface.

year: The time it takes for a planet to make one revolution around the sun. The earth's year is 365¼ days. Also see **period.**

zone of aeration: The soil, regolith, or bedrock from the earth's surface down to the water table, where the pores are only partly filled with subsurface (capillary) water; air fills the rest of the pores.

zone of saturation: The portion of the earth near the earth's surface that is below the water table, where the pores in the soil, regolith, or bedrock are filled with subsurface water (ground water).

EARTH SCIENCE
REFERENCE TABLES

Generalized Landscape Regions of New York State

Surface Ocean Currents

→ WARM CURRENTS
⇢ COOL CURRENTS

Generalized Bedrock Geology of New York State

COMPILED BY

GEOLOGICAL SURVEY

NEW YORK STATE MUSEUM

1989

GEOLOGICAL PERIODS in NEW YORK

CRETACEOUS, TERTIARY, PLEISTOCENE (Epoch) unconsolidated gravels, sands, clays (not bedrock)

LATE TRIASSIC AND EARLY JURASSIC conglomerates, red sandstones, red shales, diabase

PENNSYLVANIAN and MISSISSIPPIAN conglomerates, sandstones, shales

DEVONIAN ⎫ limestones, shales, sandstones, conglomerates
SILURIAN ⎬ *Silurian also contains salt, gypsum and hematite.*

ORDOVICIAN ⎫ limestones, shales, sandstones, dolostones
CAMBRIAN ⎬

CAMBRIAN and EARLY ORDOVICIAN sandstones, dolostones
Moderately to intensely metamorphosed east of the Hudson River.

CAMBRIAN & ORDOVICIAN (undifferentiated) quartzites, dolostones, marbles, schists
Intensely metamorphosed; includes portions of the Taconic Sequence and Cortlandt Complex.

TACONIC SEQUENCE sandstones, shales, slates. *Slightly to intensely metamorphosed rocks of*
CAMBRIAN and EARLY ORDOVICIAN *ages.*

MIDDLE PROTEROZOIC gneisses, quartzites, marbles ⎫
Lines are generalized structure trends.   ⎬ Intensely Metamorphosed Rocks
MIDDLE PROTEROZOIC anorthositic rocks   ⎭ (regional metamorphism about 1,000

Dominantly
Sedimentary
Origin

Dominantly
Metamorphosed
Rocks

m.y.a.)

Tectonic Plates

Scheme for Igneous Rock Identification

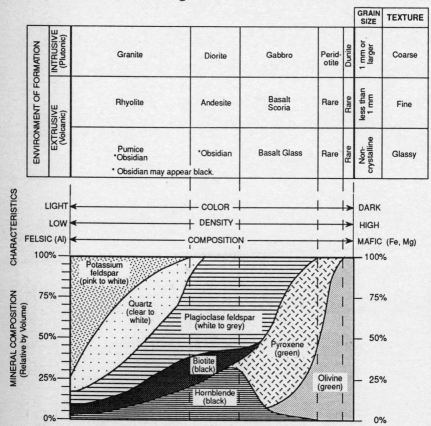

							GRAIN SIZE	TEXTURE
	INTRUSIVE (Plutonic)	Granite	Diorite	Gabbro	Perid-otite	Dunite	1 mm or larger	Coarse
ENVIRONMENT OF FORMATION	EXTRUSIVE (Volcanic)	Rhyolite	Andesite	Basalt Scoria	Rare	Rare	less than 1 mm	Fine
		Pumice *Obsidian	*Obsidian	Basalt Glass	Rare	Rare	Non-crystalline	Glassy

* Obsidian may appear black.

CHARACTERISTICS

LIGHT ← COLOR → DARK
LOW ← DENSITY → HIGH
FELSIC (Al) ← COMPOSITION → MAFIC (Fe, Mg)

MINERAL COMPOSITION (Relative by Volume)

100% — Potassium feldspar (pink to white) — 100%
75% — Quartz (clear to white) / Plagioclase feldspar (white to grey) — 75%
50% — Pyroxene (green) — 50%
Biotite (black)
25% — Hornblende (black) / Olivine (green) — 25%
0% — 0%

Note: The intrusive rocks can also occur as exceptionally coarse-grained rock, Pegmatite.

Scheme for Sedimentary Rock Identification

INORGANIC LAND-DERIVED SEDIMENTARY ROCKS

TEXTURE	GRAIN SIZE	COMPOSITION	COMMENTS	ROCK NAME	MAP SYMBOL
Clastic (fragmental)	Mixed, silt to boulders (larger than 0.001 cm)	Mostly quartz, feldspar, and clay minerals; May contain fragments of other rocks and minerals	Rounded fragments	Conglomerate	
			Angular fragments	Breccia	
	Sand (0.006 to 0.2 cm)		Fine to coarse	Sandstone	
	Silt (0.0004 to 0.006 cm)		Very fine grain	Siltstone	
	Clay (less than 0.0006 cm)		Compact; may split easily	Shale	

CHEMICALLY AND/OR ORGANICALLY FORMED SEDIMENTARY ROCKS

TEXTURE	GRAIN SIZE	COMPOSITION	COMMENTS	ROCK NAME	MAP SYMBOL
Nonclastic	Coarse to fine	Calcite		Chemical Limestone	
	Varied	Halite	Crystals from chemical precipitates and evaporites	Rock Salt	
	Varied	Gypsum		Rock Gypsum	
	Varied	Dolomite		Dolostone	
	Microscopic to coarse	Calcite	Cemented shells, shell fragments, and skeletal remains	Fossil Limestone	
	Varied	Carbon	Black and nonporous	Bituminous Coal	

Scheme for Metamorphic Rock Identification

TEXTURE	GRAIN SIZE	COMPOSITION	TYPE OF METAMORPHISM	COMMENTS	ROCK NAME	MAP SYMBOL
FOLIATED — Slaty	Fine	(CHLORITE, MICA, QUARTZ, FELDSPAR, AMPHIBOLE, GARNET, PYROXENE)	Regional	Low-grade metamorphism of shale	Slate	
FOLIATED — Schistose	Medium to coarse		Regional	Medium-grade metamorphism; Mica crystals visible from metamorphism of feldspars and clay minerals	Schist	
FOLIATED — Gneissic	Coarse		(Heat and pressure increase with depth, folding, and faulting)	High-grade metamorphism; Mica has changed to feldspar	Gneiss	
NONFOLIATED	Fine	Carbonaceous		Metamorphism of plant remains and bituminous coal	Anthracite Coal	
NONFOLIATED	Coarse	Depends on conglomerate composition		Pebbles may be distorted or stretched; Often breaks through pebbles	Meta-conglomerate	
NONFOLIATED	Fine to coarse	Quartz	Thermal (including contact) or Regional	Metamorphism of sandstone	Quartzite	
NONFOLIATED	Fine to coarse	Calcite, Dolomite		Metamorphism of limestone or dolostone	Marble	
NONFOLIATED	Fine	Quartz, Plagioclase	Contact	Metamorphism of various rocks by contact with magma or lava	Hornfels	

Inferred Properties of Earth's Interior

GEOLOGIC HISTORY OF NEW

YORK STATE AT A GLANCE

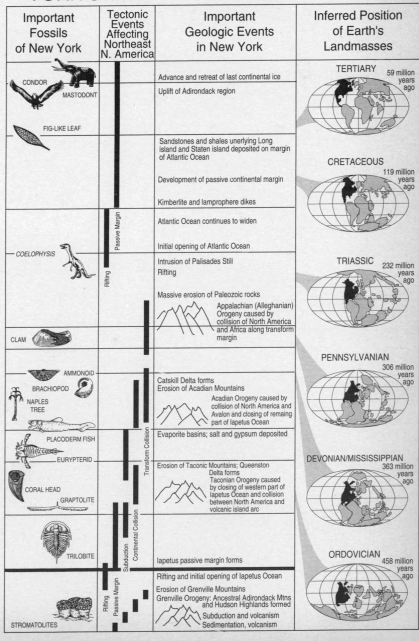

Important Fossils of New York	Tectonic Events Affecting Northeast N. America	Important Geologic Events in New York	Inferred Position of Earth's Landmasses
CONDOR MASTODONT FIG-LIKE LEAF		Advance and retreat of last continental ice	TERTIARY 59 million years ago
		Uplift of Adirondack region	
	Passive Margin	Sandstones and shales unerlying Long island and Staten island deposited on margin of Atlantic Ocean	CRETACEOUS 119 million years ago
		Development of passive continental margin	
		Kimberlite and lamprophere dikes	
COELOPHYSIS		Atlantic Ocean continues to widen	
		Initial opening of Atlantic Ocean	
	Rifting	Intrusion of Palisades Still Rifting	TRIASSIC 232 million years ago
		Massive erosion of Paleozoic rocks	
CLAM		Appalachian (Alleghanian) Orogeny caused by collision of North America and Africa along transform margin	
AMMONOID BRACHIOPOD NAPLES TREE	Transform Collision	Catskill Delta forms Erosion of Acadian Mountains	PENNSYLVANIAN 306 million years ago
PLACODERM FISH EURYPTERID		Acadian Orogeny caused by collision of North America and Avalon and closing of remaing part of Iapetus Ocean	
		Evaporite basins; salt and gypsum deposited	
CORAL HEAD GRAPTOLITE	Subduction Continental Collision	Erosion of Taconic Mountains; Queenston Delta forms Taconian Orogeny caused by closing of western part of Iapetus Ocean and collision between North America and volcanic island arc	DEVONIAN/MISSISSIPPIAN 363 million years ago
TRILOBITE		Iapetus passive margin forms	ORDOVICIAN 458 million years ago
	Rifting Passive Margin	Rifting and initial opening of Iapetus Ocean	
		Erosion of Grenville Mountains Grenville Orogeny: Ancestral Adirondack Mtns and Hudson Highlands formed	
STROMATOLITES		Subduction and volcanism Sedimentation, volcanism	

Earthquake P-wave and S-wave Travel Time

TRAVEL TIME (minutes)

EPICENTER DISTANCE (x10³ km)

Average Chemical Composition
of Earth's Crust, Hydrosphere, and Troposphere

ELEMENT (symbol)	CRUST		HYDROSPHERE	TROPOSPHERE
	Percent by Mass	Percent by Volume	Percent by Volume	Percent by Volume
Oxygen (O)	46.40	94.04	33	21
Silicon (Si)	28.15	0.88		
Aluminum (Al)	8.23	0.48		
Iron (Fe)	5.63	0.49		
Calcium (Ca)	4.15	1.18		
Sodium (Na)	2.36	1.11		
Magnesium (Mg)	2.33	0.33		
Potassium (K)	2.09	1.42		
Nitrogen (N)				78
Hydrogen (H)			66	

Electromagnetic Spectrum

Dewpoint Temperatures

Dry-Bulb Temperature (°C)	Difference Between Wet-Bulb and Dry-Bulb Temperatures (C°)														
	1	2	3	4	5	6	7	8	9	10	11	12	13	14	15
−20	−33														
−18	−28														
−16	−24														
−14	−21	−36													
−12	−18	−28													
−10	−14	−22													
−8	−12	−18	−29												
−6	−10	−14	−22												
−4	−7	−12	−17	−29											
−2	−5	−8	−13	−20											
0	−3	−6	−9	−15	−24										
2	−1	−3	−6	−11	−17										
4	1	−1	−4	−7	−11	−19									
6	4	1	−1	−4	−7	−13	−21								
8	6	3	1	−2	−5	−9	−14								
10	8	6	4	1	−2	−5	−9	−14	−28						
12	10	8	6	4	1	−2	−5	−9	−16						
14	12	11	9	6	4	1	−2	−5	−10	−17					
16	14	13	11	9	7	4	1	−1	−6	−10	−17				
18	16	15	13	11	9	7	4	2	−2	−5	−10	−19			
20	19	17	15	14	12	10	7	4	2	−2	−5	−10	−19		
22	21	19	17	16	14	12	10	8	5	3	−1	−5	−10	−19	
24	23	21	20	18	16	14	12	10	8	6	2	−1	−5	−10	−18
26	25	23	22	20	18	17	15	13	11	9	6	3	0	−4	−9
28	27	25	24	22	21	19	17	16	14	11	9	7	4	1	−3
30	29	27	26	24	23	21	19	18	16	14	12	10	8	5	1

Relative Humidity (%)

Dry-Bulb Temperature (°C)	Difference Between Wet-Bulb and Dry-Bulb Temperatures (C°)														
	1	2	3	4	5	6	7	8	9	10	11	12	13	14	15
-20	28														
-18	40														
-16	48	0													
-14	55	11													
-12	61	23													
-10	66	33	0												
-8	71	41	13												
-6	73	48	20	0											
-4	77	54	32	11											
-2	79	58	37	20	1										
0	81	63	45	28	11										
2	83	67	51	36	20	6									
4	85	70	56	42	27	14									
6	86	72	59	46	35	22	10								
8	87	74	62	51	39	28	17	6							
10	88	76	65	54	43	33	24	13	4						
12	88	78	67	57	48	38	28	19	10	2					
14	89	79	69	60	50	41	33	25	16	8	1				
16	90	80	71	62	54	45	37	29	21	14	7	1			
18	91	81	72	64	56	48	40	33	26	19	12	6	0		
20	91	82	74	66	58	51	44	36	30	23	17	11	5	0	
22	92	83	75	68	60	53	46	40	33	27	21	15	10	4	0
24	92	84	76	69	62	55	49	42	36	30	25	20	14	9	4
26	92	85	77	70	64	57	51	45	39	34	28	23	18	13	9
28	93	86	78	71	65	59	53	47	42	36	31	26	21	17	12
30	93	86	79	72	66	61	55	49	44	39	34	29	25	20	16

Weather Map Information

Lapse Rate

Temperature

Pressure

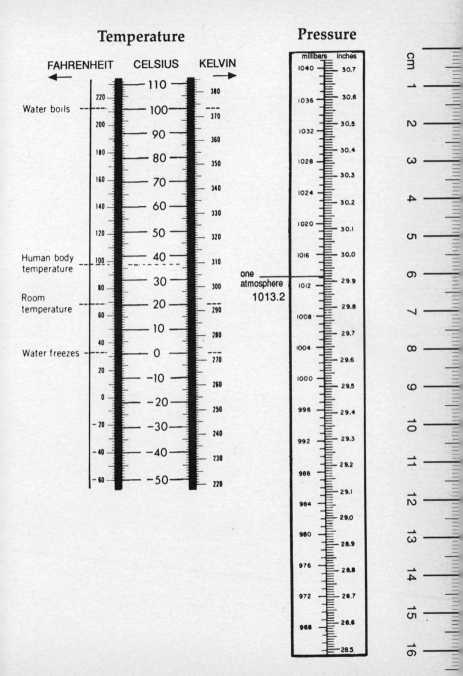

Solar System Data

Planet	Mean Distance from Sun (millions of km)	Period of Revolution	Period of Rotation	Eccentricity of Orbit	Equatorial Diameter (km)	Density (g/cm³)
MERCURY	57.9	88 days	59 days	0.206	4,880	5.4
VENUS	108.2	224.7 days	243 days	0.007	12,104	5.2
EARTH	149.6	365.26 days	23 hours 56 min 4 sec	0.017	12,756	5.5
MARS	227.9	687 days	24 hours 37 min 23 sec	0.093	6,787	3.9
JUPITER	778.3	11.86 years	9 hours 50 min 30 sec	0.048	142,800	1.3
SATURN	1,427	29.46 years	10 hours 14 min	0.056	120,000	0.7
URANUS	2,869	84.0 years	11 hours	0.047	51,800	1.2
NEPTUNE	4,496	164.8 years	16 hours	0.009	49,500	1.7
PLUTO	5,900	247.7 years	6 days 9 hours	0.250	2,300	2.0

Selected Properties of Earth's Atmosphere

Planetary Wind and Moisture Belts in the Troposphere

The drawing shows the locations of the belts near the time of an equinox. The locations shift somewhat with the changing latitude of the Sun's vertical ray. In the Northern Hemisphere the belts shift northward in summer and southward in winter.

Equations and Proportions

Equations

Percent deviation from accepted value	deviation (%) = $\dfrac{\text{difference from accepted value}}{\text{accepted value}} \times 100$
Eccentricity of an ellipse	eccentricity = $\dfrac{\text{distance between foci}}{\text{length of major axis}}$
Gradient	gradient = $\dfrac{\text{change in field value}}{\text{change in distance}}$
Rate of change	rate of change = $\dfrac{\text{change in field value}}{\text{change in time}}$
Circumference of a circle	$C = 2\pi r$
Eratosthenes' method to determine Earth's circumference	$\dfrac{\angle a}{360°} = \dfrac{s}{C}$
Volume of a rectangular solid	$V = \ell w h$
Density of a substance	$D = \dfrac{m}{V}$
Latent heat	$\left\{ \begin{array}{l} \text{solid} \longrightarrow \text{liquid} \quad Q = mH_f \\ \text{liquid} \longrightarrow \text{gas} \quad Q = mH_v \end{array} \right.$
Heat energy lost or gained	$Q = m\,\Delta T C_p$

Proportions

Kepler's harmonic law of planetary motion	(period of revolution)^2 ∝ (mean radius of orbit)^3
Universal law of gravitation	force ∝ $\dfrac{\text{mass}_1 \times \text{mass}_2}{(\text{distance between their centers})^2}$ $\left(F \propto \dfrac{m_1\,m_2}{d^2} \right)$

C_p = specific heat
C = circumference
d = distance
D = density
F = force
h = height
H_f = heat of fusion
H_v = heat of vaporization
$\angle a$ = shadow angle
ℓ = length
s = distance on surface
m = mass
Q = amount of heat
r = radius
ΔT = change in temperature
V = volume
w = width
Note: $\pi \approx 3.14$

EURYPTERID
New York State Fossil

Physical Constants

Properties of Water

Latent heat of fusion (H_f)	80 cal/g
Latent heat of vaporization (H_v)	540 cal/g
Density (D) at 3.98°C	1.00 g/mL

Radioactive Decay Data

RADIOACTIVE ISOTOPE	DISINTEGRATION	HALF-LIFE (years)
Carbon-14	$C^{14} \rightarrow N^{14}$	5.7×10^3
Potassium-40	$K^{40} \nearrow \begin{smallmatrix} Ar^{40} \\ Ca^{40} \end{smallmatrix}$	1.3×10^9
Uranium-238	$U^{238} \rightarrow Pb^{206}$	4.5×10^9
Rubidium-87	$Rb^{87} \rightarrow Sr^{87}$	4.9×10^{10}

Specific Heats of Common Materials

MATERIAL		SPECIFIC HEAT (C_p) (cal/g·C°)
Water	solid	0.5
	liquid	1.0
	gas	0.5
Dry air		0.24
Basalt		0.20
Granite		0.19
Iron		0.11
Copper		0.09
Lead		0.03

Astronomy Measurements

MEASUREMENT	EARTH	SUN	MOON
Mass (m)	5.98×10^{24} kg	1.99×10^{30} kg	7.35×10^{22} kg
Radius (r)	6.37×10^3 km	6.96×10^5 km	1.74×10^3 km
Average density (D)	5.52 g/cm³	1.42 g/cm³	3.34 g/cm³

Index

Absolute age (absolute dating), of rocks and geologic events, 183; methods of determining, 190–191

Absolute humidity, and air pressure, 83; and atmospheric moisture, 87–88

Absolute zero, 53

Absorption, of electromagnetic radiation, 53–54, 66–67; and temperature of atmosphere, 82

Abyssal areas, and deposition, 139

Actual evapotranspiration, and water budget, 111

Adiabatic temperature change, 83

Aeration, zone of, 107

Aerobic bacteria, and water pollution, 108–109

Aerosols, and insolation, 66

Age, of rocks and geologic events, 183–191

Air, see Atmosphere

Air masses, and weather, 91–93

Air pressure; see Atmospheric pressure

Altitude, of celestial object, 13; and air pressure, 83

Anaerobic bacteria, and water pollution, 109

Angle of insolation, defined, 66; and intensity, 67

Annular drainage patterns, 211 (Fig. 14-6D)

Anticyclones, and air masses, 92

Aphelion, defined, 38; and orbital speed, 39

Apparent diameter, defined, 30

Apparent motion, of celestial objects, 29, 30

Apparent solar day, defined, 40

Apparent solar time, 40

Arc, 29

Arid climates, defined, 113; and landscapes, 207–208

Ash, volcanic, 187

Astronomical Unit, defined, 40

Atmosphere, defined, 16; zones of, 16; and insolation, 65–66; and weather, 82–94; pollution of by people, 9, 212–213

Atmospheric pressure, and weather, 83–84

Atmospheric variables, 82

Atoms, and isotopes, 190

Axis, of earth, 74–75

Bacteria, and water pollution, 108–109

Balance, radiative, 72–73

Banding, in metamorphic rocks, 150

Barometric pressure, 83

Basaltic rocks, and oceanic crust, 167, 172–173

Bedding, graded, 139

Bedrock, and outcrops, 185; and landscape features, 209–212

Beds, and deposition, 139

Bench marks, and elevation, 162

Biologic processes, and rock formation, 147

Block drainage patterns, 210 (Fig. 14-6B)

Calorie, defined, 57

Capillarity, and infiltration, 108

Capillary migration, 108

Capillary water, 108

Carbon-14, and radioactive dating, 190, 191

Celestial objects, defined, 29

Cells, convection, 54

Cementation, and sedimentary rocks, 146

Change, environmental, 8–9

Chemical weathering, 127

Circulation, of atmosphere, 85

Classification, as a scientific process, 1

Clay, 129, 132, 138

Cleavage, of minerals, 154

Climate, 113–118; and weathering, 128; and landscape development, 207–208

Clouds, and insolation, 66; and atmospheric moisture, 91

Coal, as sedimentary rock, 147

Cold front, 93

Colloids, and sediment, 129, 132, 138

Color, of minerals, 154

Compounds, and composition of minerals, 154

Compression, and sedimentary rocks, 146

Compressional waves, and earthquakes, 170

Condensation, and temperature of atmosphere, 82; and dew point, 89, 91, 94

Condensation surfaces, and clouds, 91

Conduction, and transfer of energy, 54; and temperature of atmosphere, 82

Conservation, of energy, 55; of environmental resources, 213

Constituent units, of minerals, 154

Constructional forces, and landscape development, 205–207

Contact metamorphic zone, in rocks, 153

Continental climate, 115

Continental crust, 163, 165, 172–173

Continental drift, 165–166

Continental polar air mass, 92

Continental tropical air mass, 92

Continents, and climate, 115–116

Quick Review for Earth Science Regents Examination

This section provides a list of concepts and skills that have been tested most often on Earth Science regents exams. They are listed in order, from those tested most often to those tested least often. Where appropriate, the name of each concept or skill is followed by a list of the pages in this book where it is discussed. These page numbers are followed by the numbers of the corresponding questions at the end of the Topics. Finally, the related questions from recent regents exams are listed (copies of these exams are printed in the back of this book).

1. **Reading and interpreting isolines**
   Pages: 19, 20
   Questions: p. 22: 1, 6, 7, 10
   pp. 24–28: 23, 24
   1991: 8, 71–72
   1992: 13, 56–58, 60
   1993: 1, 52, 56–58, 60, 76, 77
   1994: 16, 56–60

2. **Using data from** *Geologic History of New York State at a Glance in* **the** *Earth Science Reference Tables*
   Pages: 165–166, 188
   Questions: pp. 174–182: 20
   pp. 194–202: 18, 20–26, 33, 48
   1991: 42, 44, 47
   1992: 45, 46, 52, 102
   1993: 41, 43, 44, 93, 94, 98
   1994: 48, 50, 99

3. **Using data from the** *Generalized Bedrock Geology of New York State* **map in the** *Earth Science Reference Tables*
   Questions: pp. 24–28: 18
   pp. 194–202: 1–3, 21, 22
   1991: 45, 49, 97, 99, 100
   1992: 46, 49, 54, 102, 105
   1993: 48, 99, 100
   1994: 50, 51, 91

4. **Using the** *Weather Map Information* **in the** *Earth Science Reference Tables*
   Pages: 92, 93, 95
   Questions: pp. 96–104: 51, 55–58, 60–67
   p. 105: 6–13
   1991: 18, 20
   1992: 18, 76–80
   1993: 77–79
   1994: 22, 66–68, 70

5. **Interpretations of data tables and diagrams**
   1991: none
   1992: 7, 26, 71, 72, 74
   1993: 8, 12, 53, 61, 71, 72, 86, 88, 89
   1994: 100

6. **Interpretation and extrapolation of graphs**
   Questions: pp. 96–104: 37–39
   pp. 119–125: 18–22
   1991: 53, 54, 76
   1992: 26, 67, 68, 74, 91, 95
   1993: 19, 73, 92, 94
   1994: 15, 100

7. **Using data from the** *Generalized Landscape Regions of New York State* **map in the** *Earth Science Reference Tables*
   Pages: inside back cover and two preceding pages
   Questions: pp. 214–219: 1, 5, 7
   1991: 49, 96, 97, 99, 100
   1992: 49, 54, 105
   1993: 48, 99
   1994: 51, 52

8. **Understanding how angle/intensity of insolation and duration of insolation change with the seasons on earth**
   Pages: 33–35, 67–71
   Questions: pp. 44–52: 17–22, 25
   pp. 75–81: 13–15, 17, 19–23, 25, 26, 28–30
   1991: 14, 63
   1992: 15, 61, 62, 65
   1993: 13
   1994: 63, 72–74

9. **Using data from the** *Earthquake P-wave and S-wave Travel Time* **graph in the** *Earth Science Reference Tables*
   Pages: 170–171
   Questions: pp. 174–182: 32, 34, 35, 38–42
   1991: 38
   1992: 86–90
   1993: 37, 38
   1994: 41

10. **Using data from the** *Scheme for Igneous Rock Identification* **in the** *Earth Science Reference Tables*
    Page: 149
    Questions: pp. 157–160: 8, 9, 12, 15
    1991: 101
    1992: 35, 85, 101
    1993: 103, 105
    1994: 88, 90

11. **Using the concept of superposition to determine the relative age of rock layers**
    Pages: 183–184
    Questions: pp. 194–202: 4–7, 12, 27
    1991: 86
    1992: 42, 52, 82
    1993: 45, 53, 95
    1994: 92

12. Understanding the relationships among temperature, dew point, and the chances of condensation (or sublimation) and precipitation
Page: 94
Questions: pp. 96–104: 4, 40, 42, 44
1991: 20
1992: 20, 73, 78
1993: 19, 77, 79
1994: 68

13. Using latitude and longitude to locate places on the earth
Pages: 17–19
Questions: pp. 22: 2, 5
pp. 24–28: 2, 16–18
p. 28:7
pp. 214–219: 5
1991: 64, 100
1992: 4, 105
1993: 4, 48
1994: 97, 98

14. Recognizing the location and features of erosion and deposition by streams
Pages: 131, 141
Questions: pp. 142–145: 7, 8, 11, 13
p. 145: 1, 4, 5, 7
1991: 33
1992: 97, 98
1993: 28
1994: 27, 34, 82, 85

15. Using data from the *Scheme for Sedimentary Rock Identification* in the *Earth Science Reference Tables*
Pages: 147–148
Questions: pp. 157–160: 3–5
1991: 32, 87
1992: 33
1993: 35, 97
1994: 86, 95

16. Understanding the relationships among latitude, insolation, temperature, and/or potential evapotranspiration
Pages: 68, 109, 114
Questions: pp. 119–126: 29, 40, 42
p. 160: 5
1991: 77–80
1992: 27
1993: 52
1994: 25

17. Using data from the *Relationship of Transported Particle Size to Water Velocity* graph in the *Earth Science Reference Tables*
Page: 132
Questions: pp. 133–137: 25, 30–31
1991: 82, 102
1992: 31, 99
1993: 81
1994: 76, 83

18. Using the *Radioactive Decay Data* in the *Earth Science Reference Tables*
Pages: 190–192
Questions: pp. 194–202: 37, 47
1991: 46
1992: 94
1993: 42
1994: 44, 49, 101

19. Understanding the relationship between particle size and stream velocity
Pages: 132
Questions: pp. 133–137: 25, 28–31
1991: 102
1992: 31, 32, 99
1993: 82
1994: 83

20. Understanding how weather (storms, lows, etc.) moves from southwest to northeast over most of the United States
Pages: 86, 94, 116–117
Questions: 96–104: 12, 13
pp. 119–125: 35
1991: 74
1992: 18, 80
1993: 78
1994: 69, 70

21. Using the map scale to determine distance along the earth's surface on maps
Page: 20
Questions: p. 22: 3, 4
pp. 24–28: 25
1991: 92
1992: none
1993: 59, 96
1994: 59, 70, 96

22. Using the centimeter, temperature, and pressure measurement scales in the *Earth Science Reference Tables*
Pages: 56, 83
Questions: pp. 4–7:7
pp. 60–64: 1, 10, 24
pp. 96–104: 7, 8, 44
1991: 13, 104
1992: 103
1993: 101
1994: 14

23. Understanding the causes and motions of convection and convection currents
Pages: 54, 82, 85, 168
Questions: pp. 60–64: 8, 9
pp. 96–104: 17, 19
pp. 174–182: 15, 23, 25
1991: 15, 94
1992: 12
1993: 70
1994: 5

24. Using data from *Selected Properties of Earth's Atmosphere* in the *Earth Science Reference Tables*
Page: 16
Questions: pp. 24–28: 11, 12
              pp. 96–104: 1
1991: 105
1992: 9
1993: 3, 104
1994: 4

25. Understanding the relationships of the phase change of water to latent heat and temperature, the use of latent heat data, and the equation in the *Earth Science Reference Tables*
Pages: 57–58
Questions: pp. 60–64: 30, 32, 33, 36, 40
1991: 68, 70
1992: 66, 69
1993: none
1994: 12

26. Understanding and computing rates of earth changes using the equation in the *Earth Science Reference Tables*
Page: 8
Questions: pp. 10–11: 3, 4
              pp. 60–64: 37, 39
1991: 69, 92
1992: 68
1993: 39, 96
1994: none

27. Determining compass directions on maps
Page: 20
Questions: p. 22: 8, 9
              pp. 24–28: 24
              pp. 96–104: 64
1991: 8
1992: 58, 59
1993: 58
1994: 57

28. Understanding the relationships between air mass source regions and air mass conditions
Pages: 91–92
Questions: pp. 96–104: 49, 51, 66
1991: 18
1992: 18
1993: 16
1994: 19, 67

29. Understanding the relationships among infrared radiation, the amounts of water vapor and carbon dioxide, and the greenhouse effect
Pages: 66, 67, 82, 212
Questions: pp. 75–81: 4, 7, 10–12
1991: 16
1992: 16, 75
1993: 11
1994: 13

30. Understanding the various types of environments that fossils indicate
Pages: 192–193
Questions: pp. 194–202: 48, 49
1991: 50
1992: 47
1993: 36, 91
1994: 46

31. Using data from the *Rock Cycle in Earth's Crust* in the *Earth Science Reference Tables*
Pages: 151–154
Questions: 157–160: 6, 11, 17
1991: 34
1992: 37
1993: 34
1994: 87, 88

32. Understanding how wind directions are determined by the earth's rotation and differences in air pressure
Pages: 84, 85, 92, 93
Questions: pp. 96–104: 11, 12, 17, 20
1991: 75
1992: 23
1993: 7
1994: 9, 18

33. Determining dew point temperature or percent relative humidity using the *Dewpoint Temperatures and Relative Humidity (%)* tables in the *Earth Science Reference Tables*
Pages: 89–90
Questions: pp. 96–104: 35
              p. 105: 2, 3
1991: 19
1992: 104
1993: 20
1994: 104

34. Understanding the effects of changes in amounts of water vapor (moisture) on air density and air pressure
Page: 83
Questions: pp. 96–104: 5, 19
1991: 24, 54
1992: 72
1993: 54
1994: none

35. Using the table on *Average Chemical Composition of Earth's Crust, Hydrosphere, and Troposphere* in the *Earth Science Reference Tables*
Page: 155
1991: 37
1992: 74
1993: 33
1994: 26

272   QUICK REVIEW

36. Recognizing glacial features of land-scapes
Pages: 132, 140, 208
Questions pp. 133–137: 33
pp. 142–145: 4, 9
pp. 214–219: 17, 18
1991: 81
1992: 53
1993: 46
1994: 51

37. Understanding the relationships between resistance of rocks to weathering and erosion and the shape of landscape features
Page: 210
Questions: pp. 133–137: 5
pp. 214–219: 19, 23
pp. 219–220: 7
1991: 48
1992: 84
1993: 30
1994: 93

38. Recognizing and understanding the meaning of a contact metamorphic zone or rock transition zone
Pages: 153, 183, 184
Questions: pp. 194–202: 6, 7, 29, 31
1991: 86, 90
1992: 48
1993: 27
1994: none

39. Using the density equation in the *Earth Science Reference Tables*
Pages: 2–3
Questions: pp. 4–7: 13, 16, 17, 19, 21, 22
1991: 57, 58, 60
1992: none
1993: none
1994: 105

40. Understanding the relationships among particle size permeability and infiltration
Pages: 107–108
Questions: pp. 119–125: 7–9
1991: none
1992: 26
1993: 21, 23
1994: 79

41. Understanding the oblate spheroid shape of the earth and the reasons we know the earth's shape
Pages: 12–14
Questions: pp. 24–28: 1, 3–6
1991: 52
1992: 1
1993: 2
1994: 7

42. Understanding the relationship between the altitude of Polaris (North Star) and latitude
Page: 13
Questions: pp. 24–28: 2, 5
1991: 64
1992: 64
1993: 4
1994: 3

43. Determining the relative age of an igneous intrusion
Pages: 183–184
Questions: pp. 194–202: 6, 7, 29, 31
1991: 86
1992: 48
1993: 45
1994: none

44. Understanding eccentricity of an orbit and determining eccentricity using the equation and *Solar System Data* table in the *Earth Science Reference Tables*
Page: 37
Questions: pp. 44–52: 33–35
1991: 104
1992: none
1993: 63
1994: 62

45. Differentiating between a heat source and a heat sink and understanding that energy moves from a heat source to a heat sink
Page: 55
Questions: pp. 60–64: 12, 13, 15, 16
1991: none
1992: none
1993: 7, 66, 69
1994: none

46. Understanding how climate affects rock weathering
Page: 128
Questions: pp. 133–137: 3, 7, 8
1991: 27
1992: 29
1993: 25
1994: none

47. Understanding the relationship between lack of S-wave transmission and the presence of the liquid outer core of the earth
Pages: 171–173
Questions: pp. 174–182: 37, 48
1991: 39
1992: 40
1993: 40
1994: none

REGENTS EXAMINATIONS

EARTH SCIENCE

June 18, 1991

PART I

Answer all 55 questions in this part. [55]

Directions (1–55): For *each* statement or question, select the word or expression that, of those given, best completes the statement or answers the question.

1. A measurement is best defined as
   (1) an inference made by using the human senses
   (2) a direct comparison with a known standard
   (3) an interpretation based on theory
   (4) a group of inferred properties

2. Which condition exists when the rates of water flowing into and out of a lake are balanced so that the lake's depth appears to be constant?
   (1) equilibrium   (3) hydration
   (2) transpiration   (4) saturation

3. According to the *Earth Science Reference Tables*, what is the radius of the Sun?
   (1) 69,600 km   (3) 6,960,000 km
   (2) 696,000 km   (4) 69,600,000 km

4. A student finds the mass of an igneous rock sample to be 48.0 grams. Its actual mass is 52.0 grams. What is the student's approximate percent deviation (percent of error)? [Refer to the *Earth Science Reference Tables*.]
   (1) 9.2%   (3) 7.7%
   (2) 8.3%   (4) 4.0%

5. Which graph best represents the typical relationship between population density near a lake and pollution of the lake?

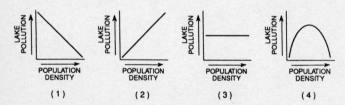

   (1)   (2)   (3)   (4)

6. The water sphere of the Earth is known as the
   (1) atmosphere   (3) lithosphere
   (2) troposphere   (4) hydrosphere

7. Which quantity has both magnitude and direction?
   (1) relative humidity of 96%
   (2) westerly wind of 10 knots
   (3) pressure of 1,012 mb
   (4) mass of 20 g

8. The map below illustrates the distribution of acid rain over the United States on a particular day. The isolines represent acidity measured in pH units.

According to the pH scale shown below the map, which region of the United States has the greatest acid rain problem?

(1) northeast
(2) northwest
(3) southeast
(4) southwest

9. The actual shape of the Earth's orbit around the Sun is best described as
(1) a very eccentric ellipse
(2) a slightly eccentric ellipse
(3) an oblate spheroid
(4) a perfect circle

10. The diagram below shows the relative positions of the Earth, Moon, and Sun for a 1-month period.

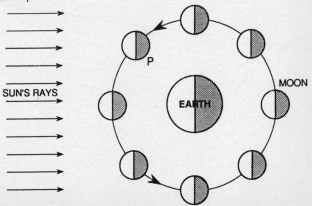

Which diagram best represents the appearance of the Moon at position *P* when viewed from the Earth?

(1)   **(2)**   **(3)**   **(4)**

11. On the Earth, a freely swinging pendulum gradually shows a change in the direction of its swing. This change is evidence that the Earth
    (1) has an elliptical orbit
    (2) is an orbiting natural satellite
    (3) rotates on its axis
    (4) revolves around the Sun

12. If viewed from the Earth over a period of several years, the apparent diameter of Mars will
    (1) decrease constantly
    (2) increase constantly
    (3) remain unchanged
    (4) vary in a cyclic manner

13. At which temperature will iron radiate the *least* electromagnetic energy?
    (1) 0°C   (3) 0°F
    (2) 230 K   (4) 32°F

14. What is the primary reason New York State is warmer in July than in February?
    (1) The Earth is traveling faster in its orbit in February.
    (2) The altitude of the noon Sun is greater in February.
    (3) The insolation in New York is greater in July.
    (4) The Earth is closer to the Sun in July.

15. The diagram below represents a large beaker of water being heated to demonstrate convection.

The movement of water upward from *A* toward *B* results primarily from
    (1) differences in density in the water
    (2) air movement across the surface of the water
    (3) capillary action within the water
    (4) the shape of the beaker

16. Two identical glass containers were placed in direct sunlight. The first container was filled with air and the second container was filled with a mixture of air and additional carbon dioxide. Each container was sealed with a thermometer inside. Temperatures were recorded at 2-minute intervals, as shown in the data table below.

Time (minutes)	Temperature (°C)	
	Container 1 (Air)	Container 2 (Air + CO_2)
0	24°	24°
2	25°	26°
4	26°	29°
6	27°	32°
8	28°	33°
10	29°	35°

Which statement best explains the results of this activity?
(1) Carbon dioxide is a good absorber of infrared radiation.
(2) Carbon dioxide causes a random reflection of energy.
(3) Carbon dioxide has no effect on the atmosphere's energy balance.
(4) Carbon dioxide converts some energy into potential energy.

17. What color and texture of a material would absorb the *least* solar radiation?
(1) black and smooth   (3) white and smooth
(2) black and rough   (4) white and rough

18. Which symbol would be used to identify an air mass originating in central Canada?
(1) mT   (3) cT
(2) mP   (4) cP

19. According to the *Earth Science Reference Tables*, what is the approximate dewpoint temperature if the dry-bulb temperature is 18°C and the wet-bulb temperature is 11°C?
(1) 1°C   (3) 7°C
(2) −10°C   (4) 4°C

20. Which weather station model indicates the greatest probability of precipitation?

(1)   (2)   (3)   (4)

21. Pollutants are most likely to be removed from the atmosphere by
(1) evaporation   (3) volcanic activity
(2) precipitation   (4) transpiration

22. Which statement best explains why a cloud is forming as shown in the diagram below?

(1) Water vapor is condensing.
(2) Moisture is evaporating.
(3) Cold air rises and compresses.
(4) Warm air sinks and expands.

23. Water will infiltrate surface material if the material is
    (1) impermeable and unsaturated
    (2) impermeable and saturated
    (3) permeable and unsaturated
    (4) permeable and saturated

24. The graph at the right shows air temperature for an area near the Earth's surface during a 12-hour period.

Which graph best illustrates the probable change in air pressure during the same time period?

25. Why do most streams in New York State have a greater stream discharge in spring than in summer?
    (1) Potential evapotranspiration is greater in spring than in summer.
    (2) More transpiration occurs in spring than in summer.
    (3) Most New York State water budgets have a deficit in spring.
    (4) Melting snow increases runoff in spring.

26. A stream is entering the calm waters of a large lake. Which diagram best illustrates the pattern of sediments being deposited in the lake from the stream flow?

27. In which climate would the chemical weathering of limestone occur most rapidly?
    (1) cold and dry   (3) warm and dry
    (2) cold and humid   (4) warm and humid

28. Which graph best represents the relationship between the surface slope of a dry, sandy soil and the infiltration rate of rain?

29. A high-pressure center is generally characterized by
    (1) cool, wet weather   (3) warm, wet weather
    (2) cool, dry weather   (4) warm, dry weather

30. The data table below shows the composition of six common rock-forming minerals.

Mineral	Composition
Mica	$KAl_3Si_3O_{10}$
Olivine	$(FeMg)_2SiO_4$
Orthoclase	$KAlSi_3O_8$
Plagioclase	$NaAlSi_3O_8$
Pyroxene	$CaMgSi_2O_6$
Quartz	SiO_2

The data table provides evidence that
(1) the same elements are found in all minerals
(2) a few elements are found in many minerals
(3) all elements are found in only a few minerals
(4) all elements are found in all minerals

31. Certain minerals usually break along flat surfaces, while other minerals break unevenly. This characteristic is due to the
(1) luster of the mineral
(2) age of the mineral
(3) internal arrangement of the mineral's atoms
(4) force with which the mineral is broken

32. According to the *Earth Science Reference Tables*, which rock most likely formed as a result of biologic processes?
(1) granite
(2) basalt
(3) sandstone
(4) limestone

33. The diagram at the right represents a stream flowing in the direction indicated by the arrows.

Which bar graph represents the relative amounts of erosion and deposition at locations A, B, C, and D in the streambed?

34. Some nonsedimentary rocks are formed as a result of
    (1) solidification of molten material
    (2) evaporation and precipitation
    (3) cementation of particles
    (4) deposition of particles

35. The chart below shows the results of an activity in which three samples of copper (A, B, and C) of equal mass were timed as they settled to the bottom of a column of water.

Sample A	Sample B	Sample C
13.10 sec	13.75 sec	13.50 sec

The differences in the settling time of the three samples are probably due to differences in their
(1) density   (3) color
(2) composition   (4) shape

36. In the diagram below, letters *A* and *B* represent locations near the edge of a continent.

A geologist who compares nonsedimentary rock samples from locations *A* and *B* would probably find that the samples from location *A* contain
(1) more granite
(2) more basalt
(3) more fossils
(4) the same minerals and fossils

37. According to the *Earth Science Reference Tables*, what is the approximate percentage by volume of oxygen in the crust of the Earth?
(1) 20%   (3) 70%
(2) 30%   (4) 90%

38. A seismographic station determines that its distance from the epicenter of an earthquake is 4,000 kilometers. According to the *Earth Science Reference Tables*, if the *P*-wave arrived at the station at 10:15 a.m., the time of the earthquake's origin was
(1) 10:02 a.m.   (3) 10:10 a.m.
(2) 10:08 a.m.   (4) 10:22 a.m.

Base your answers to questions 39 and 40 on the diagram of the Earth below showing the observed pattern of waves recorded after an earthquake.

39. The lack of *S*-waves in zone 3 can best be explained by the presence within the Earth of
    (1) density changes
    (2) mantle convection cells
    (3) a liquid outer core
    (4) a solid inner core

40. The location of the epicenter of the earthquake that produced the observed wave pattern most likely is in the
    (1) crust in zone 1
    (2) mantle in zone 2
    (3) crust in zone 3
    (4) core of the Earth

41. The diagram below represents a cross section of a portion of the Earth's crust.

    Which past activity in this region is suggested by the shape of these sedimentary rock layers?
    (1) widespread volcanic activity
    (2) horizontal sorting
    (3) glacial deposition
    (4) crustal movements

42. A skull was discovered that has human characteristics and is about 2.8 million years old. Based on this information, during which epoch could early humans have existed? [Refer to the *Earth Science Reference Tables*.]
    (1) Pliocene
    (2) Miocene
    (3) Oligocene
    (4) Eocene

43. From the study of fossils, what can be inferred about most species of plants and animals that have lived on the Earth?
    (1) They are still living today.
    (2) They are unrelated to modern life forms.
    (3) They existed during the Cambrian Period.
    (4) They have become extinct.

44. The changes observed in the fossil record from the Precambrian Eon to the Cenozoic Era best provide evidence of
    (1) sublimation
    (2) radioactive decay
    (3) evolution
    (4) planetary motion

45. According to the *Earth Science Reference Tables*, a straight line connecting which two cities would cross surface bedrock of only two geologic periods?
    (1) Watertown and Plattsburgh
    (2) Jamestown and Old Forge
    (3) Kingston and New York City
    (4) Binghamton and Syracuse

46. An igneous rock contains one-half of its original amount of potassium-40. According to the *Earth Science Reference Tables*, the age of the igneous rock is closest to
    (1) 0.7×10^9 years
    (2) 1.4×10^9 years
    (3) 2.1×10^9 years
    (4) 2.8×10^9 years

47. According to the *Earth Science Reference Tables*, which rock is most likely the oldest?
    (1) conglomerate containing the tusk of a mastodon
    (2) shale containing trilobite fossils
    (3) sandstone containing fossils of flowering plants
    (4) siltstone containing dinosaur footprints

48. The diagram below represents a cross section of a portion of the Earth's crust showing four different rock layers, *A*, *B*, *C*, and *D*.

Which rock layer shows the greatest evidence of erosion?
(1) *A*   (3) *C*
(2) *B*   (4) *D*

49. According to the *Earth Science Reference Tables,* which landscape region of New York State has a surface composed mostly of metamorphic rock?
(1) Atlantic Coastal Plain
(2) Appalachian Plateau
(3) Erie-Ontario Lowlands
(4) Adirondack Mountains

50. Living corals are found in warm, shallow seas. Coral fossils have been found in the sedimentary rocks of Alaska. These findings suggest that
(1) Alaska once had a tropical marine environment
(2) Alaska's cold climate fossilized the coral
(3) coral usually develops in cold climates
(4) ocean currents carried the coral to Alaska

51. A variety of soil types are found in New York State primarily because areas of the State differ in their
(1) amounts of insolation
(2) distances from the ocean
(3) underlying bedrock and sediments
(4) amounts of human activities

Note that questions 52 through 55 have only three choices.

52. Precise measurements of the Earth indicate that its polar diameter is
(1) shorter than its equatorial diameter
(2) longer than its equatorial diameter
(3) the same length as its equatorial diameter

53. The graph below shows the average daily temperatures and the duration of insolation for a location in the mid-latitudes of the Northern Hemisphere during a year.

KEY:
———— Surface temperature
– – – – Duration of insolation

Compared to the date of maximum duration of insolation, the date of maximum surface temperature for this location is
(1) earlier in the year
(2) later in the year
(3) the same day of the year

54. According to the graph at the right, what happens to the density of a mass of air when its water vapor content increases?
(1) Density decreases.
(2) Density increases.
(3) Density remains the same.

55. A rock contains uranium-238, which has a half-life of 4.5×10^9 years. If the rock is crushed and heated, the half-life of the uranium-238 it contains will
(1) decrease
(2) increase
(3) remain the same

PART II

This part consists of ten groups, each containing five questions. Choose seven of these ten groups. Be sure that you answer all five questions in each group chosen. [35]

Group I

If you choose this group, be sure to answer questions 56–60.

Base your answers to questions 56 through 60 on the *Earth Science Reference Tables*, the diagram below which represents a solid material of uniform composition, and your knowledge of earth science.

Density = 2.7 g/cm³

56. Which statement about this object is an inference?
    (1) The object has sharp corners.
    (2) The object is longer than it is wide.
    (3) The object is made of a naturally occurring substance.
    (4) The object has flat sides.

57. The mass of this piece of material is approximately
    (1) 0.23 g   (3) 9.3 g
    (2) 4.4 g   (4) 32 g

58. Which graph best represents the relationship between the mass and volume of various-sized pieces of this material?

Note that questions 59 and 60 have only three choices.

59. When this material is placed in a container of water, it sinks to the bottom of the container. Compared to the density of water, the density of this material is
    (1) less
    (2) greater
    (3) the same

60. If this material is heated and expands, the density of the material will
    (1) decrease
    (2) increase
    (3) remain the same

Group 2

If you choose this group, be sure to answer questions 61–65.

Base your answers to questions 61 through 65 on the diagrams below and your knowledge of earth science. The diagrams represent four locations on the Earth's surface at the same time on March 21. Lines have been drawn to represent the apparent path of the Sun across the sky. The present position of the Sun, the position of Polaris, and the zenith (Z) are shown for an observer at each location.

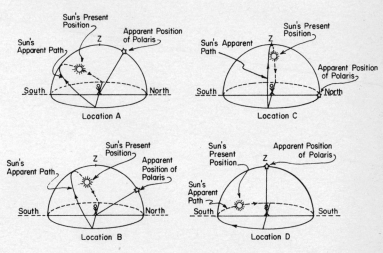

61. To an observer at location *A*, the Sun will appear to move from
    (1) east to west at 15°/hr
    (2) west to east at 15°/hr
    (3) east to west at 1°/hr
    (4) west to east at 1°/hr

62. The Sun's apparent path through the sky on this day is a direct result of the
    (1) Sun's rotation
    (2) Earth's rotation
    (3) Sun's revolution around the Earth
    (4) Earth's revolution around the Sun

63. At which location is the angle of insolation greatest at solar noon?
    (1) *A*   (3) *C*
    (2) *B*   (4) *D*

64. What is the latitude of the observer at location *D*?
    (1) 90° N   (3) $23\frac{1}{2}°$ N
    (2) $66\frac{1}{2}°$ N   (4) 0°

65. What time of day is shown by the Sun's present position at location *A*?
    (1) morning   (3) afternoon
    (2) noon   (4) midnight

Group 3

If you choose this group, be sure to answer questions 66-70.

Base your answers to questions 66 through 70 on the *Earth Science Reference Tables*, the graph below, and your knowledge of earth science. The graph shows the temperatures recorded when a sample of water was heated from −100°C to 200°C. The water received the same amount of heat every minute.

66. For the time on the graph represented by the line from point *B* to point *C*, the water was
    (1) freezing
    (2) melting
    (3) condensing
    (4) boiling

67. At which point in time would most of the water be in the liquid phase?
    (1) 1 minute
    (2) 14 minutes
    (3) 16 minutes
    (4) 4 minutes

68. How many calories were required to change 10. grams of liquid water at point *D* to water vapor at point *E*?
    (1) 500 cal
    (2) 800 cal
    (3) 1,000 cal
    (4) 5,400 cal

69. What is the rate of temperature change between points *C* and *D*?
    (1) 10 C°/min
    (2) 25 C°/min
    (3) 50 C°/min
    (4) 150 C°/min

70. The greatest amount of energy was absorbed by the water between points
    (1) *A* and *B*
    (2) *B* and *C*
    (3) *C* and *D*
    (4) *D* and *E*

Group 4

If you choose this group, be sure to answer questions 71–75.

Base your answers to questions 71 through 75 on the *Earth Science Reference Tables*, the surface weather map below, and your knowledge of earth science. The map represents a high-pressure center located over the central United States. The air pressure field lines are in millibars and the letters represent the locations of weather stations.

71. According to the *Earth Science Reference Tables*, the air pressure recorded at station *C* is equal to how many inches of mercury?
    (1) 29.95   (3) 30.12
    (2) 30.08   (4) 30.35

72. Which weather station would most likely have the same air pressure reading as station *G*?
    (1) *F*   (3) *C*
    (2) *B*   (4) *D*

73. Along which dashed line would windspeeds be greatest?
    (1) *AB*   (3) *CD*
    (2) *EF*   (4) *GH*

74. If the high-pressure center follows the typical direction of movement of an air mass across the United States, it will probably move toward the
    (1) southeast   (3) northeast
    (2) southwest   (4) northwest

75. In which diagram do the arrows best represent actual surface wind directions in this Northern Hemisphere high-pressure center?

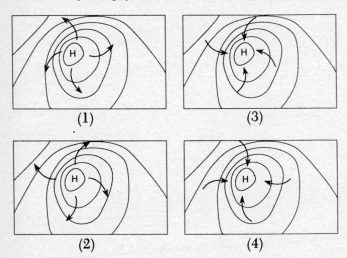

(1)   (3)

(2)   (4)

Group 5

If you choose this group, be sure to answer questions 76–80.

Base your answers to questions 76 through 80 on the climate graphs below and your knowledge of earth science. Each climate graph shows the average monthly temperature and the average monthly precipitation for a particular location. Precipitation amounts are shown by the shaded bars and are read from the scale at the left of the graph. Temperatures are shown by the solid line and are read from the scale at the right of the graph.

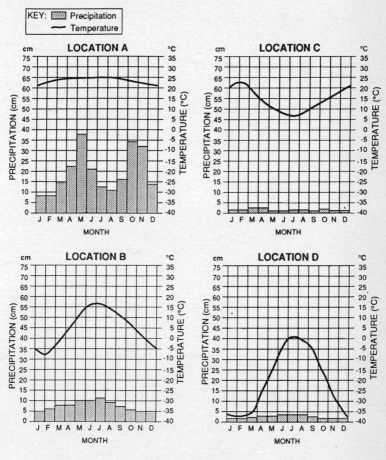

76. Which location shows the greatest amount of change in average monthly precipitation?
    (1) A
    (2) B
    (3) C
    (4) D

77. Which location would most likely have the highest average potential evapotranspiration (E_p) value for the month of July?
    (1) A
    (2) B
    (3) C
    (4) D

78. Which location is in the Southern Hemisphere?
    (1) *A*   (3) *C*
    (2) *B*   (4) *D*

79. Which location has a climate typical of a region near the North Pole?
    (1) *A*   (3) *C*
    (2) *B*   (4) *D*

80. Which statement best explains the small temperature range at location *A*?
    (1) Location *A* is far from any large body of water.
    (2) Location *A* is close to the Equator.
    (3) Location *A* has a very high elevation.
    (4) Location *A* is located in a high-pressure wind belt.

Group 6

If you choose this group, be sure to answer questions 81–85.

Base your answers to questions 81 through 85 on the *Earth Science Reference Tables*, the diagram below, and your knowledge of earth science. The diagram shows a surface and cross-sectional view of a portion of the Earth 15 kilometers from a mountain range.

81. The best explanation for the presence of an isolated boulder in this location is that the boulder was
    (1) eroded from a limestone cliff
    (2) transported there by a glacier
    (3) placed there by a volcanic eruption
    (4) deposited there by a slow-moving stream

82. What must be the size of the boulder?
    (1) less than 0.2 cm in diameter
    (2) 0.2 to 6.4 cm in diameter
    (3) 6.4 to 25.6 cm in diameter
    (4) greater than 25.6 cm in diameter

83. The processes that change the boulder and cobbles into soil are weathering and
    (1) metamorphism
    (2) cementation of sediments
    (3) biological activity
    (4) melting of rock material

84. The granite boulder and the granite cobbles have similar chemical compositions. Compared to the rate of weathering of the boulder, the rate of weathering of an equal mass of cobbles is probably
    (1) slower due to location
    (2) faster due to location
    (3) slower due to particle size
    (4) faster due to particle size

85. Which characteristic of the granite boulder would furnish the greatest amount of information about the environment in which the granite solidified?
    (1) texture   (3) hardness
    (2) density   (4) color

Group 7

If you choose this group, be sure to answer questions 86–90.

Base your answers to questions 86 through 90 on the *Earth Science Reference Tables*, the diagram below, and your knowledge of earth science. The diagram is a geologic cross section of a portion of the Earth's crust consisting of various sedimentary and nonsedimentary rock units, represented by letters *A* through *H*, which have not been overturned. Line I–II represents a fault.

86. What is the age sequence of the rock units, from oldest to youngest?
    (1) *E, F, G, H*   (3) *G, H, F, E*
    (2) *H, G, E, F*   (4) *F, E, G, H*

87. In which rock unit would unsorted rock fragments of greatly varying size most likely be found?
    (1) *A*   (3) *G*
    (2) *E*   (4) *H*

88. What is the relative age of the fault (line I–II)?
    (1) younger than rock unit *F* but older than rock unit *H*
    (2) younger than rock unit *G* but older than rock unit *H*
    (3) younger than rock unit *F* but older than rock unit *G*
    (4) younger than rock unit *H* but older than rock unit *F*

89. Evidence of a buried erosional surface (unconformity) is found at the top of unit
    (1) *A*   (3) *C*
    (2) *G*   (4) *D*

Note that question 90 has only three choices.

90. Which method of energy transfer is the primary cause of the contact metamorphism?
    (1) radiation
    (2) convection
    (3) conduction

Group 8

If you choose this group, be sure to answer questions 91-95.

Base your answers to questions 91 through 95 on the *Earth Science Reference Tables*, the diagram below, and your knowledge of earth science. The diagram shows the magnetic orientation of igneous rock on the seafloor on the east (right) side of a mid-ocean ridge. The pattern on the west (left) side of the ridge has been omitted. The age of the igneous rock and its distance from the ridge center are shown.

91. Which diagram below best represents the pattern of magnetic orientation in the seafloor on the west (left) side of the ocean ridge?

92. According to the diagram, what is the approximate rate of seafloor spreading?
    (1) 1 km/million years
    (2) 2 km/million years
    (3) 40 km/million years
    (4) 50 km/million years

93. Which inference can best be made from the diagram?
    (1) The orientation of the Earth's magnetic field has reversed with time.
    (2) The size of the continents has changed with time.
    (3) The elevation of sea level has changed with time.
    (4) The amount of fossil material preserved in the igneous rock has changed with time.

94. The occurrence of high-heat flows at the ridge center provides evidence of the
    (1) destruction of oceanic crust
    (2) destruction of continental crust
    (3) existence of ancestral mountains
    (4) existence of rising mantle convection currents

Note that question 95 has only three choices.

95. As distance from the center of the ridge increases, the age of rocks
    (1) decreases
    (2) increases
    (3) remains the same

Group 9

If you choose this group, be sure to answer questions 96–100.

Base your answers to questions 96 through 100 on the *Earth Science Reference Tables*, the map below, and your knowledge of earth science. The map shows the major landscape regions of New York State.

Generalized Landscape Regions of New York State

96. Which major landscape region covers the greatest surface area in New York State?
    (1) New England Highlands
    (2) Appalachian Uplands
    (3) St. Lawrence Lowlands
    (4) Atlantic Coastal Lowlands

97. During which period was most of the surface bedrock that separates the Adirondacks from the Catskills formed?
    (1) Precambrian
    (2) Ordovician
    (3) Jurassic
    (4) Triassic

98. In what way do plateau landscape regions differ from mountain landscape regions?
    (1) The climate of plateau regions is generally more humid.
    (2) The altitude of plateau regions is generally higher.
    (3) The bedrock of plateau regions is generally more horizontal.
    (4) The bedrock age of plateau regions is generally greater.

99. Salt deposits are often found in bedrock of Silurian age. Which landscape region in New York State most likely contains salt deposits?
    (1) Adirondack Highlands
    (2) Taconic Mountains
    (3) Atlantic Coastal Lowlands
    (4) Erie-Ontario Lowlands

100. Which landscape region contains the location 44°00′ N latitude and 74°30′ W longitude?
    (1) Adirondack Highlands
    (2) New England Highlands
    (3) Erie-Ontario Lowlands
    (4) Tug Hill Plateau

Group 10

If you choose this group, be sure to answer questions 101–105.

Base your answers to questions 101 through 105 on the *Earth Science Reference Tables* and your knowledge of earth science.

101. Which is the best description of the properties of basalt?
    (1) fine-grained and mafic
    (2) fine-grained and felsic
    (3) coarse-grained and mafic
    (4) coarse-grained and felsic

102. Which sediment is the largest that could be carried by a stream flowing at a velocity of 100 centimeters per second?
    (1) silt
    (2) sand
    (3) pebbles
    (4) cobbles

103. How much heat energy is required to raise the temperature of 10. grams of granite from 20.°C to 50.°C?
    (1) 1.9 cal
    (2) 57 cal
    (3) 300 cal
    (4) 500 cal

104. What is the approximate eccentricity of the ellipse drawn below?

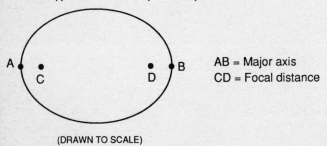

AB = Major axis
CD = Focal distance

(DRAWN TO SCALE)

    (1) 1.4
    (2) 0.73
    (3) 0.40
    (4) 0.15

105. Which layer of the atmosphere contains the most water vapor?
    (1) troposphere
    (2) stratosphere
    (3) mesosphere
    (4) thermosphere

EARTH SCIENCE

June 18, 1992

PART I

Answer all 55 questions in this part. [55]

Directions (1–55): For *each* statement or question, select the word or expression that, of those given, best completes the statement or answers the question.

1. The best evidence that the Earth has a spherical shape is provided by
   (1) photographs of the Earth taken from space satellites
   (2) the amount of daylight received at the North Pole on June 21
   (3) the changing orbital speed of the Earth in its orbit around the Sun
   (4) the cyclic change of seasons

2. According to the diagram below, at which location would the water probably be most polluted?

   (1) *A*   (3) *C*
   (2) *B*   (4) *D*

3. The predictable changes in the direction of swing of a Foucault pendulum would be influenced most by a change in the Earth's
   (1) rate of rotation
   (2) period of revolution
   (3) angle of tilt
   (4) intensity of insolation

4. The diagrams below represent four systems of imaginary lines that could be used to locate positions on a planet. Which system is most similar to the latitude-longitude system used on the Earth?

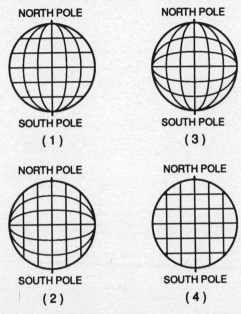

5. The diagram below represents eight positions of the Moon as it revolves around the Earth.

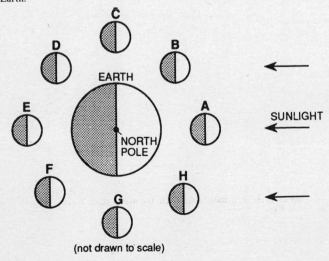

When viewed from the Earth, which phase of the Moon will be seen when the Moon is at point *E*?
(1) first quarter
(2) full moon
(3) new moon
(4) last quarter

6. The diagram below shows several positions of the Earth as it moves around the Sun.

Position D

Position A

Position C

Position B

(NOT DRAWN TO SCALE)

Which position shows the Earth during summer in the Northern Hemisphere?
(1) *A*
(2) *B*
(3) *C*
(4) *D*

7. A student collected and recorded measurements of the amount of carbon monoxide in the air at the same location each day for one week. The data are shown below.

Day	Time	Carbon Monoxide (parts per million)
1	9:10 a.m.	0.20
2	3:10 p.m.	0.38
3	10:45 a.m.	0.40
4	7:20 a.m.	1.15
5	6:00 a.m.	0.95
6	6:00 p.m.	0.65
7	7:15 p.m.	0.14

The student concluded that the amount of carbon monoxide in the air increased and then decreased during the week. A source of error in the student's investigation is that the student failed to
(1) identify the days of the week
(2) identify the month
(3) collect data at the same time each day
(4) state the method of measurement

8. Some constellations (star patterns) observed in the summer skies in New York State are different from those observed in the winter skies. The best explanation for this observation is that
(1) the Earth revolves around the Sun
(2) the Earth rotates on its axis
(3) constellations are moving away from the Earth
(4) constellations revolve around the Earth

Base your answers to questions 9 and 10 on the diagram below which shows part of the orbit of a satellite around the Earth. The distance from the satellite's orbit to the Earth's surface is 75 kilometers.

(Not drawn to scale)

9. According to the *Earth Science Reference Tables*, in which portion of the Earth's atmosphere is the satellite located?
   (1) troposphere (3) mesosphere
   (2) stratosphere (4) thermosphere

10. Which force is most directly responsible for keeping the satellite in orbit around the Earth?
    (1) friction (3) magnetism
    (2) gravity (4) Coriolis

11. An object that is a good radiator of electromagnetic waves is also a good
    (1) insulator from heat
    (2) reflector of heat
    (3) absorber of electromagnetic energy
    (4) refractor of electromagnetic energy

12. Which process is primarily responsible for the transfer of energy by air currents within the Earth's atmosphere?
    (1) convection (3) absorption
    (2) radiation (4) conduction

13. The diagram below shows the isothermal pattern obtained at a height of 1 meter above the floor in a classroom during a temperature study in November.

Which conclusion is best supported by this diagram?
(1) A heat source is located at *A*.
(2) A heat sink is located at *B*.
(3) Room temperature at the floor and at the ceiling can be determined.
(4) The isotherms indicate the temperatures at only one level in the room.

14. A diagram of the water cycle is shown below. Letters *A* through *D* represent the processes taking place.

Which arrow represents the process of transpiration?
(1) *A*   (3) *C*
(2) *B*   (4) *D*

15. Which graph best represents the intensity of insolation and the surface temperature for a location at the Equator?

16. Which form of electromagnetic energy is radiated from the Earth's surface with the greatest intensity?
    (1) x rays
    (2) infrared rays
    (3) ultraviolet rays
    (4) visible light rays

17. In the diagram below, the thermometer held 2 meters above the floor shows a temperature of 30°C. The thermometer on the floor shows a temperature of 24°C.

THERMOMETER AT 30°C

STUDENT

2 METERS

THERMOMETER AT 24°C

CHAIR

(Not Drawn to Scale)

What is the temperature gradient between the two thermometers?
(1) 6 C°/m
(2) 2 C°/m
(3) 3 C°/m
(4) 4 C°/m

18. The weather map below shows a frontal system that has followed a typical storm track.

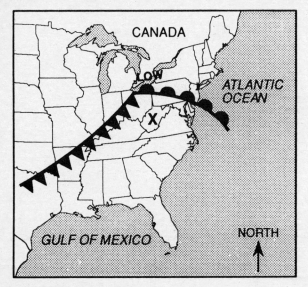

The air mass located over point *X* most likely originated over the
(1) northern Atlantic Ocean
(2) central part of Canada
(3) Gulf of Mexico
(4) Pacific Northwest

19. Which graph best represents the relationship between water droplet size and the chance of precipitation?

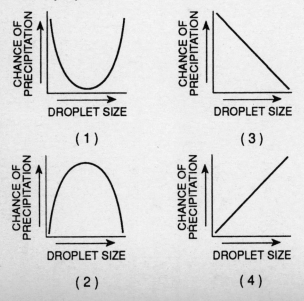

20. On a clear, dry day an air mass has a temperature of 20°C and a dewpoint temperature of 10°C.

According to the graph, about how high must this air mass rise before a cloud can form?
(1) 1.6 km   (3) 3.0 km
(2) 2.4 km   (4) 2.8 km

21. The primary source of most of the moisture for the Earth's atmosphere is
    (1) soil-moisture storage
    (2) rivers and lakes
    (3) melting glaciers
    (4) oceans

22. In which area will surface runoff most likely be greatest during a heavy rainfall?
    (1) sandy desert   (3) level grassy field
    (2) wooded forest   (4) paved city street

23. Which map correctly shows the wind directions of the high-pressure and low-pressure systems?

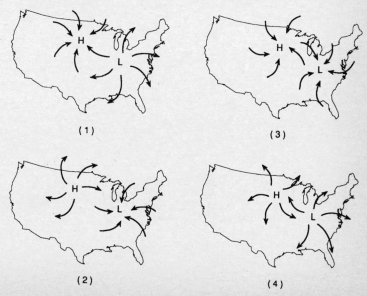

Base your answers to questions 24 and 25 on the graph below which represents the discharge of a stream at a location that has little temperature change throughout the year.

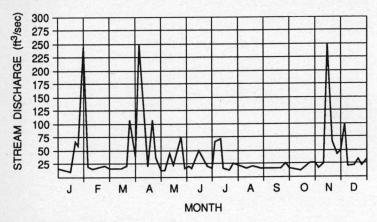

24. Which local water budget variable best accounts for the peaks in the graph?
    (1) precipitation
    (2) moisture deficit
    (3) actual evapotranspiration
    (4) potential evapotranspiration

25. During which month was the greatest amount of sediment probably transported?
    (1) February   (3) May
    (2) April   (4) October

26. Particles of uniform shape and size were placed in an open column. The time required for water to infiltrate through the column from top to bottom was recorded. The procedure was repeated using several different particle sizes. The data were plotted on the graph below.

What would be the time required for water to infiltrate the soil sample shown actual size in diagram A? [Refer to the *Earth Science Reference Tables*.]
    (1) 3–5 sec   (3) 14–16 sec
    (2) 11–13 sec   (4) 20–22 sec

27. Two locations, one in northern Canada and one in the southwestern United States, receive the same amount of precipitation each year. The location in Canada is classified as a humid climate. Why would the location in the United States be classified as an arid climate?
    (1) The yearly distribution of precipitation is different.
    (2) The soil-moisture storage in the southwestern United States is more than that in northern Canada.
    (3) The potential evapotranspiration is greater in the southwestern United States than in northern Canada.
    (4) The vegetation of the southwestern United States is different from that of northern Canada.

28. Which conditions are most likely to develop over a land area adjacent to the ocean on a hot, sunny afternoon?
    (1) lower temperatures, with winds blowing in from the ocean
    (2) lower temperatures, with winds blowing out toward the ocean
    (3) higher temperatures, with winds blowing in from the ocean
    (4) higher temperatures, with winds blowing out toward the ocean

29. In which type of climate would the rate of chemical weathering be greatest?
    (1) warm and dry   (3) cold and dry
    (2) warm and moist   (4) cold and moist

30. To investigate the effects of weathering on limestone rock chips, students placed rock chips of uniform size and shape in jars half-filled with water and shook them for different lengths of time. One rock chip was collected for each length of shaking time and these chips were arranged in a display. Which column shows the rock chips arranged from top to bottom in order of least to most shaking time?

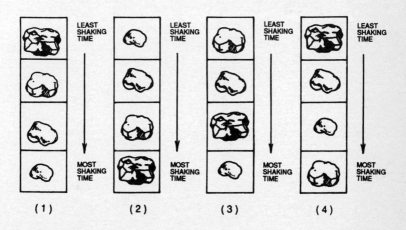

31. According to the *Earth Science Reference Tables*, which material would most likely be carried by a stream traveling at a rate of 40 centimeters per second?
    (1) clay, only
    (2) boulders, only
    (3) sand, silt, and clay
    (4) boulders, cobbles, and pebbles

32. Transported sediments are usually deposited at locations in which
    (1) the freezing and thawing of water occurs
    (2) the chemical breakdown of rocks occurs
    (3) a decrease in the speed of the agent of erosion occurs
    (4) an increase in the physical weathering of rocks occurs

33. Which rock was most likely formed from pebble-sized sediment deposited in shallow water at an ocean shoreline?
    (1) shale
    (2) basalt
    (3) siltstone
    (4) conglomerate

34. The mineral mica breaks evenly along flat sheets mainly because of its
    (1) atomic arrangement
    (2) chemical composition
    (3) hardness
    (4) density

35. According to the *Earth Science Reference Tables*, rhyolite is an example of a
    (1) monomineralic igneous rock
    (2) polymineralic igneous rock
    (3) monomineralic sedimentary rock
    (4) polymineralic sedimentary rock

36. The best evidence for determining the cooling rate of an igneous rock during its solidification is provided by
    (1) index fossils
    (2) faults in the rock
    (3) the crystal size of its minerals
    (4) the disintegration of radioactive substances

Base your answers to questions 37 and 38 on the *Earth Science Reference Tables* and the diagram below. The diagram shows two volcanoes with lava flows.

VOLCANIC CRATER

BASALT

GRANITE

37. Most of the surface bedrock in this landscape was probably formed by
    (1) burial and pressure
    (2) burial and cementation
    (3) melting and compaction
    (4) melting and solidification

38. Which map best represents the stream drainage pattern of these volcanic mountains?

39. Folded sedimentary rock layers are usually caused by
    (1) deposition of sediments in folded layers
    (2) differences in sediment density during deposition
    (3) a rise in sea level after deposition
    (4) crustal movement occurring after deposition

40. The analysis of seismic data from an earthquake shows that some locations received both P-waves and S-waves, but other locations received only P-waves. What is the best inference that can be made from these observations?
    (1) A zone of liquid rock exists within the Earth.
    (2) Iron in some rocks prevents S-waves from traveling.
    (3) Some seismographs are more sensitive than others.
    (4) S-waves are very weak.

41. Which statement best supports the theory of continental drift?
    (1) Basaltic rock is found to be progressively younger at increasing distances from a mid-ocean ridge.
    (2) Marine fossils are often found in deep-well drill cores.
    (3) The present continents appear to fit together as pieces of a larger landmass.
    (4) Areas of shallow-water seas tend to accumulate sediment, which gradually sinks.

42. Which diagram of crustal movement best shows how older rock layers may be located on top of younger rock layers?

43. Many scientists believe that convection currents in the mantle between South America and Africa caused the separation of the two continents and the formation of the Mid-Atlantic Ridge. Which diagram best represents the currents described in this theory?

44. The darkest areas on the world map below represent an earth scientist's data.

These dark areas most likely represent zones of frequent
(1) air-mass origin
(2) hurricane paths
(3) fossil correlations
(4) crustal activity

45. According to the *Earth Science Reference Tables*, approximately how many years ago did the solar system originate?
(1) 570,000,000
(2) 1,000,000,000
(3) 4,500,000,000
(4) 10,000,000,000

46. According to the *Earth Science Reference Tables*, most of the surface bedrock found in New York State was formed during which era?
(1) Precambrian
(2) Paleozoic
(3) Mesozoic
(4) Cenozoic

47. Trilobite fossils found in shale bedrock in the Albany, New York, area indicate that this area once
(1) was covered by an ocean
(2) was covered by a large forest
(3) had iron ore deposits
(4) had many land animals

48. The diagram below represents layers of rock.

Rock layer *A* is inferred to be older than intrusion *B* because
(1) layer *A* is composed of sedimentary rocks
(2) parts of layer *A* were altered by intrusion *B*
(3) layer *B* is located between layer *A* and layer *C*
(4) parts of layer *C* were altered by intrusion *B*

49. According to the *Earth Science Reference Tables*, which river begins in the Adirondack Mountains?
    (1) St. Lawrence
    (2) Niagara
    (3) Susquehanna
    (4) Hudson

50. Characteristics such as composition, porosity, permeability, and particle size are used to describe different types of
    (1) hillslopes
    (2) stream drainage patterns
    (3) soils
    (4) landscapes

51. The diagram below shows a possible sequence of evolutionary development of some vertebrates.

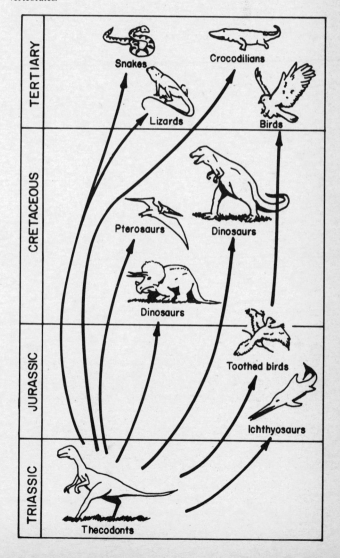

Which statement can best be inferred from the diagram?
(1) The lizard and the bird are both reptiles.
(2) The pterosaurs and the ichthyosaurs became extinct at the same time.
(3) The pterosaurs evolved into modern birds.
(4) The thecodont is the ancestor of several different types of animals.

52. A layer of shale is located below Devonian limestone and above Cambrian sandstone. Overturning has not occurred. During which period was the shale most likely deposited? [Refer to the *Earth Science Reference Tables*.]
(1) Silurian   (3) Triassic
(2) Carboniferous   (4) Tertiary

53. The diagram below represents a landscape area.

Which process is primarily responsible for the shape of the surface shown in the diagram?
(1) crustal subsidence   (3) glacial action
(2) wave action   (4) stream erosion

54. According to the *Earth Science Reference Tables*, the landscape of Rochester, New York, consists of
(1) areas of exposed metamorphic rock
(2) rounded hills of igneous rock
(3) disturbed sedimentary layers of high relief
(4) low-lying sedimentary rock

Note that question 55 has only three choices.

55. Compared to a low-density spherical particle, a high-density spherical particle of the same size will sink through water
(1) more slowly
(2) more rapidly
(3) at the same rate

PART II

This part consists of ten groups, each containing five questions. Choose seven of these ten groups. Be sure that you answer all five questions in each group chosen. [35]

Group I

If you choose this group, be sure to answer questions 56–60.

Base your answers to questions 56 through 60 on the topographic map below and your knowledge of earth science.

Contour Interval = 10 meters   NORTH

56. What is the elevation at the intersection of Jones Road and Smith Road?
    (1) 450 m   (3) 550 m
    (2) 500 m   (4) 600 m

57. What is the elevation of the highest contour line on hill *W*?
    (1) 440 m   (3) 560 m
    (2) 510 m   (4) 610 m

58. On which side of hill *X* is the steepest slope found?
    (1) north   (3) southeast
    (2) east   (4) southwest

59. In which general direction is Trout Brook flowing when it passes under Smith Road?
    (1) northeast   (3) southeast
    (2) northwest   (4) southwest

60. Which diagram best represents the profile along a straight line between points *A* and *B*?

(1)

(3)

(2)

(4)

Group 2

If you choose this group, be sure to answer questions 61–65.

Base your answers to questions 61 through 65 on the diagram below and your knowledge of earth science. The diagram represents the Earth at a specific position in its orbit. Arrows indicate radiation from the Sun. Points A through D are locations on the Earth's surface.

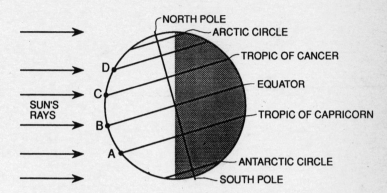

61. During which month could the Earth be in the position shown in the diagram?
    (1) February
    (2) May
    (3) October
    (4) December

62. Which location would have the greatest number of daylight hours when the Earth is in this position?
    (1) A
    (2) B
    (3) C
    (4) D

63. Locations A, B, C, D all have the same
    (1) latitude
    (2) longitude
    (3) intensity of insolation
    (4) noontime altitude of the Sun

64. As an observer travels from position B to position D, the altitude of Polaris in the nighttime sky will
    (1) decrease only
    (2) increase, only
    (3) increase, then decrease
    (4) remain the same

65. Which diagram below best represents the path of the Sun on this date as seen by an observer at location *C*?

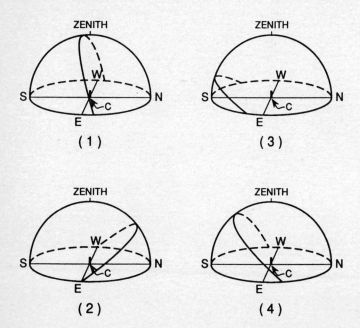

Group 3

If you choose this group, be sure to answer questions 66–70.

Base your answers to questions 66 through 70 on the *Earth Science Reference Tables*, the graph below, and your knowledge of earth science. The graph shows the results of heating 10 grams of water from −100°C to +200°C. The same amount of heat was added during each minute.

66. What is the most probable explanation for the constant temperature between points *D* and *E* on the graph?
    (1) The added heat was radiated as fast as it was absorbed.
    (2) The added heat was lost to the surroundings.
    (3) The added heat changed liquid water to water vapor.
    (4) The added heat changed water vapor to liquid water.

67. Approximately how long did it take to completely change the 10 grams of water from a solid at −100°C to a gas at +100°C?
    (1) 1 minute   (3) 11 minutes
    (2) 5 minutes   (4) 15 minutes

68. During which time interval was the rate of temperature change the greatest?
    (1) *A* to *B*   (3) *C* to *D*
    (2) *B* to *C*   (4) *D* to *E*

69. During which change would the 10 grams of water gain the most energy?
    (1) Ice at −100°C changes to ice at 0°C.
    (2) Ice at 0°C changes to liquid water at 0°C.
    (3) Liquid water at 0°C changes to liquid water at 100°C.
    (4) Liquid water at 100°C changes to water vapor at 100°C.

Note that question 70 has only three choices.

70. In which phase does water have its highest specific heat?
    (1) solid
    (2) liquid
    (3) gas

Group 4

If you choose this group, be sure to answer questions 71–75.

Base your answers to questions 71 through 75 on the *Earth Science Reference Tables*, the information and diagram below, and your knowledge of earth science.

The diagram represents a model that shows how air density is affected by the addition of water vapor to the air. Marbles with different masses, representing nitrogen, oxygen, and carbon dioxide, were used to fill a container to show a certain volume of dry air. The container was placed on a scale to find the mass of this volume of dry air.

A few marbles representing nitrogen (N_2) and oxygen (O_2) were removed and replaced with marbles representing water vapor (H_2O) to show the same volume of air with water vapor present. The relative mass of each gas, as represented by the marbles, is shown in the data table.

DATA TABLE

Molecule Symbol	Gas	Mass
N_2	Nitrogen	28 g
O_2	Oxygen	32 g
CO_2	Carbon Dioxide	44 g
H_2O	Water Vapor	18 g

71. According to the data table, which gas molecule has the *least* mass?
    (1) nitrogen
    (3) carbon dioxide
    (2) oxygen
    (4) water vapor

72. When a few of the marbles representing nitrogen and oxygen are replaced with marbles representing water vapor, the air model will become
    (1) ligher and less dense
    (2) lighter and more dense
    (3) heavier and less dense
    (4) heavier and more dense

73. After water vapor molecules enter the Earth's atmosphere, what conditions must occur before they can become liquid?
    (1) warming temperatures and condensation
    (2) warming temperatures and evaporation
    (3) cooling temperatures and condensation
    (4) cooling temperatures and evaporation

74. Which graph best represents the volume of each gas in the troposphere?

(1)

(3)

(2)

(4)

75. Which graph best represents what most likely happens to the temperature of the Earth's atmosphere as the amount of carbon dioxide in the atmosphere increases over a period of many years?

Group 5

If you choose this group, be sure to answer questions 76–80.

Base your answers to questions 76 through 80 on the *Earth Science Reference Tables*, the diagrams below, and your knowledge of earth science. The diagrams represent station models showing weather data collected at four different times during 1 day at a location in New York State.

76. At which time of day was the greatest wind velocity recorded?
    (1) 1 p.m.   (3) 7 a.m.
    (2) 10 a.m.   (4) 4 p.m.

77. What was the barometric pressure at 4 p.m.?
    (1) 26.0 mb   (3) 1,002.6 mb
    (2) 260 mb   (4) 1,026 mb

78. At what time was the probability of precipitation greatest at this location?
    (1) 1 p.m.   (3) 7 a.m.
    (2) 10 a.m.   (4) 4 p.m.

79. The change in air temperature between 7 a.m. and 10 a.m. was most likely caused by
    (1) the passage of a cold front
    (2) a decrease in cloud cover
    (3) an increase in air pressure
    (4) an increase in the angle of insolation

80. Which station model best represents the probable weather conditions at 7 p.m. if the present trend continues?

(1)

(3)

(2)

(4)

Group 6

If you choose this group, be sure to answer questions 81–85.

Base your answers to questions 81 through 85 on the *Earth Science Reference Tables*, the diagram below, and your knowledge of earth science. The diagram shows a cross section of the Grand Canyon. The rock type of layer X has been purposely left blank.

81. The Grand Canyon is primarily the result of erosion due to
    (1) wind
    (2) volcanic activity
    (3) glaciers
    (4) running water

82. Correlation of rock layers on both sides of the canyon would show that layer X is composed of
    (1) granite
    (2) limestone
    (3) sandstone
    (4) quartzite

83. This landscape area developed in an arid climate. If the climate of this region were to become humid, the hills would eventually
    (1) become more angular in shape
    (2) become more rounded in shape
    (3) erode at a slower rate
    (4) continue to erode in the same way

84. The most probable explanation for the development of the steep Redwall cliffs is that this limestone layer
    (1) is more resistant to erosion than the rock layers above and below the cliffs
    (2) was deposited in a marine environment
    (3) was uplifted by the granite intrusion
    (4) is younger than the rock layers above the cliffs

85. Which statement best describes the granite bedrock in the intrusion?
    (1) It is a dark-colored fine-grained rock.
    (2) It is a light-colored fine-grained rock.
    (3) It is a felsic coarse-grained rock.
    (4) It is a mafic coarse-grained rock.

Group 7

If you choose this group, be sure to answer questions 86–90.

Base your answers to questions 86 through 90 on the *Earth Science Reference Tables*, the map below, and your knowledge of earth science. The map shows how the epicenter of an earthquake is located using observations at seismograph stations 1, 2, and 3 in New York State. Station 4 is a seismograph station located in Canada.

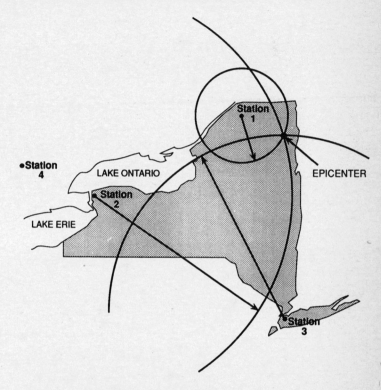

86. Using the seismic reading received at station 1 only, an observer would be able to determine
    (1) the distance of the epicenter from station 1, only
    (2) the direction of the epicenter from station 1, only
    (3) both the distance and the direction of the epicenter from station 1
    (4) neither the distance nor the direction of the epicenter from station 1

87. Which statement about the arrival times of the seismic waves at station 2 is correct?
    (1) The *P*-wave arrived first.
    (2) The *S*-wave arrived first.
    (3) The *P*-wave and *S*-wave arrived at the same time.
    (4) Only the *S*-wave arrived.

88. Another seismograph station in the United States recorded the difference in arrival times between *P*-waves and *S*-waves as 6 minutes. Approximately how far from the epicenter would this station be located?
    (1) 1.6×10^3 km   (3) 3.3×10^3 km
    (2) 9.2×10^3 km   (4) 4.4×10^3 km

89. Station 3 is approximately 400 kilometers from the epicenter of this earthquake. Approximately how much time did the *P*-wave take to travel to station 3?
    (1) 50 seconds
    (2) 2 seconds
    (3) 1 minute 40 seconds
    (4) 5 minutes

Note that question 90 has only three choices.

90. How would the difference in arrival times of the *P*-waves and *S*-waves at station 4 compare with the difference in arrival times of these waves at station 3?
    (1) The difference would be greater at station 3.
    (2) The difference would be greater at station 4.
    (3) The difference would be the same at both stations.

Group 8
If you choose this group, be sure to answer questions 91–95.

Base your answers to questions 91 through 95 on the *Earth Science Reference Tables*, the diagram below, and your knowledge of earth science. The diagram represents the radioactive decay of uranium-238 and shows the percentages of uranium-238 (U^{238}) and the stable element lead-206 (Pb^{206}) after three half-lives.

Radioactive Decay of Uranium-238

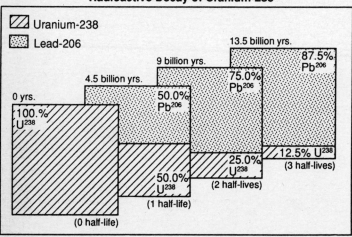

91. After three half-lives, how much of the original sample of U^{238} remains?
    (1) 12.5%   (3) 50.0%
    (2) 25.0%   (4) 87.5%

92. If an original sample of radioactive U^{238} had a mass of 400. grams, what is the total amount of the U^{238} sample that would be left after 9 billion years?
    (1) 50.0 g   (3) 100. g
    (2) 75.0 g   (4) 200. g

93. A rock sample containing uranium-238 was crushed into fragments. The half-life of the uranium-238 in each rock fragment is best described as
    (1) shorter than that of the original sample
    (2) longer than that of the original sample
    (3) the same as that of the original sample
    (4) impossible to measure

94. Which radioactive element is best suited for determining the age of wooden tools used by prehistoric humans during the last ice age?
    (1) carbon-14
    (2) potassium-40
    (3) uranium-238
    (4) rubidium-87

95. Which graph best shows the changing amounts of U^{238} and Pb^{206} in a radioactive rock sample?

Group 9

If you choose this group, be sure to answer questions 96–100.

Base your answers to questions 96 through 100 on the *Earth Science Reference Tables*, the map below, and your knowledge of earth science. The map shows a stream flowing into a lake. Letters *A* through *F* represent locations in the stream and lake.

96. Which diagram best represents the change in the stream's elevation from location A to location E?

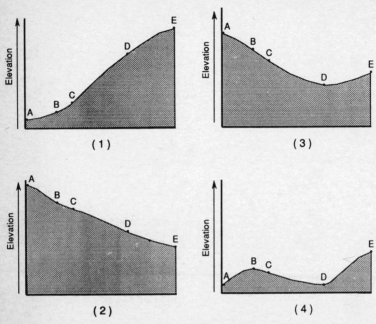

(1)

(2)

(3)

(4)

97. Which diagram best represents the cross section of the stream at location C? [Note that letters N and S represent the north and south sides of the stream.]

(1)

(2)

(3)

(4)

98. Where would the greatest amount of sediments most likely be deposited in this system?
    (1) *E*   (3) *F*
    (2) *B*   (4) *D*

99. Which kind of sediment would probably be deposited farthest out in the lake?
    (1) sand   (3) clay
    (2) silt   (4) pebbles

100. The velocity of this stream at point *B* depends on the stream's
    (1) slope, only
    (2) discharge, only
    (3) slope and discharge, only
    (4) slope, discharge, and channel shape

Group 10

If you choose this group, be sure to answer questions 101–105.

Base your answers to questions 101 through 105 on the *Earth Science Reference Tables* and your knowledge of earth science.

101. Which minerals are found in the igneous rocks gabbro and basalt?
    , (1) olivine and quartz
    (2) olivine and pyroxene
    (3) pyroxene and orthoclase
    (4) orthoclase and quartz

102. The rocks 50 kilometers east of Buffalo contains many fossils of
    (1) birds   (3) reptiles
    (2) mammals   (4) fish

103. A temperature of 73° Fahrenheit is approximately equal to a temperature of
    (1) 17° Celsius   (3) 26° Celsius
    (2) 23° Celsuis   (4) 162° Celsius

104. What is the approximate dewpoint temperature if the dry-bulb temperature is 13°C and the wet-bulb temperature is 10°C?
    (1) 7°C   (3) 3°C
    (2) 10°C   (4) −25°C

105. What type of landscape region is located at 42°30′N and 76° W?
    (1) coastal lowland   (3) plateau
    (2) mountainous area   (4) plain

EARTH SCIENCE

June 18, 1993

PART I

Answer all 55 questions in this part. [55]

Directions (1–55): For *each* statement or question, select the word or expression that, of those given, best completes the statement or answers the question.

1. The map below shows the elevation field for a 30-by-50-meter section of a parking lot on which a large pile of sand has been dumped. The isolines show the height of the sand above the surface of the parking lot in meters.

   Which map represents the most likely elevation field for the same area after several heavy rainstorms?

2. The Earth's actual shape is most correctly described as
   (1) a circle
   (2) a perfect sphere
   (3) an oblate sphere
   (4) an eccentric ellipse

3. According to the *Earth Science Reference Tables*, where are atmospheric pressure readings of 10^{-2} atmosphere found?
   (1) stratosphere
   (2) troposphere
   (3) mesosphere
   (4) thermosphere

4. The diagram below shows the altitude of Polaris above the horizon at a certain location.

What is the latitude of the observer?
(1) 10° N
(2) 40° N
(3) 50° N
(4) 90° N

5. In the Northern Hemisphere, during which season does the Earth reach its greatest distance from the Sun?
(1) winter
(2) spring
(3) summer
(4) fall

6. The Coriolis effect provides evidence that the Earth
(1) has a magnetic field
(2) has an elliptical orbit
(3) revolves around the Sun
(4) rotates on its axis

7. During the warmest part of a June day, breezes blow from the ocean toward the shore at a Long Island beach. Which statement best explains why this happens?
(1) Winds usually blow from hot to cold areas.
(2) Winds never blow from the shore toward the ocean.
(3) Air pressure over the ocean is higher than air pressure over the land.
(4) Air pressure over the land is higher than air pressure over the ocean.

Base your answers to questions 8 and 9 on the diagram below which represents the apparent daily path of the Sun across the sky in the Northern Hemisphere on the dates indicated.

(NOT DRAWN TO SCALE)

8. At noon on which date would the observer cast the longest shadow?
   (1) June 21
   (2) September 23
   (3) March 21
   (4) December 21

9. Which observation about the Sun's apparent path at this location on June 21 is best supported by the diagram?
   (1) The Sun appears to move across the sky at a rate of 1° per hour.
   (2) The Sun's total daytime path is shortest on this date.
   (3) Sunrise occurs north of east.
   (4) Sunset occurs south of west.

10. At which temperature would an object radiate the *least* amount of electromagnetic energy?
    (1) the boiling point of water (100°C)
    (2) the temperature at the stratopause (0°C)
    (3) the temperature of the North Pole on December 21 (−60°F)
    (4) room temperature (293 K)

11. Infrared radiation is absorbed in the atmosphere mainly by
    (1) nitrogen and oxygen
    (2) argon and radon
    (3) ice crystals and dust
    (4) carbon dioxide and water vapor

12. The diagram below shows part of the electromagnetic spectrum.

Which form of electromagnetic energy shown on the diagram has the lowest frequency and longest wavelength?
(1) AM radio   (3) red light
(2) infrared rays   (4) gamma rays

13. The factor that contributes most to the seasonal temperature changes during 1 year in New York State is the changing
(1) speed at which the Earth travels in its orbit around the Sun
(2) angle at which the Sun's rays strike the Earth's surface
(3) distance between the Earth and the Sun
(4) energy given off by the Sun

14. The tilt of the Earth on its axis is a cause of the Earth's
(1) uniform daylight hours   (3) 24-hour day
(2) changing length of day and night   (4) $365\frac{1}{4}$-day year

15. Which process most directly results in cloud formation?
(1) condensation   (3) precipitation
(2) transpiration   (4) radiation

16. An air mass originating over north central Canada would most likely be
(1) warm and dry   (3) cold and dry
(2) warm and moist   (4) cold and moist

17. Which graph best represents the relationship between the moisture-holding capacity (ability to hold moisture) of the atmosphere and atmospheric temperature?

18. In the diagram of a mountain below, location *A* and location *B* have the same elevation.

Prevailing winds

A

B

OCEAN

Compared to the climate at location *A*, the climate at location *B* will be
(1) warmer and drier
(2) cooler and drier
(3) warmer and wetter
(4) cooler and wetter

19. The graph below shows the air temperature and dewpoint temperature at one location at four different times during one morning.

At what time was the chance of precipitation the greatest?
(1) 1 a.m.
(2) 5 a.m.
(3) 3 a.m.
(4) 7 a.m.

20. According to the *Earth Science Reference Tables*, what is the approximate dewpoint temperature when the dry-bulb temperature is 18°C and the wet-bulb temperature is 14.5°C?
(1) 8.0°C
(2) 10°C
(3) 11°C
(4) 12°C

21. Which earth material covering the surface of a landfill would permit the *least* amount of rainwater to infiltrate the surface?
(1) silt
(2) clay
(3) sand
(4) pebbles

22. Two coastal cities have the same latitude and elevation, but are located near different oceans. Which statement best explains why the two cities have different climates?
(1) They are at different longitudes.
(2) They are near different ocean currents.
(3) They have different angles of insolation.
(4) They have different numbers of daylight hours.

23. Which graph best represents the relationship between soil permeability rate and infiltration when all other conditions are the same?

(1)   (2)   (3)   (4)

24. What most likely will happen to soil moisture when precipitation is greater than potential evapotranspiration?
    (1) Soil-moisture storage may decrease.
    (2) Soil-moisture deficit may increase.
    (3) Soil moisture may be recharged.
    (4) Soil moisture may be used.

25. In which type of climate does chemical weathering usually occur most rapidly?
    (1) hot and dry   (3) cold and dry
    (2) hot and wet   (4) cold and wet

26. A sample of rounded quartz sediments of different particle sizes is dropped into a container of water. Which graph best shows the settling time for these particles?

(1)   (2)   (3)   (4)

27. Where is metamorphic rock frequently found?
    (1) on mountaintops that have horizontal layers containing marine fossils
    (2) within large lava flows
    (3) as a thin surface layer covering huge areas of the continents
    (4) along the interface between igneous intrusions and sedimentary bedrock

28. The map below shows the top view of a meandering stream as it enters a lake.

At which points along the stream are erosion and deposition dominant?
    (1) Erosion is dominant at A and D, and deposition is dominant at B and C.
    (2) Erosion is dominant at B and C, and deposition is dominant at A and D.
    (3) Erosion is dominant at A and C, and deposition is dominant at B and D.
    (4) Erosion is dominant at B and D, and deposition is dominant at A and C.

29. The particles in a sand dune deposit are small and very well-sorted and have surface pits that give them a frosted appearance. This deposit most likely was transported by
(1) ocean currents (3) gravity
(2) glacial ice (4) wind

30. The diagram below represents a sedimentary rock outcrop.

Which rock layer is the most resistant to weathering?
(1) 1 (3) 3
(2) 2 (4) 4

31. Which property is most useful in mineral identification?
(1) hardness (3) size
(2) color (4) texture

32. The diagrams below represent four rock samples. Which rock took the longest time to solidify from magma deep within the Earth?

Bands of alternating light and dark minerals

(1)

Easily split layers of 0.0001-cm-diameter particles cemented together

(2)

Glassy black rock that breaks with a shell-shape fracture

(3)

Interlocking 0.5-cm-diameter crystals of various colors

(4)

33. According to the *Earth Science Reference Tables*, which two elements make up the greatest volume of the Earth's crust?
(1) silicon and potassium (3) iron and nickel
(2) silicon and iron (4) oxygen and potassium

34. The recrystallization of unmelted material under high temperature and pressure results in
(1) metamorphic rock (3) igneous rock
(2) sedimentary rock (4) volcanic rock

35. According to the *Earth Science Reference Tables*, which sedimentary rock would be formed by the compaction and cementation of particles 1.5 centimeters in diameter?
(1) shale (3) conglomerate
(2) sandstone (4) siltstone

36. Fossils of organisms that lived in shallow water can be found in horizontal sedimentary rock layers at great ocean depths. This fact is generally interpreted by most Earth scientists as evidence that
    (1) the cold water deep in the ocean kills shallow-water organisms
    (2) sunlight once penetrated to the deepest parts of the ocean
    (3) organisms that live in deep water evolved from species that once lived in shallow water
    (4) sections of the Earth's crust have changed their elevations relative to sea level

37. Earthquakes generate compressional waves (P-waves) and shear waves (S-waves). Compared to the speed of shear waves in a given earth material, the speed of compressional waves is
    (1) always slower
    (2) always faster
    (3) always the same
    (4) sometimes faster and sometimes slower

38. A P-wave reaches a seismograph station 2,600 kilometers from an earthquake epicenter at 12:10 p.m. According to the *Earth Science Reference Tables*, at what time did the earthquake occur?
    (1) 12:01 p.m.   (3) 12:15 p.m.
    (2) 12:05 p.m.   (4) 12:19 p.m.

39. The elevation of a certain area was measured for many years, and the results are recorded in the data table below.

Year	Elevation (m)
1870	102.00
1890	102.25
1910	102.50
1930	102.75
1950	103.00

If the elevation continued to increase at the same rate, what was most likely the elevation of this area in 1990?
    (1) 103.25 m   (3) 103.75 m
    (2) 103.50 m   (4) 104.00 m

40. The cross-sectional diagram below of the Earth shows the paths of seismic waves from an earthquake. Letter X represents the location of a seismic station.

Which statement best explains why station X received only P-waves?
(1) S-waves traveled too slowly for seismographs to detect them.
(2) Station X is too far from the focus for S-waves to reach.
(3) A liquid zone within the Earth stops S-waves.
(4) P-waves and S-waves are refracted by the Earth's core.

41. Geologists have subdivided geologic time into periods that are based on
(1) carbon dating   (3) fossil evidence
(2) rock types   (4) landscape regions

42. An ancient bone was analyzed and found to contain carbon-14 that had decayed for nearly two half-lives. According to the *Earth Science Reference Tables*, approximately how old is the bone?
(1) 1,400 years   (3) 5,600 years
(2) 2,800 years   (4) 11,000 years

43. According to the *Earth Science Reference Tables*, studies of the rock record suggest that
(1) the period during which humans have existed is very brief compared to geologic time
(2) evidence of the existence of humans is present over much of the geologic past
(3) humans first appeared at the time of the intrusion of the Palisades sill
(4) the earliest humans lived at the same time as the dinosaurs

44. The diagram below shows a cross-sectional view of part of the Earth's crust.

What does the unconformity (buried erosional surface) at line *XY* represent?
(1) an area of contact metamorphism
(2) a time gap in the rock record of the area
(3) proof that no deposition occurred between the Cambrian and Carboniferous periods
(4) overturning of the Cambrian and Carboniferous rock layers

45. The diagram below shows a cross section of the Earth's crust. Line *XY* is a fault.

Which sequence of events, from oldest to youngest, has occurred in this outcrop?

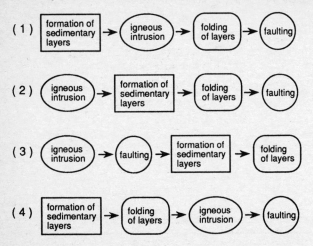

46. Which geologic evidence best supports the inference that a continental ice sheet once covered most of New York State?
    (1) polished and smooth pebbles; meandering rivers; V-shaped valleys
    (2) scratched and polished bedrock; unsorted gravel deposits; transported boulders
    (3) sand and silt beaches; giant swamps; marine fossils found on mountaintops
    (4) basaltic bedrock; folded, faulted, and tilted rock structures; lava flows

47. The boundaries between landscape regions are usually indicated by sharp changes in
    (1) bedrock structure and elevation
    (2) weathering rate and method of deposition
    (3) soil associations and geologic age
    (4) stream discharge rate and direction of flow

48. According to the *Earth Science Reference Tables*, which type of landscape region is found at 44° North latitude and 75° West longitude?
    (1) plains   (3) lowlands
    (2) plateaus   (4) mountains

49. The diagram below represents a partial cross section of a model of the Earth. The arrows show inferred motions within the Earth.

(NOT DRAWN TO SCALE)

Which property of the oceanic crust in regions *F* and *G* is a result of these inferred motions?
(1) The crystal size of the rock decreases constantly as distance from the mid-ocean ridge increases.
(2) The temperature of the basaltic rock increases as distance from the mid-ocean ridge increases.
(3) Heat-flow measurements steadily increase as distance from the mid-ocean ridge increases.
(4) The age of the igneous rock increases as distance from the mid-ocean ridge increases.

50. The diagram below shows a sample of conglomerate rock.

The oldest part of this sample is the
(1) conglomerate rock sample
(2) calcite cement
(3) limestone particles
(4) mineral vein

51. The map below shows the drainage patterns of a volcanic region.

Which two locations are most likely volcanic mountain peaks?
(1) *A* and *B*   (3) *A* and *D*
(2) *B* and *C*   (4) *B* and *D*

52. The map below shows average annual temperatures in degrees Fahrenheit across the United States.

Which climatic factor is most important in determining the pattern shown in the eastern half of the United States?
(1) ocean currents
(2) mountain barriers
(3) elevation above sea level
(4) latitude

Note that questions 53 through 55 have only three choices.

53. The diagram below shows an area where sea level gradually dropped over a period of thousands of years. A continuous sandy beach deposit stretching from *A* to *B* was created.

Which statement about the beach deposit would most likely be true?
(1) It is older at *A* than at *B*.
(2) It is older at *B* than at *A*.
(3) It is the same age at *A* and *B*.

54. As warm, moist air moves into a region, barometric pressure readings in the region will generally
(1) decrease
(2) increase
(3) remain the same

55. As surface runoff in a region increases, stream discharge in that region will usually
(1) decrease
(2) increase
(3) remain the same

PART II

This part consists of ten groups, each containing five questions. Choose seven of these ten groups. Be sure that you answer all five questions in each group chosen. [35]

Group I

If you choose this group, be sure to answer questions 56–60.

Base your answers to questions 56 through 60 on the *Earth Science Reference Tables*, the contour map below and your knowledge of earth science. Points *A*, *B*, *Y*, and *Z* are reference points on the map. Note that portions of the map are incomplete.

CONTOUR INTERVAL = 20 meters

56. Which diagram best represents the profile along line *YZ*?

57. A benchmark (B.M. 623) located at the top of the hill is shown as △. What is the elevation of the contour line that is closest to this benchmark?
    (1) 600 m
    (2) 610 m
    (3) 620 m
    (4) 630 m

58. In which general direction is Blue Stream flowing?
    (1) east
    (2) west
    (3) northwest
    (4) southeast

59. The gradient of Blue Stream between point *A* and point *B* is approximately
    (1) 26 m/km
    (2) 70. m/km
    (3) 130 m/km
    (4) 350 m/km

60. On which map is the 300-meter contour line completed correctly?

Group 2

If you choose this group, be sure to answer questions 61–65.

Base your answers to questions 61 through 65 on the *Earth Science Reference Tables*, the diagram below, and your knowledge of earth science. The diagram represents a model of the orbit of a moon around a planet. Points *A, B, C,* and *D* indicate four positions of the moon in its orbit. Points F_1 and F_2 are focal points of the orbit.

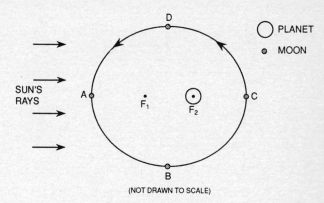

(NOT DRAWN TO SCALE)

61. If the moon takes 6.8 days to move from point *A* to point *B*, the best estimate of the time required for one complete revolution is
    (1) 20. days
    (2) 27 days
    (3) 34 days
    (4) 41 days

62. When viewed from the planet, the moon has the greatest apparent diameter at point
    (1) *A*
    (2) *B*
    (3) *C*
    (4) *D*

63. If the distance from F_1 to F_2 is 42,000 kilometers and the distance from *A* to *C* is 768,000 kilometers, what is the eccentricity of the moon's orbit?
    (1) 0.055
    (2) 0.18
    (3) 0.81
    (4) 0.94

64. For an observer on the planet, at which position in the moon's orbit does the full-moon phase occur?
    (1) *A*
    (2) *B*
    (3) *C*
    (4) *D*

65. As the moon moves in its orbit from point *D* to point *B*, the force of gravitational attraction between the moon and the planet
    (1) increases, only
    (2) decreases, only
    (3) increases, then decreases
    (4) decreases, then increases

Group 3

If you choose this group, be sure to answer questions 66–70.

Base your answers to questions 66 through 70 on the *Earth Science Reference Tables*, the diagrams below, and your knowledge of earth science. The diagrams show the steps used to determine the amount of heat held by equal masses of iron, copper, lead, and granite.

KEY

Granite

Lead

Copper

Iron

STEP A
Measure the mass of each sample.

STEP B
Place samples in boiling water.

— beaker

STEP C
Measure the temperature of water in an insulated container.

insulated container

300 mL of water at room temperature

STEP D
Transfer one sample from the boiling water and stir gently with the thermometer. Record the temperature changes of the water.

STEP E
Repeat steps C and D with each sample.

66. This method of determining the amount of heat absorbed by substances assumes that the energy lost by a heat source is
    (1) refracted by a heat sink
    (2) reflected by a heat sink
    (3) absorbed by a heat sink
    (4) scattered by a heat sink

67. Which substance has the highest specific heat?
    (1) copper
    (2) granite
    (3) iron
    (4) lead

68. Why must the water be kept boiling in step *B*?
    (1) All samples must be heated to the same high temperature.
    (2) Boiling changes the melting point of the materials being tested.
    (3) The samples must be heated above 100°C.
    (4) Less energy is lost during a phase change.

69. The granite sample is transferred from the boiling water to the room-temperature water. Why is the total heat lost by the granite greater than the total heat gained by the room-temperature water?
    (1) The granite sample had less volume than the other samples.
    (2) The granite sample lost some heat to the air as it was being transferred.
    (3) Water gained heat from the insulated container.
    (4) Water has a lower specific heat than the granite sample.

70. The movements of water molecules that transfer heat from one place to another within the water are called
    (1) radiation waves
    (2) transverse waves
    (3) conduction collisions
    (4) convection currents

Group 4

If you choose this group, be sure to answer questions 71–75.

Base your answers to questions 71 through 75 on the *Earth Science Reference Tables*, the diagrams and graph below, and your knowledge of earth science. The diagrams show the general effect of the Earth's atmosphere on insolation from the Sun at middle latitudes during both clear-sky and cloudy-sky conditions. The graph shows the percentage of insolation reflected by the Earth's surface at different latitudes in the Northern Hemisphere in winter.

INSOLATION IN THE ATMOSPHERE

CLEAR SKY

CLOUDY SKY

EARTH'S SURFACE (45° NORTH LATITUDE)

REFLECTION BY THE SURFACE

71. Approximately what percentage of the insolation actually reaches the ground at 45° North latitude on a clear day?
    (1) 100%   (3) 60%
    (2) 80%   (4) 45%

72. Which factor keeps the greatest percentage of insolation from reaching the Earth's surface on cloudy days?
    (1) absorption by cloud droplets
    (2) reflection by cloud droplets
    (3) absorption by clear-air gas molecules
    (4) reflection by clear-air gas molecules

73. According to the graph, on a winter day at 70° North latitude, what approximate percentage of the insolation is reflected by the Earth's surface?
    (1) 50%   (3) 85%
    (2) 65%   (4) 100%

74. Which statement best explains why, at high latitudes, reflectivity of insolation is greater in winter than in summer?
    (1) The North Pole is tilted toward the Sun in winter.
    (2) Snow and ice reflect almost all insolation.
    (3) The colder air holds much more moisture.
    (4) Dust settles quickly in cold air.

75. The radiation that passes through the atmosphere and reaches the Earth's surface has the greatest intensity in the form of
    (1) visible-light radiation
    (2) infrared radiation
    (3) ultraviolet radiation
    (4) radio-wave radiation

Group 5

If you choose this group, be sure to answer questions 76–80.

Base your answers to questions 76 through 80 on the *Earth Science Reference Tables*, the weather map below showing part of the United States, and your knowledge of earth science. Letters *A* through *E* represent weather stations.

76. At which weather station is the barometric pressure reading most likely to be 1,018.0 millibars?
    (1) *A*   (3) C
    (2) *B*   (4) *D*

77. Which weather station model best represents weather conditions at station *B*?

(1)   (2)   (3)   (4)

78. Which station's weather has been influenced most recently by the passage of a cold front?
    (1) *E*   (3) C
    (2) *B*   (4) *D*

79. At which weather station is precipitation most likely occurring at the present time?
    (1) *A*   (3) *E*
    (2) *B*   (4) *D*

80. If the low-pressure center follows a normal storm track, it will move toward the
    (1) southeast   (3) northeast
    (2) southwest   (4) northwest

Group 6
If you choose this group, be sure to answer questions 81–85.

Base your answers to questions 81 through 85 on the *Earth Science Reference Tables*, the information and diagrams below, and your knowledge of earth science.

A mixture of colloids, clay, silt, sand, pebbles, and cobbles is put into stream I at point *A*. The water velocity at point *A* is 400 centimeters per second. A similar mixture of particles is put into stream II at point *A*. The water velocity in stream II at point *A* is 80 centimeters per second.

STREAM I   STREAM II

81. Which statement best describes what happens when the particles are placed in the streams?
    (1) Stream I will move all particles that are added at point *A*.
    (2) Stream II will move all particles that are added at point *A*.
    (3) Stream I cannot move sand.
    (4) Stream II cannot move sand.

82. Which statement is the most accurate description of conditions in both streams?
    (1) The greatest deposition occurs at point B.
    (2) Particles are carried in suspension and by bouncing along the bottom.
    (3) The particles will have a greater velocity than the water in the stream.
    (4) The velocity of the stream is the same at point B as at point C.

83. If a sudden rainstorm occurs at both streams above point A, the erosion rate will
    (1) increase for stream I, but not for stream II
    (2) increase for stream II, but not for stream I
    (3) increase for both streams
    (4) not change for either stream

84. What will most likely occur when the transported sediment reaches lake II?
    (1) Clay particles will settle first.
    (2) The largest particles will be carried farthest into the lake.
    (3) The sediment will become more angular because of abrasion.
    (4) The particles will be deposited in sorted layers.

Note that question 85 has only three choices.

85. In lake I, as the stream water moves from point C to point D, its velocity
    (1) decreases
    (2) increases
    (3) remains the same

Group 7

If you choose this group, be sure to answer questions 86–90.

Base your answers to questions 86 through 90 on the *Earth Science Reference Tables*, the diagram below, and your knowledge of earth science. The diagram represents three cross sections of the Earth at different locations to a depth of 50 kilometers below sea level. The measurements given with each cross section indicate the thickness and the density of the layers.

86. In which group are the layers of the Earth arranged in order of increasing average density?
    (1) mantle, crust, ocean water
    (2) crust, mantle, ocean water
    (3) ocean water, mantle, crust
    (4) ocean water, crust, mantle

87. Which material is most likely to be found 20 kilometers below sea level at the continental mountain location?
    (1) basalt
    (2) granite
    (3) shale
    (4) limestone

88. Which statement about the Earth's mantle is confirmed by the diagram?
    (1) The mantle is liquid.
    (2) The mantle has the same composition as the crust.
    (3) The mantle is located at different depths below the Earth's surface.
    (4) The mantle does not exist under continental mountains.

89. Compared with the oceanic crust, the continental crust is
    (1) thinner and less dense
    (2) thinner and more dense
    (3) thicker and less dense
    (4) thicker and more dense

90. The division of the Earth's interior into crust and mantle, as shown in the diagram, is based primarily on the study of
    (1) radioactive dating
    (2) seismic waves
    (3) volcanic eruptions
    (4) gravity measurements

Group 8

If you choose this group, be sure to answer questions 91–95.

Base your answers to questions 91 through 95 on the *Earth Science Reference Tables*, the graph below, and your knowledge of earth science. The graph shows the development, growth in population, and extinction of the six major groups of trilobites, labeled *A* through *F*.

GEOLOGIC TIME ZONES

KEY TO SYMBOLS:

■ Population based on fossil record

▨ Population presumed: fossil evidence rare

------ Assumed evolutionary relationship

91. The fossil evidence that forms the basis for this graph was most likely found in
    (1) lava flows of ancient volcanoes
    (2) sedimentary rock that formed from ocean sediment
    (3) granite rock that formed from former sedimentary rocks
    (4) metamorphic rock that formed from volcanic rocks

92. Which group of trilobites became the most abundant?
    (1) *A*
    (2) *B*
    (3) *C*
    (4) *D*

93. During which period did the last of these trilobite groups become extinct?
    (1) Cretaceous   (3) Permian
    (2) Triassic   (4) Carboniferous

94. Which inference is best supported by the graph?
    (1) All trilobites evolved from group *A* trilobites.
    (2) The trilobite groups became most abundant during the Devonian Period.
    (3) Precambrian trilobite fossils are very rare.
    (4) Trilobites could exist in present-day marine climates.

95. The diagrams below represent rock outcrops in which the rock layers have not been overturned. Which rock outcrop shows a possible sequence of the trilobite fossils?

Group 9
If you choose this group, be sure to answer questions 96–100.

Base your answers to questions 96 through 100 on the *Earth Science Reference Tables*, the diagrams below, and your knowledge of earth science. Diagram I shows a map of Niagara Falls and part of the Niagara River Gorge. The past locations of the edge of the river gorge are labeled in calendar years from 1678 to 1969. The lines show the changing locations of the edge of the Horseshoe Falls as it receded (eroded upstream) due to weathering and undercutting. Diagram II shows a geologic cross section of the rock layers at the edge of the Niagara River Gorge.

DIAGRAM I

DIAGRAM II

96. According to the map and scale, what is the approximate rate at which the Horseshoe Falls receded upstream from point *A* in 1678 to point *B* in 1969?
    (1) 1 meter per year
    (2) 0.1 meter per year
    (3) 10 meters per year
    (4) 200 meters per year

97. According to the geologic cross section (diagram II), the top rock layer at Niagara Falls consists of
    (1) crystals from chemical precipitation and evaporation
    (2) crystalline minerals resulting from melting and solidification
    (3) banded and distorted layers due to extreme pressure
    (4) metamorphosed clay, sand, and volcanic ash

98. Most scientists believe that the Niagara River started flowing at the end of the last ice age. During which geologic epoch did this ice age occur?
    (1) Early Triassic   (3) Miocene
    (2) Paleocene   (4) Pleistocene

99. In which New York State landscape region is Niagara Falls located?
    (1) Appalachian Plateau
    (2) Tug Hill Plateau
    (3) Erie-Ontario Lowlands
    (4) St. Lawrence Lowlands

100. What is the age of the surface bedrock at Niagara Falls, New York?
    (1) Devonian   (3) Ordovician
    (2) Silurian   (4) Cambrian

Group 10

If you choose this group, be sure to answer questions 101–105.

Base your answers to questions 101 through 105 on the *Earth Science Reference Tables* and your knowledge of earth science.

101. A barometric pressure reading of 28.97 inches is equal to
    (1) 981 mb   (3) 1,006 mb
    (2) 984 mb   (4) 1,008 mb

102. A student incorrectly converted 20°C to 64°F instead of 68°F. What is the student's approximate percent error?
    (1) 44%   (3) 6.3%
    (2) 5.9%   (4) 4%

103. A fine-grained igneous rock contains 11% plagioclase, 72% pyroxene, 15% olivine, and 2% hornblende. This rock would most likely be classified as
    (1) granite   (3) gabbro
    (2) rhyolite   (4) basalt

104. What do the tropopause, stratopause, and mesopause all have in common?
    (1) Each is a point of maximum temperature in its layer of the atmosphere.
    (2) Each is an interface between two layers of the atmosphere.
    (3) Each is a region of increasing pressure within the atmosphere.
    (4) Each is a zone of decreasing water vapor content within the atmosphere.

105. Which relative concentrations of elements are found in a felsic rock?
    (1) a high concentration of aluminum and a low concentration of iron
    (2) a high concentration of iron and a low concentration of aluminum
    (3) a high concentration of magnesium and a low concentration of iron
    (4) a high concentration of magnesium and a low concentration of aluminum

EARTH SCIENCE

June 17, 1994

PART I

Answer all 55 questions in this part. [55]

Directions (1–55): For *each* statement or question, select the word or expression that, of those given, best completes the statement or answers the question.

1. Which statement about a mineral sample found in a field in New York State is most likely an inference?
   (1) The sample was transported by a glacier.
   (2) The sample is white in color.
   (3) The sample is rectangular, with sharp, angular corners.
   (4) The sample is 8 cm long, 5 cm wide, and 3 cm high.

2. The use of a triple-beam balance to determine the mass of a rock is an example of measuring by using
   (1) all of the five senses
   (2) inferences and interpretations
   (3) a direct comparison with a standard
   (4) a combination of dimensional quantities

3. Which graph best represents the relationship between the latitude of an observer and the observed altitude of Polaris above the northern horizon?

(1)

(3)

(2)

(4)

4. According to the *Earth Science Reference Tables,* as altitude increases from the tropopause to the mesopause, the atmospheric temperature will
   (1) decrease, only
   (2) increase, only
   (3) decrease, then increase
   (4) increase, then decrease

5. Which diagram best illustrates the heat transfer movement in fluids?

(1)

(3)

(2)

(4)

6. The diagrams below represent fossils found at different locations.

When classified by similarity of structure, which three fossils should be grouped together?
(1) *A, F,* and *H*
(2) *C, F,* and *J*
(3) *E, G,* and *H*
(4) *B, D,* and *I*

7. From which set of polar and equatorial diameters can the actual shape of the Earth be inferred?
(1) polar diameter = 12,714 km
equatorial diameter = 12,714 km
(2) polar diameter = 12,756 km
equatorial diameter = 12,756 km
(3) polar diameter = 12,714 km
equatorial diameter = 12,756 km
(4) polar diameter = 12,756 km
equatorial diameter = 12,714 km

8. The best evidence that the distance between the Moon and the Earth varies is provided by the apparent change in the Moon's
(1) shape
(2) diameter
(3) altitude
(4) phase

9. Earth's atmospheric winds are deflected in a predictable manner because of the Earth's
(1) rotation
(2) revolution
(3) gravity
(4) inclination

10. Approximately how many hours of daylight are received at the North Pole on June 21?
(1) 0
(2) 12
(3) 18
(4) 24

11. In general, good absorbers of electromagnetic radiation are also good
(1) refractors
(2) radiators
(3) reflectors
(4) convectors

12. An increase in latent heat can cause liquid water to
(1) melt
(2) condense
(3) freeze
(4) evaporate

13. The average air temperature on the Earth may increase as a result of the ability of carbon dioxide and water vapor to absorb
(1) visible light
(2) radio waves
(3) gamma radiation
(4) infrared radiation

14. According to the *Earth Science Reference Tables,* an air pressure of 29.47 inches of mercury is equal to
    (1) 996 mb
    (2) 998 mb
    (3) 1,002 mb
    (4) 1,014 mb

15. The graph below shows the changes in height of ocean water over the course of 2 days at one Earth location.

Which statement concerning these changes is best supported by the graph?
    (1) The changes are cyclic and occur at predictable time intervals.
    (2) The changes are cyclic and occur at the same time every day.
    (3) The changes are noncyclic and occur at sunrise and sunset.
    (4) The changes are noncyclic and may occur at any time.

16. On which map of temperatures across the United States is the 60°F isotherm drawn correctly?

17. The diagram below shows the apparent paths of the Sun in relation to a house in New York State on June 21 and December 21.

(not drawn to scale)

Which statement best explains the cause of this apparent change in the Sun's path?
(1) The Sun's orbital velocity changes as it revolves around the Earth.
(2) The Earth's orbital velocity changes as it revolves around the Sun.
(3) The Earth's axis is tilted 23½°.
(4) The Sun's axis is tilted 23½°.

18. In the Northern Hemisphere, what is the direction of surface wind circulation in a high-pressure system?
(1) clockwise and outward from the center
(2) clockwise and toward the center
(3) counterclockwise and outward from the center
(4) counterclockwise and toward the center

19. Which abbreviation indicates a warm air mass that contains large amounts of water vapor? [Refer to the *Earth Science Reference Tables.*]
(1) cP   (3) mT
(2) cT   (4) mP

20. Which gas in the atmosphere has the most influence on day-to-day weather changes?
(1) ozone   (3) water vapor
(2) oxygen   (4) carbon dioxide

21. Which condition most likely exists when precipitation is greater than potential evapotranspiration and soil water storage is at the maximum?
(1) usage   (3) recharge
(2) runoff   (4) drought

22. Which station model represents an atmospheric pressure of 1,009.2 millibars and a temperature of 75°F?

23. The diagram below represents snow falling on the Tug Hill Plateau in New York State.

(NOT DRAWN TO SCALE)

The best explanation for the formation of snow under these conditions is that
(1) dry air rises and warms
(2) moist air rises and cools
(3) moist air rises and warms
(4) dry air sinks and cools

24. The diagram below represents the Earth's orbital path around the Sun. The Earth takes the same amount of time to move from A to B as from C to D.

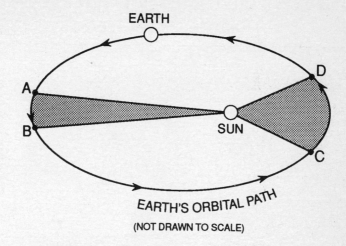

EARTH

SUN

EARTH'S ORBITAL PATH

(NOT DRAWN TO SCALE)

Which values are equal within the system?
(1) The shaded sections of the diagram are equal in area.
(2) The distance from the Sun to the Earth is the same at point A and at point D.
(3) The orbital velocity of the Earth at point A equals its orbital velocity at point C.
(4) The gravitational force between the Earth and the Sun at point B is the same as the gravitational force at point D.

25. The graph below represents the average temperature of a city for each month of the year.

Where is this city most likely located?
(1) inland in the Northern Hemisphere, in a middle latitude
(2) inland in the Southern Hemisphere, in a middle latitude
(3) on a coast near the Equator
(4) on a coast in the Antarctic

26. According to the *Earth Science Reference Tables*, which element is most abundant by mass in the Earth's crust?
    (1) nitrogen
    (3) silicon
    (2) oxygen
    (4) iron

27. The photograph below shows a fan-shaped accumulation of sediment.

SEDIMENT

This accumulation of sediment is the direct result of
(1) weathering of bedrock
(3) deposition by running water
(2) erosion by wind
(4) transport by glaciers

28. What is the best explanation for the two statements below?

    ● Some mountains located near the Earth's Equator have snow-covered peaks.
    ● Icecaps exist at the Earth's poles.

    (1) High elevation and high altitude have a similar effect on climate.
    (2) Both mountain and polar regions have arid climates.
    (3) Mountain and polar regions receive more energy from the Sun than other regions do.
    (4) An increase in snowfall and an increase in temperature have a similar effect on climate.

29. During winter, Lake Ontario is generally warmer than adjacent land areas. The primary reason for this temperature difference is that
    (1) water has a higher specific heat than land has
    (2) water reflects sunlight better than land does
    (3) land is more dense than water is
    (4) winds blow from land areas toward the water

30. As a particle of sediment in a stream breaks into several smaller pieces, the rate of weathering of the sediment will
    (1) decrease due to a decrease in surface area
    (2) decrease due to an increase in surface area
    (3) increase due to a decrease in surface area
    (4) increase due to an increase in surface area

31. When minerals are dissolved, how are the resulting ions carried by rivers?
    (1) by precipitation
    (2) by tumbling and rolling
    (3) in suspension
    (4) in solution

32. The relative hardness of a mineral can best be tested by
    (1) scratching the mineral across a glass plate
    (2) squeezing the mineral with calibrated pliers
    (3) determining the density of the mineral
    (4) breaking the mineral with a hammer

33. The diagrams below show how plant materials are changed into the three forms of coal by natural processes.

START ⟶ FINISH

Pressure of overlying sediments

Decayed plant material

Lignite coal

Bituminous coal

Anthracite coal

By which process is anthracite coal formed from bituminous coal? [Refer to the *Earth Science Reference Tables*.]
(1) solidification
(2) metamorphism
(3) deposition
(4) intrusion

34. In the diagram below, the arrow shows the direction of stream flow around a bend.

    At which point does the greatest stream erosion occur?
    (1) *A*   (3) *C*
    (2) *B*   (4) *D*

35. Which is an accurate statement about rocks?
    (1) Rocks are located only in continental areas of the Earth.
    (2) Rocks seldom undergo change.
    (3) Most rocks contain fossils.
    (4) Most rocks have several minerals in common.

36. The size of the mineral crystals found in an igneous rock is directly related to the
    (1) density of the minerals
    (2) color of the minerals
    (3) cooling time of the molten rock
    (4) amount of sediments cemented together

37. Which statement best explains why the direction of some seismic waves changes sharply as the waves travel through the Earth?
    (1) The Earth is spherical.
    (2) Seismic waves tend to travel in curved paths.
    (3) The temperature of the Earth's interior decreases with depth.
    (4) Different parts of the Earth's interior have different densities.

38. The diagram below represents a cross section of a portion of the Earth's crust and mantle. Letters *A, B, C, D,* and *X* identify locations within the crust.

The age of oceanic crust increases along a line between location *X* and location

(1) *A*   (3) *C*

(2) *B*   (4) *D*

39. In a soil sample, the particles have the same shape but different sizes. Which graph best represents the relationship between particle size and settling time when these particles are deposited in a quiet body of water?

40. The best evidence of crustal uplift would be provided by

   (1) marine fossils in the Rocky Mountains

   (2) sediment in the Gulf of Mexico

   (3) trenches in the Pacific Ocean floor

   (4) igneous rock deep within the Earth

41. According to the *Earth Science Reference Tables*, what is the approximate total distance traveled by an earthquake's *P*-wave in its first 9 minutes?
    (1) 2,600 km
    (2) 5,600 km
    (3) 7,600 km
    (4) 12,100 km

42. Which evidence supports the theory of ocean-floor spreading?
    (1) The rocks of the ocean floor and the continents have similar origins.
    (2) In the ocean floor, rocks near the mid-ocean ridge are cooler than rocks near the continents.
    (3) The pattern of magnetic orientation of rocks is similar on both sides of the mid-ocean ridge.
    (4) The density of oceanic crust is greater than the density of continental crust.

43. A layer of volcanic ash may serve as a time marker because the ash is
    (1) generally deposited only on land
    (2) composed of index fossils
    (3) deposited rapidly over a large area
    (4) often a distinct color

44. One similarity between uranium-238 and carbon-14 is that both
    (1) decay at a predictable rate
    (2) have the same half-life
    (3) are normally found in large quantities in living matter
    (4) are found in granite

45. The diagram below represents a series of brachiopod fossils showing progressive changes during the Early Mississippian Epoch. The fossils are drawn to scale.

BEGINNING OF EARLY MISSISSIPPIAN EPOCH

END OF EARLY MISSISSIPPIAN EPOCH

One explanation for this process of change is the theory of
    (1) superposition
    (2) evolution
    (3) dynamic equilibrium
    (4) fossilization

46. What is the best interpretation of the two statements below?

    • Corals are marine animals that live in warm ocean water.
    • Fossil corals are found in surface bedrock in areas of New York State.

    (1) Corals once lived on land.
    (2) Corals have migrated northward.
    (3) Parts of New York State are now covered by warm ocean water.
    (4) Parts of New York State were once covered by warm ocean water.

47. Which feature often indicates a boundary between landscape regions?
    (1) a highway cutting through a mountain region
    (2) resistant bedrock composed of more than one type of mineral
    (3) a long, meandering stream flowing across a large, level region
    (4) a change in slope between adjoining bedrock types with different structures

48. According to the *Earth Science Reference Tables*, when did the intrusion of the Palisades Sill occur?
    (1) before the Appalachian Orogeny
    (2) during the late Triassic Period
    (3) during the Paleozoic Era
    (4) after the extinction of dinosaurs and ammonites

49. According to the *Earth Science Reference Tables,* what are the respective decay products of uranium, potassium, and rubidium?
    (1) lead (Pb), argon (Ar), and strontium (Sr)
    (2) carbon (C), oxygen (O), and nitrogen (N)
    (3) hydrogen (H), lithium (Li), and helium (He)
    (4) silicon (Si), oxygen (O), and aluminum (Al)

50. According to the *Earth Science Reference Tables,* at which location could a geologist find shale containing eurypterid fossils?
    (1) Old Forge   (3) New York City
    (2) Syracuse   (4) Long Island

51. The advance and retreat of continental ice sheets produced deposits of sands and gravels during the Pleistocene Epoch. According to the *Earth Science Reference Tables,* in which New York State landscape region were such sands and gravels deposited over Cretaceous and Tertiary materials?
    (1) Atlantic Coastal Plain
    (2) Erie-Ontario Lowlands
    (3) Adirondack Mountains
    (4) Tug Hill Plateau

52. According to the *Earth Science Reference Tables,* in which type of landscape region is Elmira, New York, located?
    (1) mountains   (3) plateau
    (2) plain   (4) lowlands

53. The block diagrams below show a river and its landscape during four stages of erosion.

A   C

B   D

In which order should the diagrams be placed to show the most likely sequence of river and landscape development?
(1) *A, D, B, C*   (3) *C, B, A, D*
(2) *B, D, C, A*   (4) *D, A, C, B*

54. Which condition is a characteristic of a landscape region in dynamic equilibrium?
    (1) a balance between uplifting and erosion
    (2) a balance between weathering and erosion
    (3) more erosion than uplifting
    (4) more uplifting than weathering

Note that question 55 has only three choices.

55. A person in New York State observes a star that is due east and just above the horizon. During the next hour, the distance between the star and the horizon will appear to
    (1) decrease
    (2) increase
    (3) remain the same

PART II

This part consists of ten groups, each containing five questions. Choose seven of these ten groups. Be sure that you answer all five questions in each group chosen. [35]

Group 1

If you choose this group, be sure to answer questions 56-60.

Base your answers to questions 56 through 60 on the *Earth Science Reference Tables*, the contour map below, and your knowledge of Earth science. Letters *A* through *K* represent locations in the area. Hachure lines (⊔⊔⊔⊔) show depressions.

Contour interval = 20 meters
⊔⊔⊔⊔ Hachure lines show depression

56. Which hilltop could have an elevation of 1,145 meters?
    (1) *D* (3) *G*
    (2) *F* (4) *H*

57. Toward which direction does Moose Creek flow?
    (1) southeast (3) southwest
    (2) northeast (4) northwest

58. Which graph best represents the map profile along a straight line from point *C* through point *A* to point *K*?

(1)

(3)

(2)

(4)

59. Which equation would be used to determine the stream gradient along Moose Creek between points *J* and *K*?

    (1) gradient $= \dfrac{1.8 \text{ km}}{80 \text{ m}} \times 100$

    (2) gradient $= \dfrac{0.8 \text{ km}}{60 \text{ m}}$

    (3) gradient $= (1{,}040 \text{ m} - 960 \text{ m}) \times 20 \text{ m}$

    (4) gradient $= \dfrac{80 \text{ m}}{1.8 \text{ km}}$

60. What is the *lowest* possible elevation of point *B*?
    (1) 981 m (3) 961 m
    (2) 971 m (4) 941 m

Group 2

If you choose this group, be sure to answer questions 61–65.

Base your answers to questions 61 through 65 on the *Earth Science Reference Tables,* the diagram below, and your knowledge of Earth science. The diagram shows the Earth's position in its orbit around the Sun at the beginning of each season. The Moon is shown at various positions as it revolves around the Earth.

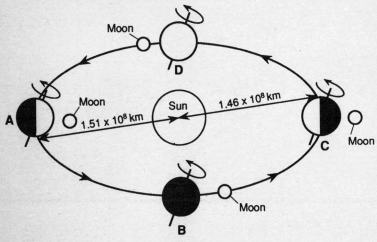

(not drawn to scale)

61. What is most likely represented by the symbol ⟲ near the Earth's axis at each position?
    (1) the direction of Earth's rotation
    (2) the path of the Sun through the sky
    (3) the changing tilt of Earth's axis
    (4) convection currents in the atmosphere

62. The Earth's orbit around the Sun is best described as
    (1) a perfect circle
    (2) an oblate spheroid
    (3) a very eccentric ellipse
    (4) a slightly eccentric ellipse

63. Which position of the Earth represents the beginning of the winter season for New York State?
    (1) *A*   (3) *C*
    (2) *B*   (4) *D*

64. Which position of the Earth shows the Moon located where its shadow may sometimes reach the Earth?
    (1) *A*   (3) *C*
    (2) *B*   (4) *D*

65. As the Earth moves from position *B* to position *C*, what change will occur in the gravitational attraction between the Earth and the Sun?
    (1) It will decrease, only.
    (2) It will increase, only.
    (3) It will decrease, then increase.
    (4) It will remain the same.

Group 3

If you choose this group, be sure to answer questions 66–70.

Base your answers to questions 66 through 70 on the *Earth Science Reference Tables*, the weather map of the United States below, and your knowledge of Earth science.

66. Which kind of frontal system is located northwest of Miles City, Montana?
    (1) cold front
    (2) warm front
    (3) stationary front
    (4) occluded front

67. The air mass over Memphis, Tennessee, most likely originated in
    (1) the North Pacific
    (2) central Canada
    (3) the central United States
    (4) the Gulf of Mexico

68. According to the map, at which city is precipitation most likely occurring?
    (1) Boise, Idaho
    (2) Omaha, Nebraska
    (3) Albuquerque, New Mexico
    (4) New York City

69. If the low-pressure systems follow the path of most weather systems in the United States, in which direction will they move?
    (1) northwest
    (2) southwest
    (3) northeast
    (4) southeast

70. The weather front west of Memphis, Tennessee, is moving at a speed of 50 kilometers per hour. What is the most likely weather forecast for Memphis for the next 12 hours?
    (1) showers followed by clearing skies and cooler temperatures
    (2) showers followed by warm, humid conditions
    (3) clearing skies followed by warm, dry conditions
    (4) a continuation of the present weather conditions

Group 4

If you choose this group, be sure to answer questions 71–75.

Base your answers to questions 71 through 75 on the *Earth Science Reference Tables*, the data table below, and your knowledge of Earth science. The table shows the time of sunrise and sunset and the total amount of insolation received on the Earth's surface for four locations, *A, B, C,* and *D*, at the beginning of each season. The locations have the same longitude, but are at different latitudes. Data were collected on clear, sunny days.

Location A — 66° North Latitude

Date	Sunrise	Sunset	Total Insolation (cal/cm^2)
March 21	6:00 a.m.	6:00 p.m.	373
June 21	12:51 a.m.	11:09 p.m.	1,014
September 23	5:48 a.m.	6:12 p.m.	393
December 21	11:06 p.m.	12:54 a.m.	1

Location B — 43° North Latitude

Date	Sunrise	Sunset	Total Insolation (cal/cm^2)
March 21	6:00 a.m.	6:00 p.m.	674
June 21	4:24 a.m.	7:36 p.m.	1,023
September 23	5:54 a.m.	6:06 p.m.	682
December 21	7:33 a.m.	4:27 p.m.	284

Location C — 0° Latitude

Date	Sunrise	Sunset	Total Insolation (cal/cm^2)
March 21	6:00 a.m.	6:00 p.m.	923
June 21	6:00 a.m.	6:00 p.m.	814
September 23	6:00 a.m.	6:00 p.m.	909
December 21	6:00 a.m.	6:00 p.m.	869

Location D — 23° South Latitude

Date	Sunrise	Sunset	Total Insolation (cal/cm^2)
March 21	5:57 a.m.	6:03 p.m.	851
June 21	6:42 a.m.	5:18 p.m.	545
September 23	6:00 a.m.	6:00 p.m.	827
December 21	5:15 a.m.	6:45 p.m.	1,044

71. Which location received the greatest total insolation on June 21?
    (1) *A*   (3) *C*
    (2) *B*   (4) *D*

72. At which location would an observer see the Sun in the northern sky at noon on March 21?
    (1) *A*   (3) *C*
    (2) *B*   (4) *D*

73. A comparison of the times of sunrise and sunset in New York State on December 21 and June 21 shows that, in December, the Sun
    (1) rises later and sets earlier
    (2) rises earlier and sets later
    (3) rises and sets earlier
    (4) rises and sets later

74. Which statement best explains why surface temperatures are higher at 43° N than at 66° N on June 21?
    (1) At 66° N, there is complete darkness.
    (2) At 66° N, winter is beginning.
    (3) At 43° N, summer is ending.
    (4) At 43° N, the angle of insolation is greater.

75. Why are the times of sunrise and sunset for March 21 and September 23 nearly the same at each location?
    (1) The Sun's altitude at noon is the same everywhere on Earth on these days.
    (2) The Earth is at its closest and farthest points from the Sun on these days.
    (3) The Sun's insolation reaches its maximum intensity on these days.
    (4) The Sun is directly above the Equator on these days.

Group 5

If you choose this group, be sure to answer questions 76–80.

Base your answers to questions 76 through 80 on the *Earth Science Reference Tables*, the diagrams below, and your knowledge of Earth science. The diagrams represent cross sections of four samples of loosely packed, uniformly sorted soil particles. The diameter of the particles is given below each diagram. All soil samples consists of solid spherical particles.

A (0.9 cm)   B (0.7 cm)   C (0.5 cm)   D (0.3 cm)

(not drawn to scale)

76. Particles of the sizes shown are classified as
    (1) cobbles   (3) sand
    (2) pebbles   (4) silt

77. Which graph best represents the capillarity of these soil samples?

(1)

(3)

(2)

(4)

78. Water can infiltrate these soils if they are
    (1) saturated and impermeable
    (2) saturated and permeable
    (3) unsaturated and impermeable
    (4) unsaturated and permeable

79. Which sample has the greatest permeability?
    (1) *A*   (3) *C*
    (2) *B*   (4) *D*

Note that question 80 has only three choices.

80. Some particles from sample *D* are mixed with particles from sample *A*. Compared
    to the original porosity of sample *A*, the porosity of the resulting mixture will be
    (1) less
    (2) greater
    (3) the same

Group 6

If you choose this group, be sure to answer questions 81–85.

Base your answers to questions 81 through 85 on the *Earth Science Reference Tables*, the diagram below, and your knowledge of Earth science. The diagram represents a profile of a stream. Points *A* through *E* are locations along the stream.

(not drawn to scale)

81. The primary force responsible for the flow of water in this stream is
    (1) solar energy   (3) wind
    (2) magnetic fields   (4) gravity

82. Between which two points is potential energy changing to kinetic energy most rapidly?
    (1) *A* and *B*   (3) *C* and *D*
    (2) *B* and *C*   (4) *D* and *E*

83. The largest particles of sediment transported by the stream at location *C* are sand particles. What is the approximate velocity of the stream at location *C*?
    (1) 50 cm/sec   (3) 300 cm/sec
    (2) 200 cm/sec   (4) 600 cm/sec

84. In what way would a sediment particle most likely change while it is being transported by the stream?
    (1) It will become more dense.   (3) Its size will decrease.
    (2) It will become more angular.   (4) Its hardness will increase.

85. At which location would the amount of deposition be greatest?
    (1) *A*   (3) *E*
    (2) *B*   (4) *D*

Group 7

If you choose this group, be sure to answer questions 86–90.

Base your answers to questions 86 through 90 on the *Earth Science Reference Tables*, the diagrams below of five rock samples, and your knowledge of Earth science.

BASALT

GNEISS
(METAMORPHIC)

CONGLOMERATE

GRANITE

SANDSTONE

86. Which sample is composed of sediments 0.006 centimeter to 0.2 centimeter in size that were compacted and cemented together?
   (1) conglomerate   (3) gneiss
   (2) sandstone   (4) granite

87. If granite were subjected to intense heat and pressure, it would most likely change to
   (1) conglomerate   (3) gneiss
   (2) sandstone   (4) basalt

88. The basalt was most likely formed by
   (1) heat and pressure
   (2) melting and solidification
   (3) compaction and cementation
   (4) erosion and deposition

89. Which sample would most likely contain fossils?
   (1) gneiss   (3) sandstone
   (2) granite   (4) basalt

90. Which sample is igneous and has a coarse texture?
   (1) sandstone   (3) basalt
   (2) conglomerate   (4) granite

Group 8

If you choose this group, be sure to answer questions 91–95.

Base your answers to questions 91 through 95 on the *Earth Science Reference Tables*, the diagram below, and your knowledge of Earth science. The diagram shows a cross section of bedrock where the Niagara River flows over Niagara Falls.

91. The Niagara River begins at
    (1) the Genesee River
    (2) Niagara Falls
    (3) Lake Erie
    (4) the St. Lawrence River

92. Which is the youngest rock unit?
    (1) Lockport dolostone
    (2) Queenston shale
    (3) Whirlpool sandstone
    (4) Rochester shale

93. Which rock layers appear to have weathered and eroded most?
    (1) Irondequoit limestone and Whirlpool sandstone
    (2) Power Glen shale and Queenston shale
    (3) Lockport dolostone and Reynales limestone
    (4) Thorold sandstone and Rochester shale

94. A sedimentary layer resembling the Rochester shale is located in another section of New York State. The best way to correlate these two rock units would be to compare the
    (1) thickness of the layers
    (2) index fossils contained in the layers
    (3) minerals cementing the sediments
    (4) color of the layers

95. Which rock unit was most likely formed from chemical precipitates?
    (1) Lockport dolostone
    (2) Whirlpool sandstone
    (3) Rochester shale
    (4) Thorold sandstone

Group 9

If you choose this group, be sure to answer questions 96–100.

Base your answers to question 96 through 100 on the *Earth Science Reference Tables*, the map and information below, and your knowledge of Earth science.

The map shows the location of major islands and coral reefs in the Hawaiian Island chain. Their ages are given in millions of years.

The islands of the Hawaiian chain formed from the same source of molten rock, called a hot plume. The movement of the Pacific Plate over the Hawaiian hot plume created a trail of extinct volcanoes that make up the Hawaiian Islands. The island of Hawaii (lower right) is the most recent island formed. Kilauea is an active volcano located over the plume on the island of Hawaii.

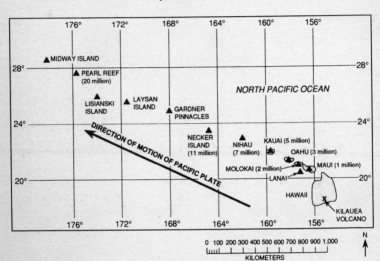

96. Approximately how far has the Pacific Plate moved since Necker Island was located over the hot plume at *X*?
    (1) 300 km
    (2) 1,100 km
    (3) 1,900 km
    (4) 2,600 km

97. What is the location of Lisianski Island?
    (1) 26° N 174° E
    (2) 26° N 174° W
    (3) 26° S 174° E
    (4) 26° S 174° W

98. Approximately how long will it take the noon Sun to appear to move from Kauai to Pearl Reef?
    (1) 1 hour
    (2) 2 hours
    (3) 15 minutes
    (4) 45 minutes

99. What kinds of animals were common in New York State 20 million years ago, when Pearl Reef was forming?
    (1) primitive humans
    (2) early reptiles
    (3) dinosaurs and ammonites
    (4) grazing mammals

100. Which graph shows the general relationship between the age of individual islands in the Hawaiian chain and their distance from the hot plume?

(1) (2) (3) (4)

Group 10

If you choose this group, be sure to answer questions 101–105.

Base your answers to questions 101 through 105 on the *Earth Science Reference Tables* and your knowledge of Earth science.

101. Which radioactive element has a half-life of 4.5×10^9 years?
(1) carbon-14   (3) uranium-238
(2) rubidium-87   (4) potassium-40

102. Students calculated the circumference of a globe to be 60. centimeters. The actual circumference of the globe is 63 centimeters. The percent deviation of the students' calculation was
(1) 0.48 %   (3) 5.0%
(2) 4.8%   (4) 21%

103. In the Earth's interior, which zone has a temperature higher than its melting point?
(1) crust   (3) inner core
(2) stiffer mantle   (4) outer core

104. What is the dewpoint temperature when the dry-bulb temperature is 22°C and the wet-bulb temperature is 15°C?
(1) 7° C   (3) 12° C
(2) 10° C   (4) 14° C

105. A pebble has a mass of 35 grams and a volume of 14 cubic centimeters. What is its density?
(1) 0.4 g/cm^3 (3) 490 g/cm^3
(2) 2.5 g/cm^3 (4) 4.0 g/cm^3

5. HUDSON-MOHAWK LOWLANDS. The rocks of this region are distorted sedimentary rocks of Paleozoic age that have lower resistance than the surrounding rocks. They have therefore been leveled by weathering, and by the erosion of the Mohawk and Hudson Rivers, to generally low elevations. Variations in slope are associated with escarpments that have been formed by resistant layers and the valleys carved by the rivers. South of Albany the Hudson River has an elevation of sea level and may be considered an inlet of the ocean.

6. ALLEGHENY PLATEAU. This part of the Appalachian Plateau is composed of horizontal sedimentary rocks, mostly of Paleozoic age. Much leveling by streams and glaciers has resulted in steep slopes and much change in elevation, so that some sections, such as the Catskills (area 6B), resemble mountains. Elevations range from about 500 meters in the west to over 1,250 meters in the Catskills. The region contains many lakes, such as the Finger Lakes, which are the result of glacial erosion and deposition.

7. ERIE-ONTARIO LOWLANDS. This region is a plain of horizontal sedimentary rocks of Paleozoic age, covered by much glacial transported sediment. The northern section is especially smooth because of deposition of sediments from glacial lakes that were the ancestors of Lakes Erie and Ontario. In some places, resistant rocks have been eroded to

escarpments up to 500 meters in elevation, but elevations and slopes are generally small throughout the region.

8. TUG HILL PLATEAU. This plateau of horizontal sedimentary rocks of Paleozoic age has a resistant surface layer that has resulted in fairly uniform elevations of about 600 to 700 meters. However, steep slopes occur where rivers have cut valleys, such as the Black River Valley that separates this region from the Adirondacks.

9. ADIRONDACK MOUNTAINS. These are mature mountains composed mostly of metamorphic rocks of Precambrian age. There are moderate elevations in the western section, but the highest elevations in the state (over 1,600 meters at mountain peaks) occur in the eastern section. The landscape is rugged, with much change in elevation and steep slopes, and with valleys related to faults and rocks of lesser resistance. Stream drainage patterns are of radial and trellis types except where glacial deposition has blocked the former drainage paths, resulting in many swamps and lakes.

10. ST. LAWRENCE-CHAMPLAIN LOWLANDS. This plain is composed generally of horizontal sedimentary rocks of lower resistance than rocks of surrounding regions, and therefore has lower elevations. The St. Lawrence section (10 A) is mostly flat, with changes in elevation usually no more than 30 meters. Some steep slopes exist in the Champlain section (10 B) as the result of uplift and subsidence caused by faults. Lake Cham-

LANDSCAPE REGIONS OF NEW YORK STATE AND THEIR CHARACTERISTICS

New York has a greater number of different landscape regions than any other state. The chief reason for this variety of landscape regions is the great variation in age, structure, and resistance of the bedrock found within the state. The present climate of the state is uniformly humid and has not been a major factor in producing variations in landscape development.

Almost all of New York was affected by the Pleistocene glaciation that ended in New York about 10,000 years ago. As a result, glacial depositional features are observed throughout the state, superimposed on the other characteristics of the different landscape regions. One of the most important features left by the glaciers is the transported soils, which are young and have small and incomplete profiles.

The landscape regions that are numbered on the facing map have the following distinguishing characteristics.

1. ATLANTIC COASTAL PLAIN. The bedrock consists of horizontal sedimentary rocks of late Mesozoic and Cenozoic age, with elevations near sea level, covered by thick glacial deposits reaching elevations of about 125 meters above sea level in some areas. The features of glacial deposition result in minor changes of slope on a generally smooth plain. Waves and ocean currents have created many typical shore features, such as bars, beaches, and lagoons.

2. NEWARK LOWLANDS. This region is composed of weak sedimentary rocks of early Mesozoic age, which have been leveled to lower elevations than the surrounding landscape regions. The generally smooth landscape has moderate changes in slope caused by faults. A volcanic intrusion called the Palisades Sill borders the Hudson River. Because of its greater resistance, it forms a cliff that ranges up to more than 150 meters above sea level.

3. HUDSON HIGHLANDS—MANHATTAN PRONG. These two regions are extensions of the New England Highlands to the east. These mountains in the mature and old-age stages are composed of highly distorted metamorphic rocks, mostly early Paleozoic and Precambrian in age and more resistant than the rocks of surrounding regions. In the northern parts of the region (3A, Hudson Highlands) there are elevations up to 500 meters with steep slopes; in the southern parts (3B, Manhattan Prong), the rocks have been eroded to low elevations and little slope typical of the plain-like topography of mountains in old age.

4. TACONIC MOUNTAINS. These greatly eroded mountains were originally uplifted in the Paleozoic Era. They consist mostly of metamorphic nonsedimentary rocks that are highly folded and faulted. Today they have moderate elevations (up to about 600 meters) and gradual changes in slope, so that the topography has the form of rolling hills.

(Continued on other side)